ANATOMY AND PHYSIOLOGY

OF

FARM ANIMALS

R. D. Frandson, B.S., D.V.M., M.S.

*Professor, Department of Anatomy, College of Veterinary Medicine,
Colorado State University, Fort Collins, Colorado*

231 Illustrations, 2 in color

Lea & Febiger

Philadelphia

Reprinted April, 1966

Reprinted January, 1968

Reprinted May, 1969

Reprinted July, 1970

Reprinted August, 1972

ISBN 0–8121–0089–1

Library of Congress Catalog Card Number: 65–19429

Printed in the United States of America

DEDICATION

To Z., R., S., and M.

PREFACE

This book is written as a text for undergraduate students who are majoring in animal husbandry, dairy production, or agriculture. For a number of years, I have taught students who are pursuing these majors, so I have purposely slanted the book in a direction I hope will be of most value to them. It should also prove useful as a reference book for high-school students who are studying vocational agriculture, for 4-H club members, and for livestock men in the field.

There are no special prerequisites for understanding this text, although previous courses in animal husbandry and zoology or biology will be of assistance.

Initially the text covers the fundamentals of anatomy and physiology as they apply to all animals; then it considers species differences. The cow and horse are discussed in greatest detail; the sheep, hog, and dog are also described where important differences from the cow or horse exist. Special emphasis has been given to the digestive system and to the reproductive systems, with chapters on the mammary glands, milk secretion, and endocrinology.

Clarity of expression has been one of my chief objectives, with the expectation that everyone who reads this book can gain an understanding of the principles of anatomy and physiology and their application to farm animals. Technical terms are used throughout the book, but most terms not found in an ordinary college dictionary are defined within the text.

Where controversial subjects are treated, the generally accepted view is given in greatest detail; however, important differences from this view are also mentioned or discussed. Rather than subject the reader to an extensive discussion of divergent opinions, I have assumed responsibility for presenting what I consider to be the most logical explanation of subjects still open to question. A list of references is included for those students who wish to pursue these subjects further.

R. D. FRANDSON

Fort Collins, Colorado

ACKNOWLEDGMENTS

Acknowledgment of all sources of information and assistance in preparation of this book obviously is impossible. However, I would like to thank specifically the following colleagues and friends for their many and varied contributions.

Dr. Rue Jensen, Dean, College of Veterinary Medicine, Colorado State University; Dr. Robert W. Davis, Head, Department of Anatomy, Colorado State University; Dr. Nicholas Booth, Head, Department of Physiology, Colorado State University; Dr. T. H. Belling Jr., New Mexico State University; Dr. Neil May, University of Queensland; and Mr. John Foss.

Staff members at Colorado State University: Dr. Y. Z. Abdelbaki, Miss Elsie Bergland, Dr. H. E. Bredeck, Dr. G. P. Epling, Dr. R. A. Kainer, Dr. H. Meyer, Dr. D. Will and Mr. K. Nakamoto.

Artists: Mrs. D. Dietemann, Miss M. Haff, Miss R. Haff, Mrs. D. Jeffry, Mrs. W. Musslewhite, Mrs. S. Nuss, and Mrs. B. Sparks.

The many publishers who loaned illustrations and tables.

CONTENTS

CHAPTER 1

INTRODUCTION TO ANATOMY AND PHYSIOLOGY

GENERAL

THE term *anatomy* has come to refer to that science which deals with the form and structure of all organisms. Literally the word means "to cut apart" and was used by early anatomists when speaking of a complete dissection of a cadaver.

In contrast to anatomy, which deals primarily with structure, *physiology* is the study of functions of the animal body or any of its parts.

When detailed anatomy courses and detailed physiology courses are taught separately, the approach to the laboratory portion of each course is considerably different. Study in a typical *gross* anatomy laboratory is based primarily on dissection of animals. These animals usually have been preserved by embalming, and one or more parts of the vascular system has been injected with a colored material to facilitate identification of the vessels. Careful dissection coupled with close observation gives the student a concept of the shape, texture, location, and relations of those structures visible to the unaided eye that can be gained in no other way. The use of the microscope with properly prepared tissue sections on slides is equally essential for an understanding of the structures that are so small they cannot be seen without optical assistance.

In the physiology laboratory the student repeats a number of classical experiments, frequently with living animals, to gain a better understanding of normal function of the body and the effects of changes in environment (both internal and external) on the normal animal. This often includes the use of drugs, changes in temperature, and the use of electric current to produce changes in the animal body.

The anatomist and physiologist working in research use some of the same techniques that are used in the teaching laboratory, but with considerable refinement. Both types of scientists borrow a great deal of equipment and methods from the physical sciences, particularly chemistry and physics. The anatomist applies the principles of physics in the different microscopes he uses and applies a knowledge of chemistry in the staining of various parts of cells and tissues. The combination of chemistry and microscopic anatomy is a field known as *histochemistry*.

The physiologist uses many chemicals for altering the environment of the experimental animal and adapts much electronic equipment from physics and electrical engineering for monitoring responses of the animal or some part of the animal to the experimental treatment.

Although both disciplines, anatomy and physiology, commonly are pursued more or less independently, they are both facets of the total study of the animal body. A thorough knowledge of structure imparts a great deal of information about its function. A mere description of structure without some implication of possible function would be of little practical value. Conversely, it is impossible to gain a thorough understanding of function without a good basic knowledge of the structures involved.

The science of anatomy has become so extensive that it is now divided into many specialized branches. In fact, Dorland's *Medical Dictionary* defines thirty subdivisions of anatomy. We are chiefly interested in *gross (macroscopic) anatomy*. This is the study of the form and relations (relative positions) of the structures of the

study of anatomy is called *ultrastructural cytology* and deals with portions of cells and tissues as they are visualized with the aid of the electron microscope. The term "fine structure" is used frequently in reference to structures seen in electron micrographs (photographs made with the electron microscope).

Our approach to the study of anatomy will be chiefly by systems. This method of study is referred to as *systematic anatomy*. To name the study, the suffix "ology" which means "branch of knowledge or science" is added to the root word referring to the system. The following table indicates the commonly accepted systems, the name of the study of those systems, and the chief structures involved in each system.

System	*Name of Study*	*Chief Structures*
Skeletal system	Osteology	Bones
Articular system	Arthrology	Joints
Muscular system	Myology	Muscles
Digestive system	Splanchnology	Stomach and intestines
Respiratory system	"	Lungs and air passages
Urinary system	"	Kidneys and bladder
Reproductive system	"	Ovaries and testes
Endocrine system	Endocrinology	Ductless glands
Nervous system	Neurology	Brain, spinal cord, nerves
Circulatory system	Angiology	Heart, vessels
Integumentary system	Dermatology	Skin
Sensory system	Esthesiology	Eye, ear

body which can be seen with the unaided eye.

Comparative anatomy is a study of the structure of various species of animals with particular emphasis on those characteristics that aid in classification.

Embryology is the study of developmental anatomy covering the period from conception (fertilization of the egg within the dam) to birth.

Another large branch of anatomy consists of the study of those tissues and cells which can be seen only with the aid of a microscope. This is known as *microscopic anatomy* and is sometimes called histology.

The most recent development in the

DESCRIPTIVE TERMS USEFUL IN THE STUDY OF ANATOMY

When giving geographical locations, we make use of certain arbitrary frames of reference known as meridians of latitude and longitude. However, since an animal is rarely oriented exactly with a line on the earth's surface, our frames of reference must be in relation to the animal itself and must apply regardless of the position or direction of the animal.

In order to meet these requirements, the following arbitrary planes are used as frames of reference in locating any given part of an animal body:

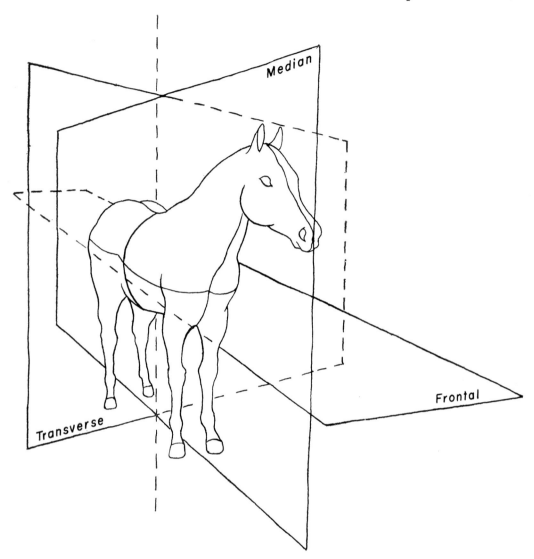

Fig. 1–1.—Imaginary planes of reference. (After Julian and Tyler. *Lab. Dissection Guide for Functional Anatomy of the Domestic Animals.*)

Cranial and *anterior* are directional terms meaning toward the head. The shoulder is cranial to the hip—it is closer to the head than is the hip.

Caudal and *posterior* mean toward the tail. The rump is caudal to the loin.

The *median plane* is an imaginary plane passing through the body craniocaudally which divides the body into equal right and left halves. A beef carcass is split into two halves on the median plane.

A *sagittal plane* is any plane parallel to the median plane. The median plane is sometimes called the *midsagittal* plane.

A *transverse plane* is a plane which is at right angles to the median plane and divides the body into cranial and caudal segments. A cross section of the body would be made on a transverse plane. The surcingle of a milker defines a transverse plane through the abdomen of a cow.

A *frontal plane* is a plane which is at right angles to both the median plane and transverse planes. The frontal plane divides the body into dorsal (upper) and ventral (lower) segments. If a cow walks into a lake till the water comes above the chest, the surface of the water

away from the median plane. The ribs are lateral to the lungs. They are farther from the median plane.

Dorsal is a directional term meaning toward or beyond the backbone or vertebral column. The kidneys are dorsal to the intestines. They are closer to

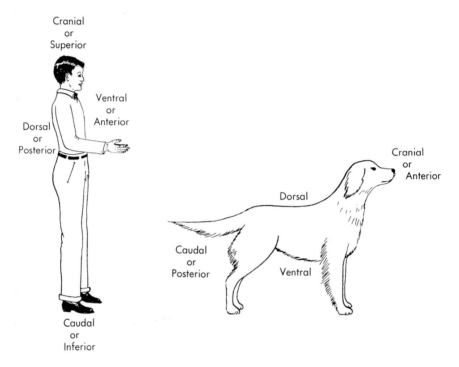

Cranial
or
Superior

Ventral
or
Anterior

Dorsal
or
Posterior

Caudal
or
Inferior

Cranial
or
Anterior

Dorsal

Caudal
or
Posterior

Ventral

Fig. 1–2.—Terminology of quadruped and human compared. (After King and Showers, *Human Anatomy and Physiology*, W. B. Saunders Co.)

represents a frontal plane in relation to the cow.

In addition to the planes of reference, certain other descriptive terms are valuable in locating an area we wish to discuss. Some of these include:

Medial is an adjective meaning close to or toward the median plane. The heart is medial to the lungs. It is closer to the median plane than are the lungs. The chestnut is located on the medial side (inside) of a horse's leg. It is on the side closest to the median plane.

Lateral is the antonym of medial; means

the vertebral column. Dorsum is the noun referring to the dorsal portion or back. A saddle is placed on the dorsum of a horse.

Ventral means away from the vertebral column or toward the mid-abdominal wall. The udder is the most ventral part of the body of a cow. It is the part of the body farthest from the vertebral column.

Deep and *internal* refer to closeness to the center of gravity or the center of an extremity. The humerus (arm bone) is deep to all other structures in the arm.

Superficial and *external* refer to proximity

to the skin or surface of the body or surface of an extremity. Hair is superficial to all other structures of the body.

Proximal means relatively closer to a given part, usually the vertebral column, body, or center of gravity. Proximal is generally used in reference to portions of an extremity or limb. The knee is proximal to the foot.

Distal means relatively farther from the vertebral column. The hoof is distal to the carpus or knee.

Volar refers to the flexion or caudal surface of the forelimb distal to (below) the elbow. *Dorsal* when used in reference to forelimbs refers to the opposite or cranial side.

Plantar refers to the caudal surface of the hind limb below the hock, and dorsal refers to the side directly opposite (the cranial side).

Prone refers to a position in which the dorsal aspect or dorsum of the body or any extremity is uppermost. *Pronation* refers to the act of turning toward a prone position.

Supine refers to the position in which the ventral aspect of the body or volar or plantar aspect of an extremity is uppermost. *Supination* refers to the act of turning toward a supine position.

MICROSCOPIC ANATOMY— ANIMAL CELLS AND TISSUES

All living things, both plants and animals, are constructed of small units called *cells*. The simplest animals, such as the ameba, consist of a single cell that is capable of performing all functions commonly associated with life. These functions include growth (increase in size), metabolism (utilization of food), response to stimuli (such as moving toward light), contraction (shortening in one direction), and reproduction (development of new individuals of the same species).

A typical cell consists of three main parts, the *cytoplasm*, the *nucleus*, and the

cell membrane. Detailed structure of the cell will be described in Chapter 3, but tissues will be discussed in the present chapter.

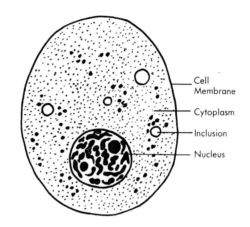

FIG. 1–3.—A cell as seen with the light microscope.

When the number of cells increases in animals, certain cells become specialists in one or more of the functions of the animal body. Specialized cells grouped together are called *tissues*. For example, cells that specialize in conducting impulses make up nervous tissue. Cells that specialize in holding structures together make up connective tissue.

Various tissues are associated in functional groups called *organs*. The stomach is an organ that functions in digestion of food.

A group of organs that are involved in a common enterprise make up a *system*. The stomach, liver, pancreas, and intestines are all part of the digestive system.

The primary types of tissues include: (1) *epithelial tissues*, which cover the surface of the body, line body cavities, and form the active parts of glands; (2) *connective tissues*, which support and bind other tissues together; (3) *fluid tissues*, which transport nutrients and waste products; (4) *muscle tissues*, which specialize in contracting; and (5) *nervous tissues*, which conduct impulses from one part of the body to another.

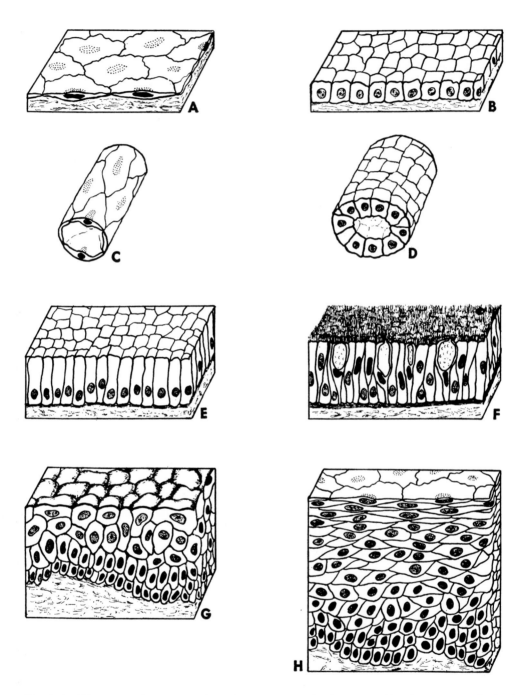

Fɪɢ. 1–4.—Diagrammatic representation of types of epithelial tissues. *A,* Simple squamous; *B,* simple cuboidal; *C,* simple squamous in tubular arrangement; *D,* simple cuboidal forming a small duct; *E,* simple columnar; *F,* pseudostratified columnar with cilia; *G,* transitional; *H,* stratified squamous (moist type). (Finerty and Cowdry, *A Textbook of Histology,* Lea & Febiger.)

EPITHELIAL TISSUES

In general the epithelial tissues are classified as *simple* (single layered), and *stratified* (many layered). Each of these types is further subdivided according to the shape of the individual cells.

Simple epithelium includes squamous (plate-like) cells, cuboidal (cube-shaped) cells, columnar (cylindrical-shaped) cells, and pseudostratified columnar cells.

Simple squamous epithelium consists of thin, plate-like cells. They are much expanded in two directions but have very little thickness. The edges are joined somewhat like mosaic tile covering a floor. A layer of simple squamous epithelium has very little tensile strength and is found only as a covering layer for stronger tissues. Simple squamous epithelium is found where a smooth surface is required to reduce friction. The coverings of viscera and the linings of body cavities and blood vessels are all composed of simple squamous epithelia.

Cuboidal epithelial cells are about equal in all dimensions. They are found in some ducts and passageways in the kidneys. The active tissue of many glands is composed of cuboidal cells.

Columnar epithelial cells are cylindrical in shape. They are arranged somewhat like the cells in a honeycomb or the cartridges in a box. Some columnar cells have, extending from the free extremity, whip-like projections called cilia. The cells lining the trachea (windpipe) are of this type. The cilia wave in such a manner as to move any foreign material in the trachea toward the mouth where it can be coughed out.

Pseudostratified columnar epithelium is composed of columnar cells. However, they vary in length, giving the appearance of more than one layer or stratum. This type of epithelium is found in the upper respiratory tract where the lining cells are ciliated.

Stratified epithelium consists of more than one layer of epithelial cells, and includes stratified squamous, stratified columnar, and transitional epithelium.

Stratified squamous epithelium forms the outer layer of the skin and the lining of the first part of the digestive tract as far as the stomach. In ruminants, stratified squamous epithelium also lines the fore stomachs.

Stratified squamous epithelium is the thickest and toughest of the epithelia, consisting of many layers of cells. The deepest layers, known as the stratum germinativum, are the actively growing and multiplying cells. These cells are somewhat cuboidal in shape, but as they are pushed toward the surface away from the food supply they become flattened and lifeless and are in the constant process of peeling off. This layer of dead cells becomes very thick in areas subjected to friction. Calluses are formed in this manner.

Stratified columnar epithelium is composed of more than one layer of columnar cells and is found lining part of the pharynx and salivary ducts.

Transitional epithelium forms the lining of those portions of the urinary system that are subjected to considerable stretching. These areas include the bladder and ureters. This transitional epithelium has the ability to pile up many cells thick when the bladder is relaxed, yet stretch out to a single layer when completely filled.

Glandular epithelium, which often is either cuboidal or columnar, has the ability to secrete various products. The cells may be arranged as single goblet cells which produce mucus, or they may consist of aggregations of many cells, such as are found in most glands. Glands are described in more detail on page 34 in this chapter.

CONNECTIVE TISSUES

Connective tissues, as the name implies, serve to connect other tissues. They give form and strength to many organs and often serve for protection and leverage. Connective tissues include yellow elastic tissue, collagenous (white fibrous) tissue, reticular (net-like) tissue, adipose (fat) tissue, cartilage (gristle), and bone.

Yellow elastic tissue contains kinked fibers which tend to regain their original shape after being stretched. This tissue is found in the ligamentum nuchae, a strong band which helps support the head. Yellow elastic tissue also is found in the abdominal tunic, in the ligamenta flava of the spinal canal, in elastic arteries, and mixed with other tissues wherever elasticity is needed.

Collagenous (white fibrous) tissue is found throughout the body in various forms. Individual cells (fibroblasts) produce long fibers of collagen which have considerable tensile strength.

In dense regular connective tissue the fibers are arranged in parallel bundles forming cords or bands of considerable strength. These are the *tendons*, which connect muscles to bones, and the *ligaments*, which connect bones to bones.

The fibers of dense irregular connective tissue are arranged in a thick mat with fibers running in all directions. The dermis of the skin, which may be tanned to make leather, consists of dense irregular connective tissue. This forms a strong covering that resists tearing and yet is flexible enough to move with the surface of the body.

Areolar connective tissue is found throughout the body wherever protective cushioning and flexibility are needed. For example, blood vessels are surrounded by a sheath of areolar connective tissue which permits the vessels to move and yet protects them.

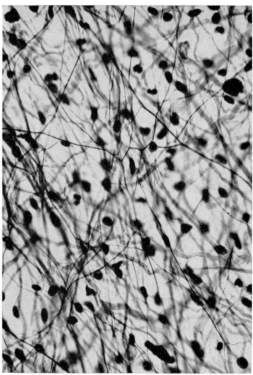

Fig. 1–6.—Areolar (loose) connective tissue. (Turtox Biological Supplies, courtesy of General Biological Supply House, Inc.)

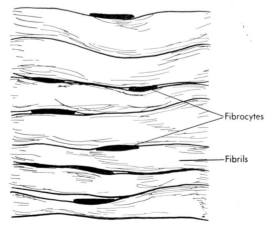

Fig. 1–5.—Diagram of dense regular connective tissue (longitudinal section of a tendon).

Beneath the dermis is a layer of loosely arranged areolar connective tissue fibers which attach the skin to underlying muscles. This attachment is flexible enough to permit considerable movement of the skin. It also permits the formation of a thick layer of fat between the skin and underlying muscles. Whenever the skin is adherent to bony prominences be-

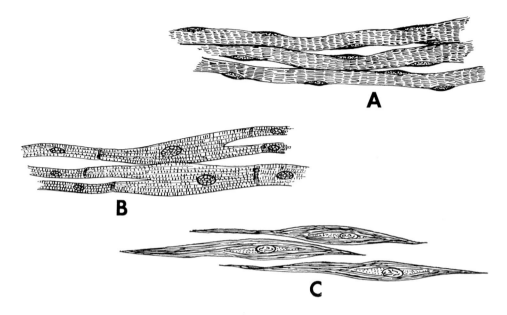

Fig. 1–11.—Types of muscle tissue. *A*, Striated voluntary muscle; *B*, Cardiac muscle; and *C*, Smooth muscle.

supply in order to contract, and when stimulated to contract it will do so to the maximum of its ability. This property of maximal contraction is known as the "*all-or-none*" *principle.* Striated muscle tissue plus some connective tissue makes up the flesh of meat-producing animals.

Smooth muscle cells are spindle-shaped cells that contain one centrally located nucleus per cell. They are found in the walls of the digestive tract, in the walls of blood vessels, and in the walls of urinary and reproductive organs. These cells contract more slowly than striated muscle and respond to a variety of stimuli.

Cardiac muscle is also known as *involuntary striated muscle* because it is not under conscious control, yet does have cross striations. The heart is composed of a complex branched arrangement of cardiac-muscle cells. Modified muscle cells called *Purkinje's fibers* conduct impulses within the heart much as nerve fibers do in other parts of the body, and the impulses travel throughout the heart causing a spreading contraction wave.

NERVOUS TISSUE

The essential cell making up nervous tissue is the *neuron (nerve cell).* This consists of a nerve cell body and two or more nerve processes (nerve fibers). The processes are called *axons* if they conduct impulses away from the cell body and *dendrites* if they conduct impulses toward the cell body.

The cord-like structures commonly referred to as nerves consist of thousands of nerve processes or fibers. By examining a nerve fiber either grossly or with a microscope it is impossible to determine whether impulses were carried toward or away from the cell body. Some authorities, therefore, prefer to consider the longest process as the axon and shorter processes as dendrites.

A nerve fiber may be covered by a myelin sheath, or by a neurolemma, or by both.

The special connective tissues of the nervous system proper are called *neuroglia* and are found only in the central nervous system. Outside the central nervous system ordinary white fibrous tissue serves as a protective covering for the nerves and bundles of nerve fibers.

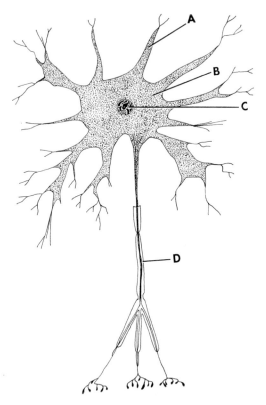

Fig. 1–12.—A typical neuron. *A*, Dendrites; *B*, Nerve cell body; *C*, Nucleus; and *D*, Axon. (After Francis, *Introduction to Human Anatomy*, courtesy of C. V. Mosby Co.)

THE GENERAL PLAN OF
THE ANIMAL BODY

All farm animals are classified as vertebrates and as such have a vertebral column. The body (with the exception of a few internal organs) exhibits bilateral symmetry. This means that the right and left sides of the body are nearly identical, but are mirror images of each other. Similar right and left structures are called paired structures such as a pair of gloves that are similar but not interchangeable. Most unpaired structures are located on or near the median plane, and, of course, only one such structure exists in any given animal. The tongue, trachea, vertebral column, and heart are examples of unpaired structures. The ribs, limbs, eyes, and most muscles are examples of paired structures in the animal body.

A medial view of the body shows two cavities; a dorsal cavity containing the brain and spinal cord and a ventral cavity containing most of the viscera (soft structures) of the body. The ventral cavity is subdivided by the diaphragm into the thoracic cavity cranially and the abdominopelvic cavity (which includes the abdominal cavity and the pelvic cavity) caudally.

The *thoracic cavity* contains the *pericardial sac*, which surrounds the heart, and two *pleural sacs*, which surround the two lungs. These sacs are formed by *serous membranes*.

The *abdominal cavity* contains the kidneys, most of the digestive organs, and a variable amount of the internal reproductive organs in both sexes. The *pelvic cavity* contains the terminal part of the digestive system (the rectum) and all of the internal portions of the uro-genital system not found in the abdominal cavity. The serous membrane that surrounds the abdominal viscera and part of the pelvic viscera is called *peritoneum*.

A transverse section through the abdominal cavity illustrates the general plan of the body as a tube (digestive tract and its derivatives) within a tube (body wall). The potential space between the two tubes is the ventral body cavity, which is derived from the embryonic *celom*. Normally there are very few actual air-filled spaces in the animal body except in the respiratory system and the ear. However, for the sake of clarity, many illustrations show a considerable separation between structures that in the animal body are actually in contact.

The layers of the body wall and the layers of the digestive tract show a re-

CHAPTER 2

EMBRYOLOGY

GENERAL

EMBRYOLOGY is the study of the early prenatal development of an animal. It begins with the fertilization of the ovum by a spermatozoon to form a zygote, which in turn becomes a morula, a blastula, a gastrula, and finally a fetus. Strictly speaking, the period of the embryo terminates when the various organs and organ systems are formed. The embryo then becomes a fetus that more or less resembles an adult of the same species. In cattle the embryo becomes a fetus at about the end of the second month of gestation. The fetus becomes a newborn animal at parturition (birth).

The ovum contains a large amount of food material (yolk) that provides energy for the early stages of cell division. The ovum and spermatazoon each contribute one-half of the chromosomes to the newly formed zygote (see Fig. 4–7, p. 61).

EMBRYOLOGY OF AMPHIOXUS

The embryology of amphioxus, a primitive chordate, is studied because of its simplicity. In amphioxus, the first mitotic divisions, known as cleavage, increase the number of cells (blastomeres) with little if any increase in actual volume, because cleavage occurs so rapidly that there is not enough time for the customary growth of daughter cells before a new division occurs. However, the nuclei of the daughter cells are of normal size and contain a full complement of chromosomes. The mass of small cells resulting from cleavage has a lobulated appearance resembling a mulberry; hence the name "morula" given to this stage.

The morula then becomes a hollowed sphere, the *blastula*. One pole (end) of the blastula is called the *animal pole*. The animal pole consists of cells that contain very little yolk material and eventually form the *ectoderm*, the outer germ layer. The opposite end of the blastula is called the *vegetal pole*. It consists of cells with a much higher yolk content than the cells of the animal pole. These vegetal pole cells will form the *endoderm*, the inner germ layer.

Because the yolk material in the vegetal pole cells inhibits *mitosis*, the cells of the animal pole multiply much more rapidly. These very rapidly multiplying animal pole cells soon overlap the vegetal pole cells and produce a double-layered invaginated ball called a *gastrula*.

The two layers of the gastrula grow into close apposition, effacing the cavity of the blastula. The new cavity formed by the invagination is called the *archenteron* (*primitive gut*), which eventually forms the lumen of the digestive and respiratory systems. The archenteron opens to the exterior by way of the blastopore.

The embryo in this gastrula stage elongates and begins to differentiate in a number of ways.

A series of paired outpouchings on each side of the dorsal junction of endoderm and ectoderm form the *somites* (segments) which eventually give rise to most of the body wall. These mesodermal (middle skin) structures appear to originate from the dorsal endoderm. The cavities coalesce to form the celom (body cavity), bounded by outer and inner layers of *mesoderm*. The outer layer of mesoderm fuses with the ectoderm to form the *somatopleure* (body wall), and the inner layer fuses with the endoderm to form the *splanchnopleure* (gut wall). At the same time, the dorsal plate of ectoderm evaginates longitudinally to form first a groove, then a tube (*neural tube*) which is the forerunner of the nervous system. Concurrently the roof of the archenteron forms the *notochord*, the basis of the skeleton.

MAMMALIAN EMBRYOLOGY

When the mammalian embryo reaches the uterus the morula becomes a blastula (or blastocyst) consisting of several cells or cell masses, each termed a blastomere. The blastula is a hollow ball consisting of a layer of cells, the trophoblast, that surrounds the blastocele, a cavity into which the inner cell mass protrudes (from the trophoblast). The inner cell mass eventually forms the body of the embryo. In

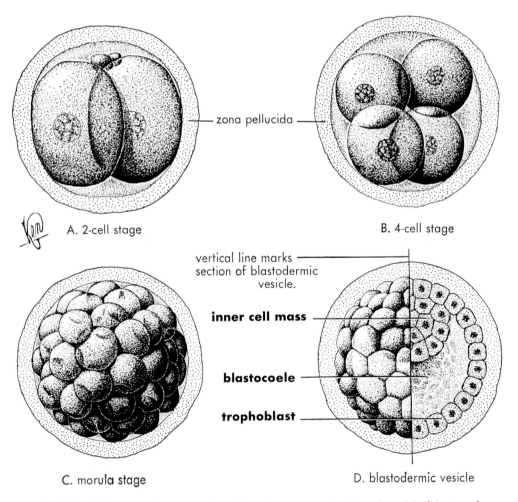

zona pellucida

A. 2-cell stage

B. 4-cell stage

vertical line marks section of blastodermic vesicle.

inner cell mass

blastocoele

trophoblast

C. morula stage

D. blastodermic vesicle

Fig. 2–1.—Diagrams of human embryos from cleavage to blastodermic vesicle (blastocyst). (Crouch, *Functional Human Anatomy*, Lea & Febiger.)

this process three germ layers are produced.

The ectoderm (outer skin) develops from the outer cells of the inner cell mass and is continuous with the trophoblast. The endoderm (inner skin) grows into the blastocele just deep to the trophoblast to form the archenteron or primitive gut. The mesoderm (middle skin) grows between the ectoderm and endoderm and splits into two layers forming a cavity, the celom, between the two layers.

The outer layer of the mesoderm and the adjacent ectoderm make up the somatopleure, which forms part of the body wall and also enters into the formation of the fetal membranes. The inner layer of the mesoderm and the endoderm form the splanchnopleure, which forms the wall of the gut.

The dorsal surface of the embryonic disc (the forerunner of the embryo) develops an elongated thickening called the primitive streak and a rod-shaped mass, the notochord. Mesodermal cells on each side of the notochord form the segmentally arranged somites, which in turn develop into vertebrae and muscles.

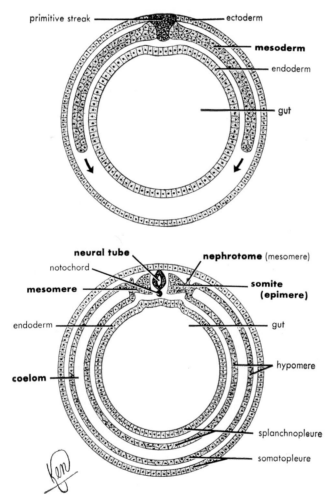

FIG. 2–2.—Diagrammatic representation to show spread and differentiation of the mesoderm. The hypomere includes an inner splanchnic mesoderm and an outer somatic mesoderm. The splanchnic mesoderm and endoderm form the splanchnopleure. The somatic endoderm and ectoderm form the somatopleure. (Modified from Arey—Crouch, *Functional Human Anatomy*, Lea & Febiger)

Other areas of mesoderm produce urogenital organs and blood vascular organs.

The ectoderm above the notochord forms a groove that becomes the neural tube which eventually forms the central nervous system. The epidermis of the skin is also derived from the ectoderm.

and organs develop, but very little is known about why these changes take place. It has been established that the *DNA* (*deoxyribonucleic acid*) of the nucleus in the form of chromosomes contains the information that influences development of all the various parts of the animal.

TABLE 2–1.—THE GERM-LAYER ORIGIN OF TISSUES (Arey)*

Ectoderm	Mesoderm (including mesenchyme)	Endoderm

1. Epidermis, including:
    Cutaneous glands.
    Hair; nails; lens.
 2. Epithelium of:
    Sense organs.
    Nasal cavity; sinuses.
    Mouth, including:
      Oral glands; enamel.
    Anal canal.
 3. Nervous tissue, including:
    Hypophysis.
    Chromaffin tissue.
	1. Muscle (all types).
	 2. Connective tissue; cartilage; bone; notochord.
	 3. Blood; bone marrow.
	 4. Lymphoid tissue.
	 Epithelium of:
	 5. Blood vessels; lymphatics.
	 6. Body cavities.
	 7. Kidney; ureter.
	 8. Gonads; genital ducts.
	 9. Suprarenal cortex.
	 10. Joint cavities, etc.
		Epithelium of:
		 1. Pharynx, including:
		    Root of tongue.
		    Auditory tube, etc.
		    Tonsils; thyroid.
		    Parathyroids; thymus.
		 2. Larynx; trachea; lungs.
		 3. Digestive tube, including:
		    Associated glands.
		 4. Bladder.
		 5. Vagina (all?); vestibule.
		 6. Urethra, including:
		    Associated glands.

* Arey, *Developmental Anatomy*, courtesy of W. B. Saunders Co.

As the above changes are occurring, the trophoblast becomes elongated and attached to the lining of the uterus where it absorbs nutrients from the uterine glands. The actual fetal membranes develop later.

Differentiation of the relatively indifferent cells of each of the three germ layers to form specialized tissue cells is called *histogenesis*. A great deal is known about when and where various tissues

In general, the ectoderm forms the outer epithelium and nervous system, the endoderm forms the lungs and gut epithelium and its derivatives, and the mesoderm forms muscles, connective tissues, blood, and most of the urogenital system (organs associated with the urinary system and reproductive system).

The subject of embryology is well covered in a large number of standard textbooks on embryology.

CHAPTER 3

STRUCTURE OF THE CELL

GENERAL

DISCOVERY of living cells would have been difficult, if not impossible, before the compound microscope was invented by Zacharias Jansen of Holland in 1590. Robert Hooke of England applied the term "cell" to the cavities he saw in sections of cork. Hooke published a description of cork cells in 1665, based on a study he made with his improved compound microscope. Ten years later, 1675, Marcello Malpighi published an *Anatomy of Plants* the first systematic study of cell structure.

In 1839 Matthias Schleiden, a German botanist, and Theodor Schwann, an animal anatomist, formulated the cell theory which set forth the concept that "the elementary parts of all tissues are formed of cells in an analogous, though very diversified, manner, so that it may be asserted that there is one universal principle of development for the elementary parts of organisms, however different, and that this principle is the formation of cells."

DEFINITIONS

The word cell comes from the Latin "cella" meaning "a small chamber." In biology, particularly animal biology, the term cell refers more specifically to the individual units of living structure rather than the compartments in which they may be located. There actually are no compartments as such in most tissues (with the exception of bone and cartilages) but the living units, cells, are found in groups in which individual cells are restrained mainly by adjacent cells. As early as 1772 Corti observed the jelly-like material in the cell that later was called protoplasm.

It is difficult if not impossible to give a satisfactory definition of life. However, for many years the properties of protoplasm and of the cell have been equated with life. These properties include growth, reproduction, absorption, respiration, excretion, secretion, irritability, conductivity, and contractibility.

Growth refers to increase in size, usually by increase in the amount of protoplasm. Increase in size of a cell or organ beyond normal is called *hypertrophy*.

Reproduction of a cell or of an organism implies the ability to produce more cells or more organisms which are essentially the same as the original. Increase in size of a structure because of increased number of cells is called *hyperplasia*.

Absorption refers to the process of taking dissolved materials into the substance of the cell. This may be a passive process dependent on such forces as diffusion and osmosis, or it may be an active process requiring the expenditure of energy. There is much yet to be learned about the mechanism of absorption.

If the material taken in is not dissolved, but is in the form of particles, the process is called *phagocytosis*, and cells with this ability are called *phagocytes*. Phagocytosis is an engulfing process in which the cell flows around the foreign object until it is completely surrounded. This ability is frequently found in unattached cells such as the white blood cells.

Pinocytosis is believed to be a somewhat similar method for taking fluid into a cell.

Respiration (internal respiration) refers to the utilization of food by the cell, con-

Irritability consists of the property of reacting to stimuli. The reaction to a stimulus must necessarily consist of one of the other properties of protoplasm such as conduction or contraction.

Conductivity is the property of transmitting an impulse of some nature from one point in the cell to another. Nerve cells are specialized for the function of conductivity and irritability.

Contractility is the property of shortening in one direction. Muscle cells are specialized for contraction, although other cells protrude and withdraw pseudopodia (foot-like processes), a process which involves small contractions.

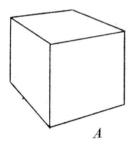 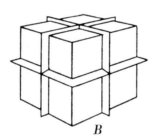 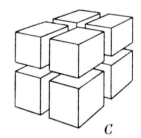

A   *B*   *C*

Fig. 3–1.—Relationship of surface area and volume. *A*, Cube 1 centimeter on a side has a volume of 1 cubic centimeter and area of 6 square centimeters. *B*, Three complete cuts produces eight small cubes. *C*, Eight small cubes have a total volume of 1 cubic centimeter but total surface area of 12 square centimeters.

sisting essentially of oxidation of carbon and hydrogen to carbon dioxide and water, with the release of energy. This is not like burning but is a slow, controlled, stepwise process that is discussed in Chapter 21, p. 304. Oxidation not only includes the addition of oxygen, but also refers to the removal of hydrogen or the removal of electrons.

Excretion and *secretion* at the cellular level refer to loss of material from the cell. If waste products are lost, the process is called excretion; if useful products are extruded, the process is called secretion. Both active and passive excretion and secretion are described, but the exact mechanism of each is still in question.

CELL SIZE

Most cells range in diameter from about 10 to 100 μ (micra), with cells that are multiplying ranging from about 20 to 30 μ in diameter. (1 μ = 1/1000 mm. (millimeter), and there are about 25 mm. in 1 inch; 1 μ = 1/25,000 inch.) Sizes of cells vary considerably from one type of cell to another, but with the exception of yolks of birds' eggs (which are considered to be single cells), the distance from the interior of the cell to some portion of the cell membrane (surface of the cell) is seldom over 50 μ. For efficient functioning, all parts of the protoplasm must be relatively close to a source of nutrition and route of waste excretion. This automatically limits the size of cells, because too large a cell could not transport nutrients to the center of the cell or eliminate waste products from the center of the cell.

A large surface area in comparison to the volume results from small cell size. This relationship is also an important factor in efficient cell functioning.

The cell wall is extremely thin—70 to 100 Å in thickness. 1 Å (Angstrom) = 1/10,000,000 mm., which is about the diameter of a hydrogen atom. Regardless of its composition, a membrane of this dimension (100 Å thick) can have little tensile strength. This is another reason cells must be small. As an analogy, a ton of grain could be handled reasonably well if it were placed in small paper sacks, but it would be completely unmovable in one large sack made of paper the same thickness.

The uniformly small size of cells and much smaller size of structures within the cell has made effective study of cells very difficult. As noted earlier, the existence of cells was not confirmed before the microscope was invented. Details of the actual structure of the various parts of cells have not been known with any degree of certainty until the development and use of the electron microscope made this possible. The study of gross anatomy goes back in history several centuries, but an understanding of the finer structure of the animal body had to wait on technological developments.

LIGHT MICROSCOPY

Some cells are located in tissues that are thin enough to be illuminated from one side and observed with a microscope from the opposite side. This is true of the web of the foot of the frog, the mesentery attaching to the intestine, and a few other tissues. In these instances living cells can be observed directly, and this technique is useful for the study of blood circulation. Specific cells may also be taken from a living animal and grown on artificial media by a technique called *tissue culture*. These cells may then be studied in the living state, even at rather high magnifications.

Except for the above situations (naturally thin tissues or tissue culture), cells usually are studied after more or less manipulation, so that what is actually seen with the microscope bears little resemblance to the living cell.

A fairly typical treatment of tissue before it can be examined with a light microscope includes:

1. Fixation with some agent such as formalin that will coagulate the protein and prevent further changes in the tissue, such as autolysis and bacterial action.

2. Embedding the tissue in a material that will permit cutting very thin sections. Paraffin and nitrocellulose are commonly used for this purpose. Since most embedding media are not water soluble, the fixed tissue must be dehydrated and then infiltrated with some material such as xylene which is miscible with the embedding medium.

3. Sectioning the tissue into very thin slices (generally between 2 and 20 μ in thickness) so the sections may be placed on a glass slide. An instrument called a microtome is used for this purpose. It consists of a very sharp knife blade and a mechanism for moving the tissue past the blade and then advancing it a definite amount after each cutting.

4. Staining the section so that different cells or different parts of cells can be differentiated according to color. *Hematoxylin* and *eosin* are stains commonly used together and are termed *H & E stain*. The hematoxylin tends to stain acid portions of a cell dark blue or purple (these are called basophilic areas), and the eosin tends to stain the basic portions of a cell pink to red (these are called acidophilic areas). A great deal may be

learned by applying a variety of stains to a tissue to determine how different portions react with various chemicals. This type of study is known as histochemistry.

5. The last step, of course, is the actual examination of the stained section of tissue on the slide by means of a microscope and light transmitted through the section.

This approach to the study of the animal body has been standard for many years and will continue to be of great use regardless of newer developments. A number of factors should be kept in mind when studying sections or photographs of sections.

The relationship between the tissue sections and the actual tissue is about the same as the relationship of a sack of potato chips and a growing potato. Both the sections and potato chips have been processed so that actual resemblance to the original structure is practically nil. Both are seen in two dimensions, length and width, with thickness being of little importance as far as visualization is concerned.

A technique known as *wax plate reconstruction* is sometimes used to visualize microscopic structures in three dimensions. By this method the structures seen on a slide are magnified and projected onto a wax plate, and the unwanted portions are then cut away. This process is repeated with the next section that was cut from the block of tissue and corresponding areas of this wax plate are matched with the preceding wax plate. After a number of repetitions, a reconstruction has been produced that resembles the original tissue except that it is much larger and consists of wax rather than tissue. This is a very time-consuming and meticulous technique, but the results are quite gratifying, since it is about the only way to gain a good three-dimensional concept of microscopic structures.

The light microscope can magnify objects to a maximum of about 1500 times the original size. This is known as the magnification, or power, of the microscope. Resolving power refers to the property of showing two objects as separate structures. The light microscope can resolve (separate) two structures that are as close as about $\frac{1}{3}$ μ apart. This resolving power is determined in part by the wave length of the light used. Sodium light has a wave length of about 0.6 μ which gives the above resolving power of $\frac{1}{3}$ μ. A fairly recent development in light microscopy is the *phase contrast microscope*, which can be used with unstained and/or living cells because it depends on differences in refraction of various parts of a cell for image formation.

ELECTRON MICROSCOPY

The most exciting and productive development in recent years is the *electron microscope*. Using an electron beam as a source of illumination and electromagnets as lenses the electron microscope can resolve structures as close as 1/1000 μ (a distance equivalent to the diameter of 10 hydrogen atoms) and can magnify up to 300,000 times the size of the original structure. Since the electron microscope is not suitable for extended study of the image on a fluorescent screen, photographs are taken, and enlarged prints are then studied. If projection slides are made, the image can be projected onto a screen, giving a total magnification of the order of 1,000,000 times, a fantastic increase in size. The new perspective available with the electron microscope might be compared with the new insight of a person who had tried to study a forest from a distance of several miles and then was finally permitted to wander at will among the trees. Some of the same problems affect the electron microscopist as would beset the hypothetical explorer. There are such vast areas to uncover that

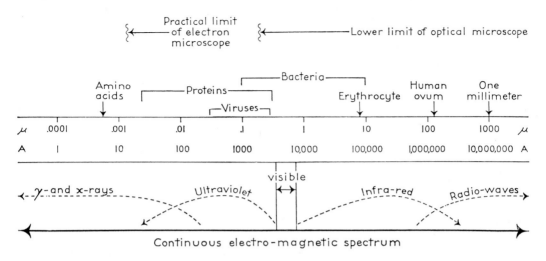

FIG. 3–2.—Comparison of sizes of amino acids, proteins, and living units with wave lengths of different kinds of radiation. (Bloom and Fawcett, *A Textbook of Histology*, courtesy of W. B. Saunders Co.)

many are studied only superficially, and some erroneous conclusions are undoubtedly drawn because of insufficient data. Because so much more detail can be seen in a very small area, tissue preparation is a great deal more exacting and much more time-consuming.

The best means of fixation involves the applying of a fixative (*osmium tetroxide* is commonly used) to living tissue, either directly to the surface or by perfusion of the fixative into blood vessels of an anesthetized animal. If this type of fixation is impracticable, a biopsy specimen may be removed and fixed, or a piece of tissue may be removed immediately following slaughter. In either case, the time from the living state to immersion in the fixative should not exceed two minutes, and the size of tissue should not exceed 1 mm. on a side.

Osmium tetroxide acts both as a fixative and as a stain. Other heavy metals including lead may be used as so-called stains. The term "stain" may be used somewhat loosely, because the areas where the metals concentrate inhibit the passage of electrons, giving an electron-dense appearance that shows up as a dark area in the final photographic print.

After fixation, the tissue is dehydrated and infiltrated with plastic and then embedded in plastic for sectioning. The sections are cut extremely thin (less than 300 Å in thickness), placed on a grid, and examined with the electron microscope.

The picture of the typical cell as viewed with the electron microscope still shows most of the structures described by light microscopists, but in much greater detail.

The classical separation of the cell into presumed living *organelles* and non-living *metaplastic inclusions* has become somewhat blurred by findings with the electron microscope and the discovery that genetic information is carried from cell to cell and organism to organism only by *DNA* (*deoxyribonucleic acid*). Although the mechanisms of life are becoming clearer, the definition of life is more difficult.

GENERAL ANATOMY OF THE CELL

The typical cell seen in light microscopy consists of a nucleus and cytoplasm surrounded by the cell membrane. The nucleus contains a nucleolus and *chromatin material* that forms into *chromosomes* during cell division and is surrounded by a nuclear membrane. The cytoplasm contains a number of different structures, including the *Golgi apparatus, mitochondria*, and inclusions that can be demonstrated by special preparation and staining techniques. The cell wall seen in light microscopy was the subject of much difference of interpretation.

THE PLASMA MEMBRANE

The plasma membrane (also called the cell wall and cell membrane) has long been believed to be of great importance because it presumably controls what enters the cell and what leaves the cell. Electron micrographs have shown the plasma membrane to be a rather uniform structure of the order of 70 to 100 Å in thickness. The plasma membrane as well as many other membranous structures within the cell consists of three visible layers. The most superficial layer of the plasma membrane and the deepest layer both appear to be protein in nature, and the middle layer of the "sandwich" appears to be a lipid or a phospholipid. Although this shows a great deal more than was ever seen in light microscopy, the question still remains as to how the plasma membrane functions to help maintain cytoplasm that is of a considerably different composition from the fluid outside the cell.

The presence of *pores* (small holes) in the plasma membrane has been described and also denied. A "pumping mechanism" to move water and other molecules and ions into and out of the cell has been postulated, but not explained very well. Invaginations of the cell wall (called *caveoli*) are sometimes seen in close proximity to small membrane-bound vesicles (called *pinocytotic vesicles*). These structures suggest that fluid may enter the cell by a process called *pinocytosis*, in which small blebs formed by an inpouching of the plasma membrane break off within the cells as vesicles. It is also conceivable that these vesicles may be formed in the cell and discharge their contents to the exterior by joining the cell membrane and then opening to the exterior in that manner.

Regardless of how it functions, the plasma membrane is a major factor in *homeostasis* within the cell. This is the phenomenon of maintaining a constant internal environment.

Modifications of the plasma membrane occur largely on the free surface of cells, a surface not adjacent to any other cells. These modifications usually increase the cell surface and presumably function in absorption or secretion. The *striated border* (*brush border*) seen in light microscopy appears in electron micrographs to consist of remarkable uniform finger-like projections of a constant height and width, at least for a given cell type. Less regular projections, called *stereocilia*, are irregular branched extensions of the cell cytoplasm that are not motile. Microvilli are somewhat similar to stereocilia, except they are smaller and unbranched.

Motile cilia (*kinocilia*) are quite complex elongated finger-like projections from cell surfaces found in areas where material is moved past the surface, as in the lining of the trachea and lining of the Fallopian tubes. Each cilium is associated with a basal body that resembles a centriole normally seen in the cytoplasm of all cells. From the basal body nine pairs of peripheral tubules and one central pair of tubules extend into and throughout most of the length of the related cilium. These tubules are parallel with the long axis of the cilium and are presumed to produce movement of the cilium in some manner.

THE NUCLEUS

The *nucleus* contains the genetic material of the cell: chromatin in the nondividing cell, and chromosomes in the dividing cell. That the nuclei of somatic cells contain the information necessary for determining the form and structure of new cells and that the nuclei of sex cells contain the information necessary to determine the characteristics of a new individual has been known for many years. However, until the concept of DNA and *RNA* (*ribonucleic acid*) activity became known, the mechanism involved in cell division was hardly even suspected. The appearance of chromosomes during cell division has been worked out quite well with techniques of light microscopy. The electron microscope has not added a great deal to the knowledge of the interior of the nucleus, except to show the chromosomes as largely DNA.

The *nuclear membrane* in electron micrographs shows two distinct membranes separated by a space of about 200 Å. The outer membrane is believed to be continuous with the endoplasmic reticulum. Ribosomes are frequently found outside the outer membrane. Pores (small holes) have been described in the nuclear membrane. These pores permit continuity between the protoplasm of the nucleus and the cytoplasm outside the nucleus.

The *nucleoli* in the nucleus appear to consist largely of clustered RNA granules and consequently show up as electron-dense structures. The DNA in the nucleus appears much less dense in electron micrographs. Fine filaments may also be seen scattered throughout the nucleus.

Organelles in the cytoplasm beside the nucleus include the endoplasmic reticulum (either smooth-surfaced or rough-surfaced), mitochondria, Golgi apparatus, centrioles, free ribosomes, various types of vesicles (including multivesicular bodies, microbodies, droplets, and lysosomes).

THE ENDOPLASMIC RETICULUM

The *endoplasmic reticulum* consists of a system of tubes or flattened sacs located in the cytoplasm of practically all cells. The outer nuclear membrane often shows continuity with the endoplasmic reticulum, and the plasma membrane has been described as joining the endoplasmic reticulum. Some authorities do not believe the plasma membrane is ever continuous with the endoplasmic reticulum.

Occasionally dilations occur in the endoplasmic reticulum. These dilations are called *cisternae* and presumably may contain products of secretion. Some endoplasmic reticulum appears to be covered with scattered RNA (*ribosomes*) on the outer surface. This type is called *rough-surface endoplasmic reticulum* (also *alpha cytomembrane* and *ergastoplasm*). RNA functions in protein synthesis, so the amount of rough-surface endoplasmic reticulum is suggestive of the amount of protein synthesis occurring in the cell.

Smooth-surface endoplasmic reticulum (also called *beta cytomembrane*) has no visible RNA granules on the surface of the membrane. The smooth-surface endoplasmic reticulum appears to be associated with glycogen formation in the cell and may be related to the Golgi apparatus or may possibly be continuous with it.

MITOCHONDRIA

Mitochondria are usually oval structures found in the cytoplasm of cells. They range in size from spheres $0.2\,\mu$ in diameter to elongated structures $25\,\mu$ long. On section, each mitochondrion shows an outer enclosing membrane and an inner folded membrane. The inner membrane is thrown into inward-projecting folds called *cristae*. Knob-like projections have also been described attaching to the cristae. Mitochondria contain many of the enzymes associated with oxidation occurring in the citric acid cycle and the concurrent storing of energy by means of the change of ADP to ATP (see Chapter 21, p. 302). Cells undergoing active metabolism have large numbers of mitochondria in the cytoplasm.

THE GOLGI APPARATUS

The *Golgi apparatus* usually appears as a series of flattened membranous sacs near the nucleus. The electron microscope has definitely proven the Golgi apparatus is not an artifact of fixation or staining as some believed from the evidence of light microscopy. However, the function of the Golgi apparatus is not settled. Some believe the Golgi apparatus is the first place that secretory products of cells appear in the cytoplasm. Golgi membranes resemble smooth-surface endoplasmic reticulum quite closely, and the two may be associated or even continuous.

OTHER COMPONENTS OF THE CELL

Microsomes resemble rough-surface endoplasmic reticulum and may in fact be segments of rough-surface reticulum. They can be separated by ultra centrifugation from other parts of homogenized (ground) cells, being somewhat lighter than the mitochondria and nuclei.

The granules seen on the surface of various membranes in the cell and also seen as clumps of granules or as individual granules are called *ribosomes*. These consist almost entirely of RNA, either in the form of large molecules or as a coating of RNA on some other structure. If the granules are unattached, they are called *free ribosomes*.

Less constant structures are the various types of vesicles that may contain stored material such as lipid or glycogen, secretory material, or enzymes as in the lysosomes.

Some vesicles are membrane bound and some appear to be unbounded accumulations of products within the cytoplasm.

The relative quantities of the different cell constituents seem to vary with the specialization and function of different types of cells. Some of these differences will be pointed out when specific tissues are discussed in subsequent chapters.

CHAPTER 4

PHYSIOLOGY OF THE CELL

GENERAL

Physiology of the cell is a broad field. It involves the physical and chemical changes that occur in the normal functioning of the cell. This implies application of most laws of physics and chemistry as they pertain to living cells. The findings of cellular physiologists must be interpreted in the light of structures identified with various techniques, including the use of the electron microscope, the phase-contrast microscope, the ordinary light microscope, x-ray, diffraction, histochemistry, isotope studies, and others. As De Robertis *et al.*, 1960 (p. 2) states, "We believe today that form and function constitute an inseparable unity: the living organism."

CHEMICAL COMPOSITION OF THE CELL

Chemical composition of various parts of the cell plays an important role in cellular function. Approximate percentage composition of protoplasm is: water 85, protein 10, lipid 2, inorganic matter 1.5, and miscellaneous substances 1.5. Of equal or greater importance is the arrangement of molecules, particularly the proteins, amino acids, and lipids.

WATER

Water is by far the largest constituent of protoplasm and certainly one of the most important. The amorphous portion of the cell, the protoplasm proper, is largely a colloidal solution in water. Water also acts as a solvent for inorganic substances and enters into many reactions that occur in the cell.

Water occurs in the cell as free water, which is available for use in metabolism, and as bound water that is adsorbed to the surface of protein molecules. The bound water actually forms a part of the protoplasm, as it is held to the protein by hydrogen bonds.

Although some water is formed by oxidation of hydrogen during the utilization of food, so much is lost by evaporation from the skin and lungs and by excretion in urine and feces that additional water must be taken in from outside the animal. The quantity of water taken in varies considerably with the environment to which the animal is adapted. The time required for a complete turnover of the amount of water equal to the body weight varies with the species. De Robertis *et al.*, 1960 give this time for the ameba as seven days, man four weeks, the camel three months, the tortoise one year and some cacti 29 years.

PROTEINS

Proteins are next to water in quantity in protoplasm. Proteins and related substances are involved in many functions of protoplasm and the cell. The large size of many protein molecules makes them an important factor in maintaining osmotic pressure within the cell so that the water content of the cell is maintained at a relatively constant level. These large molecules, called macromolecules, have a variety of definite forms which permits some to function as enzymes in metabolic reactions, some to act as structural material such as collagen of connective tissue, some to aid in transmission of genetic information from cell to cell and from generation to generation, and some to function in other ways.

LIPIDS

Although lipids (fatty substances) account for a relatively small percentage of protoplasm, they are of importance in forming a part of the plasma membrane and other membranous constituents of the cell. In addition, lipids are found in some vitamins and in some hormones and, of course, provide a convenient way to store energy in the form of body fat.

CARBOHYDRATES

Carbohydrates make up a part of the "miscellaneous substances" listed earlier. Relatively little carbohydrate is found in protoplasm, even though carbohydrate forms a major part of the food of most animals.

Energy can be stored more efficiently as fat than as carbohydrate in the animal body because most of both the carbon and hydrogen of fats can be oxidized, but the hydrogen and oxygen of carbohydrates are in the same proportion as in water, so in effect only the carbon is available for oxidation. In plants the carbohydrates not only serve for storage of energy, but also are of structural importance. Several sugars are found in combination with proteins to form much of the ground substance (non-cellular portion) of connective tissues and some of the special fluid of the body, such as synovial fluid and the liquids of the eye.

The sugar deoxyribose is found in combination with nucleic acid to form the very important *DNA* (*deoxyribonucleic acid*) which has been accepted as the carrier of all genetic information from generation to generation and from cell to cell, and perhaps is ultimately in control of all functions of the cell. DNA is found almost exclusively in the nucleus of the cell. A related substance, *RNA* (*ribonucleic acid*), includes the sugar ribose combined with nucleic acid. RNA is believed to be intimately associated with synthesis of the many proteins within the cell.

INORGANIC SUBSTANCES

Inorganic substances in protoplasm may exist as ionizable salts such as NaCl, or they may be combined with proteins, fats, or carbohydrates. Iodine is an essential part of the hormone *thyroxine*; iron is necessary in *hemoglobin*; and phosphorus, joined with *adenosine* to form *ADP* (*adenosine diphosphate*) or *ATP* (*adenosine triphosphate*), is vital for energy relationships in almost all living matter.

Inorganic salts aid in maintaining a constant pH and help regulate osmotic pressure.

various substances can be moved across the plasma membrane (either into or out of the cell) against osmotic pressure, against hydrostatic pressure, and against electrochemical pressure. This movement of substances through the plasma membrane which requires work is called *active transport*.

The fact that sodium usually is found in greater concentration outside the cell and potassium is found in greater concentration inside the cell suggests some form of active transport of at least the sodium ions. This mechanism has been called the *"sodium pump"* or more generally the *"ion pump."*

Some materials are actively absorbed by kidney cells, and other materials are actively excreted by kidney cells. Active transport appears to be associated with metabolism of the cell, because metabolic poisons and other injuries to the cell destroy active transport and frequently increase the permeability of the plasma membrane to many substances.

Theories as to how active transport is accomplished are related both to the plasma membrane and to the cytoplasm. Structure of the membrane, including electrical activity of the proteins and possibly electric charges at the pores, has been suggested as contributing to the function of active transport. Current thinking seems to lean toward the idea that some type of carrier (probably enzymatic in nature) is involved in active transport. The theory is that the carrier forms a compound with the material to be transported across the plasma membrane and that energy is used in forming the combination of carrier and material or in separating the carrier from the material or both.

PINOCYTOSIS

Pinocytosis is a method cells may use to take in fluid from the surrounding medium by forming invaginations of the plasma membrane into the cell. These invaginated blebs then pinch off, forming small vacuoles surrounded by plasma membrane but located in the cytoplasm. Many of these vacuoles are so small that they can be seen only with the electron microscope. Pinocytosis has been observed in single-cell animals and in a number of mammalian cells, including white blood cells and cells believed to be active in fluid transport, such as cells of the kidney and cells lining the intestine.

Pinocytosis permits cells to take in molecules that are too large to pass through the plasma membrane of the cell. However, the fate of these large molecules (such as proteins and hormones) after entering the cell in this manner is not known.

A process that is essentially the reverse of pinocytosis has been described. The membrane surrounding vacuoles within the cytoplasm of the cell may fuse with the plasma membrane and then rupture at the point of junction, extruding the contents of the vacuole outside the cell. This process is difficult to differentiate from that of pinocytosis by the electron microscope, as they have an almost identical appearance. The expulsion of the contents of vacuoles as described above may function as a means of excretion of waste products or of secretion of products, or in some cases it may be a part of water transport across the cell.

Many of the modifications of the surface of cells, such as *microvilli* and *stereocilia*, presumably function to increase the surface area of the cell for either absorption, secretion, or excretion. Pinocytosis often occurs in cells equipped with microvilli.

INTERCELLULAR CONTACT

All vertebrates develop from subdivision of a single cell, the fertilized egg. Unicellular animals also develop by subdivision of a single parent cell. When the parent cell of a unicellular animal divides, the resulting daughter cells each

ULTRASTRUCTURE OF THE COMMON
CELL ORGANELLES AND INCLUSIONS

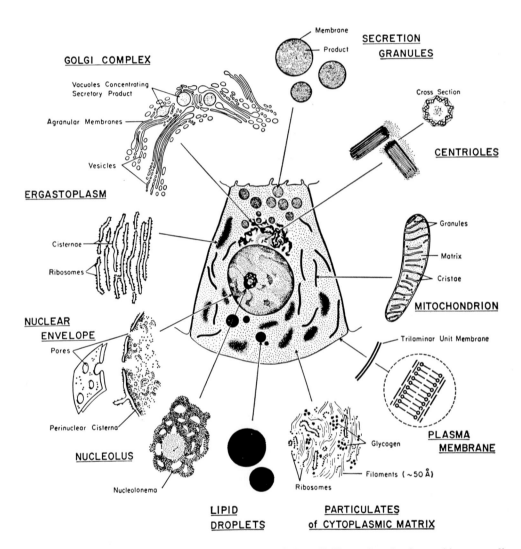

FIG. 4–5.—In the center of this figure is a diagram of the cell illustrating the form of its organelles and inclusions as they appear by light microscopy. Around the periphery are representations of the finer structure of these same components as seen in electron micrographs. The ergastoplasm of light microscopy consists of aggregations of submicroscopic membrane-limited elements with granules of ribonucleoprotein adhering to their outer surface. This component is now also called the *granular endoplasmic reticulum.* The illustration of the plasma membrane encircled by an interrupted line does not show structure that has been directly observed but represents one possible interpretation of the arrangement of lipid and protein molecules that may be related to the trilaminar appearance of cell membranes in electron micrographs. (Bloom and Fawcett, *A Textbook of Histology,* courtesy of W. B. Saunders Co.)

go their own separate way, but the daughter cells of the fertilized ovum of a multicellular animal for some reason stay together and eventually differentiate into cells making up different tissues. The problem of what holds these cells together and why they differentiate is still largely unanswered, although some incorrect ideas have been dispelled by the use of the electron microscope. Light microscopists described such things as intercellular bridges and intercellular cement which cannot be visualized with the electron microscope. Generally the plasma membranes of adjacent cells appear to be separated by a rather constant space of about 200 Å. Although it is difficult to prove there is no cement between these plasma membranes, it is equally difficult to identify the nature of a cementing substance if it exists. The *desmosomes* seen in electron micrographs were once called intercellular bridges. However, desmosomes appear to be simply localized thickenings of adjacent plasma membranes with tiny fibrils (*tonofibrils*) radiating from the thickening into the cytoplasm of the respective cell, with no continuity between cells.

Terminal bars resemble desmosomes when seen in cross section. They are ribbon-like thickenings of the plasma membrane just below the free surface of columnar cells. Each terminal bar passes completely around the periphery of the cell at the same level as the terminal bars of adjacent cells. In light microscopy the terminal bars were described as cementing substance.

Interdigitation of adjacent plasma membranes no doubt helps keep some cells together. This consists of finger-like projections from one cell that fit appropriate invaginations of adjacent cells.

THE GOLGI APPARATUS

The Golgi apparatus (a membranous structure near the nucleus) appears rather constantly in nearly all cells but differs in size and location in cells of different tissues. Its smooth membranous structure resembles that of smooth-surfaced endoplasmic reticulum, and they may in fact be continuous with each other. Function of the Golgi apparatus is not known, but it may be associated in some way with storage and/or transport of secretory products. The fact that there are no RNA (ribonucleic acid) granules associated with the Golgi apparatus suggests that it does not function in protein synthesis.

THE ENDOPLASMIC RETICULUM

The *endoplasmic reticulum* is a membranous network found throughout the cytoplasm of the cell. It was first described in the endoplasm (the cytoplasm deepest in the cell), giving rise to the name endoplasmic reticulum. Although still called the endoplasmic reticulum, it has been observed in all parts of the cytoplasm and may even be continuous with the plasma membrane and outer nuclear membrane. The endoplasmic reticulum may be in the form of tubules or sheets, with occasional enlarged sacs or vesicles called *cisternae*.

The fact that granules of RNA (ribonucleic acid) are found associated with endoplasmic reticulum, particularly in cells that actively synthesize protein, has led to the suggestion that the endoplasmic reticulum is associated with secretory activities and protein synthesis in cells. The endoplasmic reticulum also contains enzymes that may be involved in lipid (fat) metabolism.

RIBOSOMES

Free RNA granules are called *ribosomes*, and, because the ribonucleic acid is presumed to be associated with a protein, the term *RNP* (*ribonucleic protein*) granules is also used. RNA granules may also be attached to endoplasmic reticulum, in which case the membranous structure is known as granular or rough-surfaced endoplasmic reticulum. If no granules are associated with the membranes, it is called smooth-surfaced endoplasmic reticulum.

Both the free ribosomes and granular endoplasmic reticulum have an important function in protein synthesis. Smooth-surfaced endoplasmic reticulum may be involved in synthesis of *glycogen*. The endoplasmic reticulum of muscle cells is believed to act as a conductor for the impulse causing muscle contraction.

Fragments of endoplasmic reticulum found in homogenized cells are called *microsomes*. They can be separated from other cell portions by the centrifuge and analyzed chemically.

MITOCHONDRIA AND THE KREBS CYCLE

Mitochondria are next to nuclei in specific gravity, as shown by sedimentation or centrifuging cellular homogenate. The double membrane of the mitochondrion with the cristae projecting into the interior gives a large amount of surface for attachment of enzymes. Studies of fragmented mitochondria indicate that all the enzymes associated with oxidation of nutrients to carbon dioxide and water are found in the mitochondria. Thus all of the enzymes and coenzymes involved in the Krebs cycle appear to be largely localized in the mitochondria. The Krebs cycle is the final method of breakdown of carbohydrates, fatty acids, and amino acids. The energy released by oxidation of the carbon and hydrogen to carbon dioxide and water in the Krebs cycle is largely stored in the form of high-energy phosphate bonds in the compound ATP (adenosine triphosphate). ATP is formed by adding inorganic phosphate to ADP (adenosine diphosphate). The energy used to add the extra phosphate is readily available for any cellular activities that require energy, such as synthesis of protein, secretory activity, and muscle contraction. Energy is released in reconversion of ATP to ADP and inorganic phosphate. Most of these processes requiring energy are located outside of the mitochondria, although some synthesis may occur within the mitochondria.

LYSOSOMES

Lysosomes are larger than ribosomes but smaller than mitochondria. They are surrounded by a membrane and contain hydrolytic enzymes. The function of lysosomes is not known, but they may dissolve dead cells.

CELL DIVISION

The *nucleus* has been accepted as an important part of the cell for a long time. Its functions in cell division and transmission of genetic characteristics are well known. Nuclear control of cytoplasmic activities, particularly control of synthetic activity, is still being studied extensively.

MITOSIS

Mitosis, the division of somatic cells, as seen with the light microscope, has been well described for many years. Use of the electron microscope has added some information, but not as much as had been hoped. The period between active cell divisions is called the *interphase* and may vary from a matter of minutes in actively proliferating tissue to practically a permanent condition in cells that no longer divide, such as neurons in mature tissues.

The nuclear changes in a mitotic cycle include the following divisions: prophase, prometaphase, metaphase, anaphase, and telophase.

The stimulus for initiating cell division is not definitely known, although several factors have been suggested, including absolute cell size, disproportionate size of nucleus and cytoplasm and doubling of quantity of genetic material in the nucleus. Enough exceptions can be found to each of the above factors to exclude any one of them as the only stimulus for cell division.

Prophase

During *prophase* there is an increase in refractivity (bending of light), turgidity, and surface tension of the cell. The cytoplasm tends to become more viscous, and the nucleus tends to become less viscous. The chromosomal material becomes visible as a twisted filamentous mass that formerly was believed to be one continuous filament called the *spireme*. It is now believed that each chromosome, even in the prophase period, is a separate entity consisting of two chromatids (spiral elements) parallel with each other but not fused. As prophase progresses, the chromosomes become more definite, they thicken and shorten, and move toward

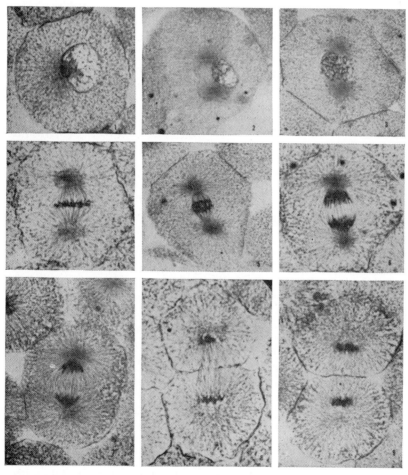

Fig. 4–6.—States of mitosis in cells of the Whitefish blastula: *1*, Interphase, with cell center adjacent to nucleus; *2*, early prophase showing development of astral centers; *3*, late prophase, with astral centers at opposite ends of the cell; *4*, metaphase; *5*, early anaphase; *6*, late anaphase; *7*, early telophase; *8*, mid-telophase, showing cleavage furrow; *9*, telophase-interphase following separation of daughter cells. (Courtesy of Mr. Philip G. Coleman, Michigan State University.)

the nuclear membrane, and a clear circular zone (the *centromere*) becomes more easily visible. The *centriole* (a small dark staining structure) splits, and an *aster* forms from each half. The aster is a figure composed of fibers radiating from each new centriole.

Prometaphase

The beginning of *prometaphase* is marked by disappearance of the nuclear membrane, followed by increasing fluidity of the central part of the cell. The chromosomes then begin to migrate toward the *equator* of the cell.

Metaphase

During *metaphase* the chromosomes become arranged at the equator and some of the astral fibers appear to attach to the centromere, the clear circular zone in the center of each chromosome.

Anaphase

Division of each centromere followed by separation of the chromatids marks the beginning of *anaphase*. As anaphase continues, the chromatids separate still farther.

Telophase

When separation of the two groups of chromatids is complete, *telophase* begins. During telophase each daughter nucleus reverts to the interphase appearance. The nuclear membrane, nucleoli, and nuclear sap reappear, and the chromosomes lose their identity. During telophase the cytoplasm also prepares for separation, called *cytokinesis*. The cytoplasmic organelles are divided about equally in each of the daughter cells. There is difference of opinion as to when and how replication of these cytoplasmic structures occurs, but eventually each daughter cell has essentially the same structure as the parent cell.

MEIOSIS

Meiosis (reduction division) differs from mitosis in a number of ways. It occurs during *gametogenesis*, the formation of ova (eggs) in the female and spermatazoa in the male (see Fig. 4–7). Since fertilization produces a doubling of the number of chromosomes in the fertilized ovum (an equal number is contributed by the male and by the female), there must be a mechanism to reduce the somatic or diploid, number of chromosomes before fertilization takes place. Otherwise chromosome numbers would increase in geometric ratio, a constant number of chromosomes in a species could not be maintained, and reproduction would cease after a few generations because of the massive numbers of chromosomes produced.

Meiosis not only reduces the somatic (diploid) number of chromosomes by one-half to the haploid number; it also increases the genetic variability of the offspring by a process called "crossing over." Homologous chromosomes in the primary sex cells pair up during prophase of meiosis. Homologous chromosomes are similar chromosomes, one contributed by the dam and one by the sire. These paired homologous chromosomes may then cross over and exchange similar areas such as one end, the middle portion, or both ends, resulting in two new chromosomes, each of which is different from either parent chromosome.

Crossing over is then followed by the so-called two meiotic divisions. In the first division one of the new chromosomes from each homologous pair goes to each daughter cell. In the second division half of each chromosome then goes to a new daughter cell, with the final result of four new cells, called gametes, each of which is likely to differ from the other three.

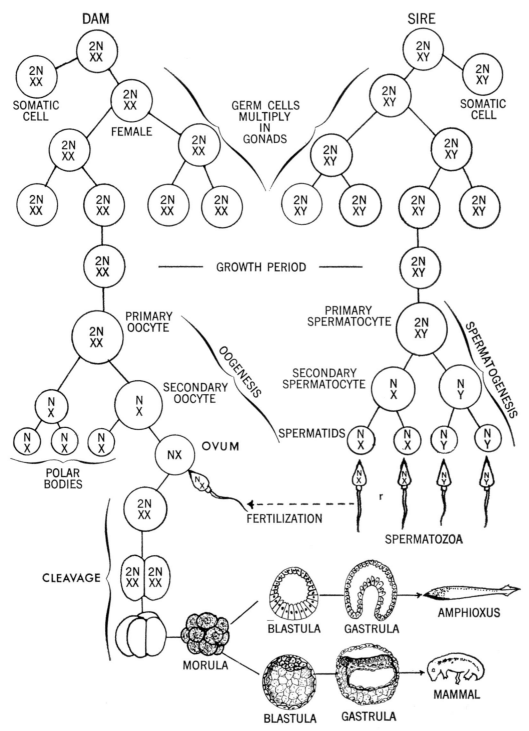

Fig. 4–7.—Diagram illustrating gametogenesis (oogenesis in the dam and spermatogenesis in the sire), cleavage, and development of the embryo in amphioxus and in a mammal. (After Alexander, *Biology*, Barnes and Noble.)

THE NUCLEUS

Experiments with amebae have shown that functional activity and even continued life of the cytoplasm is dependent on the presence of a nucleus. A cell with the nucleus removed gradually ceases activity and finally dies. However, replacement of a nucleus from one ameba of the same species or a very closely related species into the cytoplasm will restore function of the enucleated ameba. An isolated nucleus soon dies, even in a physiological salt solution.

Constituents of the nucleus can be identified by chemical analysis, and the location of many of them can be determined by histochemical methods, in which specific substances are stained and their location observed in tissue sections. The nuclei of all cells contain DNA (deoxyribonucleic acid) RNA (ribonucleic acid), proteins, lipids, and inorganic compounds. Most of the RNA in the nucleus appears to be located in the nucleolus, and there may be a small amount of DNA in the periphery of the nucleolus. Some proteins, including enzymes, are also present in the nucleolus. It is presumed that the nucleolus functions in some manner in the manufacture of RNA and possibly of proteins. Some RNA has also been described near the chromosomes.

DNA (DEOXYRIBONUCLEIC ACID) AND RNA (RIBONUCLEIC ACID)

DNA appears to be present largely in the nucleolus of interphase nuclei but in the chromosomes themselves during metaphase. If chromosomes are separated from nuclei and the DNA removed, there is still a residual protein left that apparently forms the framework of the chromosome. When the protein is removed from isolated chromosomes, the DNA remaining has been described as a series of discs (see Fig. 4–8).

It has been suggested that the structure of the chromosome consists of linked helices of DNA attached end to end and also attached to a protein core of some nature, or that the helices of DNA are not attached to each other but that each DNA helix is attached by one end to the protein core, and that the helix projects at right angles to the core. It has been impossible to correlate the gene concept exactly with electron micrographs of chromosomes. However, a quantitative relationship can be established between the DNA content of a nucleus and the number of chromosomes in the interphase nucleus (resting cell). In a dividing cell the quantity of DNA is doubled in late interphase or early prophase in preparation for doubling the number of chromosomes. *RNA* appears to leave the nucleus and enter the cytoplasm at this time, and the RNA content of the cytoplasm increases appreciably. During starvation of a cell the RNA and protein may decrease, but the DNA remains constant. RNA contents of the cell reflects quite closely the metabolic activity of the cell. As cellular activity increases, the quantity of RNA increases.

The DNA of the nucleus is essential for continued production of enzymes and other proteins by the cell. It is presumed that the RNA of the ribosomes is directly involved in protein synthesis, but that information must be obtained from the DNA of the nucleus in some manner as to the arrangement of amino acids in the proteins. A so-called "messenger RNA" has been postulated that functions by bringing the coded information from DNA of the nucleus to the RNA of the ribosomes in the cytoplasm.

Viruses consist largely of either DNA or RNA. Upon entering a cell the virus in some manner substitutes its own messenger RNA in place of the original messenger RNA from the nucleus of the cell. Thus the cell is induced to manufacture protein and DNA or RNA to the specifications laid down by the virus.

DNA and RNA both consist of many small units (*monomers*) joined to form long chains. Each monomer, called a *nucleotide*, is made up of a phosphate, a sugar, and either a *purine* or *pyrimidine* base. The sugar in RNA is ribose, but the sugar in DNA is called deoxyribose because it lacks one oxygen atom that is present in ribose.

The two purines, *adanine* and *guanine*, and the pyrimidine *cytosine* are found as bases in both DNA and RNA. However, the pyrimidine *thymine* occurs only in DNA, and the pyrimidine *uracil* occurs only in RNA.

The presumed structure of DNA was determined by Watson and Crick to be a double helix something like a circular stair or twisted metal ladder. The rails consist of two long chains of sugar-phosphate molecules, and the rungs are made up of paired bases that hold the two parts of the double helix together. Adenine is always paired with thymine, and guanine is always paired with cytosine.

Apparently all genetic information carried by the chromosomes from one generation of cells to the next is coded by the specific sequence of purine and pyramidine bases in a DNA molecule. This sequential arrangement of bases and its control of heredity both on the cellular level and species level has been referred

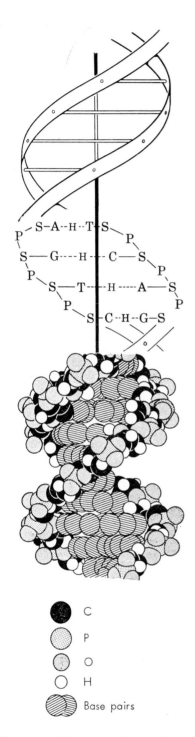

C
P
O
H
Base pairs

Fig. 4–8.—(*See opposite column for legend.*)

Fig. 4–8.—The helix of DNA, with three different ways of representing the molecular arrangement. *Top*, general picture of the double helix, with the phosphate-sugar combinations making up the outside spirals and the base pairs the cross-bars; *middle*, a somewhat more detailed representation: phosphate *P*, sugar *S*, adenine *A*, thymine *T*, guanine *G*, cytosine *C*, and hydrogen *H*; *bottom*, detailed structure showing how the space is filled with atoms; carbon *C*, oxygen *O*, hydrogen *H*, phosphorus *P* and the base pairs. (Carl P. Swanson, *The Cell*, courtesy of Prentice-Hall, Inc.)

to as the *genetic code* and also as the language of life. Eventually the code is interpreted by the cell largely as specific proteins, particularly enzymes.

The two strands of the DNA double helix are not identical but are complementary. In other words, wherever adanine appears on one strand, thymine will be in the same position on the opposite strand, and wherever guanine is located on one strand, cytosine is found in the same position on the opposite strand. Replication of DNA results by splitting of the double helices at the point of junction of complementary bases. Each separated strand then serves as a template or model for the formation of its complementary strand, thus resulting in two double DNA helices identical with the original DNA double helix.

Messenger RNA in some way receives coding information from DNA of the nucleus. This may occur in a fashion similar to the duplication of DNA, except that uracil in RNA pairs with the adenine of DNA. The messenger RNA then appears to leave the nucleus and then transmits the information it received from DNA to the RNA of the cytoplasm, the ribosomes. The RNA of the ribosomes in turn determine the configuration of protein that the cell produces from amino acids in the cytoplasm.

A *transfer RNA* has been described that functions to bring amino acids from the cytoplasm of the cell to the ribosomes for assembly into protein.

Although many details of this process are yet to be worked out, it appears that the same general principles of information transfer apply regardless of whether the cell is producing secretory products for use outside the cell or additional cytoplasmic structures and enzymes for use within the cell. These same principles also seem to apply to all living things from viruses, through plants and lower animals, to vertebrates, including man.

CHAPTER 5

ANATOMY OF THE NERVOUS SYSTEM

GENERAL

IRRITABILITY and conductivity are two of the properties associated with life which a single cell organism such as the ameba possesses.

In order to adjust to changes in the external environment, the single cell must be receptive to stimuli such as changes of light, temperature, osmotic pressure, pH, and touch. In other words, it must be irritable. Not only are the stimuli received, but they must be transmitted to the portion of the cell which will take appropriate action. This transmission represents conductivity.

As organisms evolve into more complex forms, these two activities are performed by specialized cells which are the forerunners of nerve cells, called neurons. These cells must have contact both with the surface of the animal, where changes in environment are most noticeable, and with deeper (effector) cells, such as muscle cells or gland cells, which specialize either in contraction or secretion. Certain epithelial cells at first produce elongated processes to facilitate this type of nervous activity.

Thus, the origin of the nervous system of higher animals is seen logically to come from the ectoderm, or external layer of the animal.

The nervous system of early multicellular forms such as the hydra consists of a fine network of individual nerve cells without any brain or special co-ordinating center. As organisms become more complex, the specialization of nerve cells increases, with some cells (sensory, or afferent) conducting stimuli from the surface to the central portion of the organism, where each contacts another neuron (motor or efferent). This neuron, in turn, is responsible for relaying the impulse from the central region to the effector cells, producing the required action.

The next step is the development of an integrative mechanism, or central nervous system, to coordinate activities according to the stimuli received by the sensory neurons. This co-ordination is produced largely by neurons interposed between afferent and efferent neurons which are called *intercalated neurons, internuncial neurons, association neurons, connector neurons*, or simply *interneurons*. Much of the central nervous system (brain and spinal cord) of higher animals consists of interneurons which connect neurons from various levels or segments and integrate their activity.

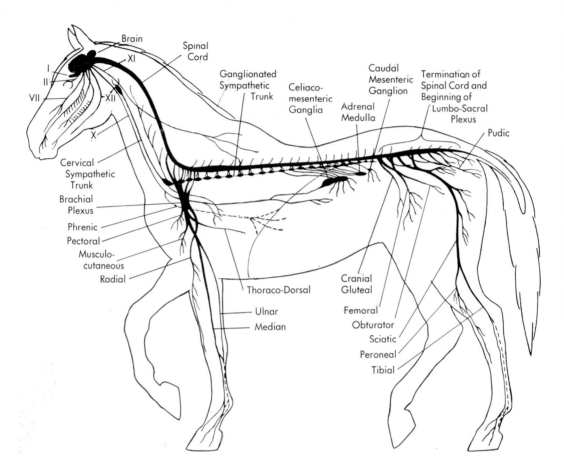

FIG. 5–1.—Nervous system of the horse.

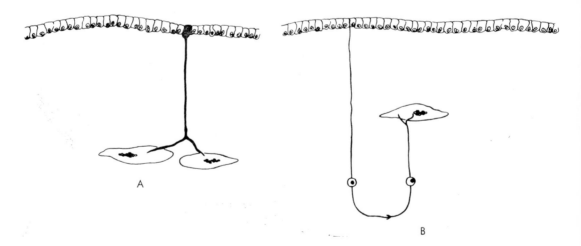

FIG. 5–2.—Early stages in evolution of nervous tissue. *A*, Modified ectodermal cell extends from surface to   uscle cells. *B*, Chain of two modified ectodermal cells (neurons) extending from surface to muscle cell. (After Ham, *Histology*, J. B. Lippincott Co.)

ORGANIZATION OF THE NERVOUS SYSTEM

Perception of changes in external environment (everything associated with the animal but external to it) and changes of internal enviroment (the entire internal makeup of the animal) as well as the ability to adapt to these changes basically depend upon the proper functioning of the individual neurons or nerve cells which constitute the nervous system of an animal.

Each neuron consists of a nerve cell body and one or more nerve processes. The nerve processes are called *dendrites*, or *dendrons*, if they conduct impulses toward the cell bodies; they are called *axons* (also called axis-cylinder processes, neuraxons, or neurites) if they conduct away from the cell bodies.

The junction of the axon of one neuron with a dendrite of another neuron is called a *synapse*. The synapse is the point of contact between neurons that are functionally related. This contact may be between the axon of one neuron and a dendrite of another or it may be between the axon of one neuron and the cell body of another neuron. Of course, any given neuron may synapse with axons or dendrites of many other neurons. While a nerve impulse can travel in all directions in a neuron, the synapse conducts in only one direction, from the afferent, or sensory, neuron toward the efferent, or motor, neuron. Thus the synapse acts as a one-way valve so that reflex action can be produced only by stimulation of the receptor (afferent) neuron. Stimulation of a motor neuron cannot initiate a reflex.

The synapse appears to be subject to fatigue and is much more sensitive than the neuron to drugs such as *nicotine*, *strychnine*, *caffeine*, and *morphine*. It is assumed that the physiological properties of the synapse are due to its membrane characteristics, although much is still to be learned about the fine structure of the synapse.

The many classifications and subdivisions of the nervous system will seem considerably less formidable if one remembers that they are all arbitrary names for geographic or physiologic groupings of nerve cells and/or nerve processes.

Groups of nerve cell bodies within the brain or spinal cord are generally called *nuclei*, while groups of nerve cell bodies outside the brain and spinal cord are usually called *ganglia*. This type of nucleus should not be confused with the central body of a cell which is also called a nucleus. Similarly, bundles of nerve processes within the brain or spinal cord are frequently called *tracts*, or *fasciculi*, while bundles of processes outside the central nervous system are called nerves.

The following classification is an arbitrary division of the nervous system of mammals which groups various portions for convenience of description. It should be remembered that the nervous system is an integrated unit and that any separation into parts is a man-made invention.

Central nervous system
　Brain—enclosed in cranial part of skull
　Spinal cord—enclosed in vertebral canal
Peripheral nervous system
　Cranial nerves—emerge through cranial foramina of skull
　Spinal nerves—emerge through intervertebral foramina
　Autonomic nervous system
　　Sympathetic nervous system — Thoraco-lumbar portion
　　Parasympathetic nervous system — Cranio-sacral portion

HISTOLOGY OF THE NERVOUS SYSTEM

Nervous tissue consists not only of neurons but also of supporting tissue. In the central nervous system (brain and spinal cord) the supporting tissue is called *neuroglia*, while the supporting tissue of the peripheral nervous system is ordinary white fibrous connective tissue.

Structure of the Neuron

The *neuron* consists of the nerve cell body and all of its processes. The cell body consists of a relatively large mass of cytoplasm, a nucleus, and one or more nucleoli. The cytoplasm is sometimes called *neuroblasm*. Among the important parts of the cytoplasm are the organelles (living structures) which include *mitochondria*, *fibrils*, *Golgi network*, and a *centrosome*.

The most common non-living inclusion seen in nerve cell cytoplasm are the *Nissl bodies*, or *tigroid bodies*, which are dark-

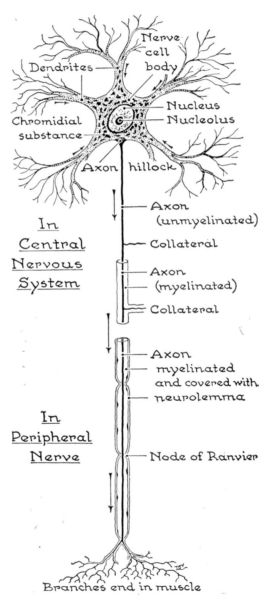

Fig. 5–3.—Diagram of a multipolar neuron. (Ham and Leeson, *Histology*, 4th ed., courtesy of J. B. Lippincott Co.)

staining granules. The term "tigroid bodies" comes from the striped appearance they impart to some cells. Other inclusions found in the cytoplasm include fat and pigments. A yellow-brown *lipochrome* pigment and black *melanin* pigment are commonly present.

Neurons may be classified according to the number of nerve processes. Unipolar neurons have one process, bipolar neurons have one dendrite and one axon, and multipolar neurons have a number of dendrites but usually only one axon. Dendrites are short protoplasmic processes that branch repeatedly. The cytoplasm of the cell body extends into the dendrites. The axon arises from a conical mound of cytoplasm, the *axon hillock.*

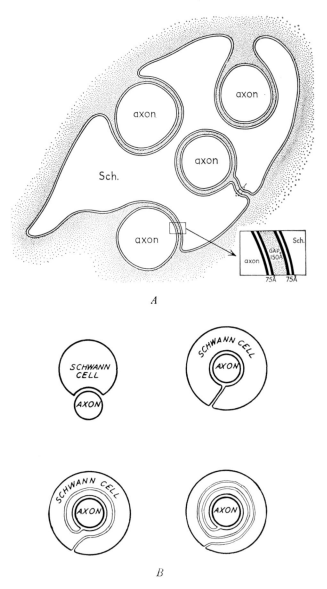

FIG. 5–4.—*A*, Diagram of nonmyelinated fibers in relation to a neurilemma cell. (Causey, G., *The Cell of Schwann*, Edinburgh, Livingstone.)

B, Diagram to illustrate the process of myelinization of axons as outlined by Geren and Schmitt, 1957. (Finerty and Cowdry, *A Textbook of Histology*, 5th ed., Lea & Febiger.)

Although only one axon leaves the cell body, it frequently gives off right-angle collateral branches along its course which end in more or less profuse terminal arborizations, or *telodendria*, as does the main axon.

In a motor nerve each terminal branch supplies a single muscle fiber. The entire unit, motor nerve plus all muscle fibers it supplies, is termed a motor unit.

Nerve fibers may be myelinated or unmyelinated. Myelinated fibers are surrounded by a white sheath of fatty material. Studies with the electron microscope have shown the myelin sheath actually to consist of many layers of cell membrane of a Schwann cell wrapped around the nerve fiber in such a manner that in cross section the myelin sheath resembles a slice of jelly roll. The nerve fibers that were described as lacking both myelin sheath and neurolemma when observed with light microscopy have been found to be invaginated into the cell membrane of a Schwann cell so that all nerve fibers are covered by at least one layer of cell membrane. Several un-myelinated fibers may be invaginated into separate areas of the same Schwann cell (see Fig. 5–4*A* and *B*).

EMBRYOLOGY OF THE NERVOUS SYSTEM

Whether the development of the nervous system is considered from the standpoint of developmental anatomy of the individual or from that of the evolutionary development of the race, the steps are similar.

The very early embryo first shows a thickening of ectodermal cells on the dorsum just anterior to the *primitive streak*. The primitive streak is one of the first areas of cellular differentiation, and it indicates the longitudinal axis of the embryo. This thickening, the *neural plate*, grows faster along the lateral margins than in the center, thus forming the

neural groove. Next, the edges of the groove come into apposition dorsally to form the *neural tube*. The entire central nervous system is formed from the neural tube. The lumen of the neural tube persists in the adult as the *central canal* of the spinal cord and as the two *lateral ventricles*, the *third ventricle* and the *fourth ventricle* of the brain.

Neural crest cells lateral to the neural tube eventually form sensory ganglia and some of the sympathetic ganglia.

Although the rostral (cranial) end of the embryonic brain develops earliest and is the largest, closure of this portion is slower than the more caudal parts which will form the cranial part of the spinal cord.

In this early period the segmental nature of the organism is indicated by the development of *somites* in the *mesoderm*. These are serially arranged paired thickenings on each side of the neural tube eventually form sensory ganglia be supplied by a pair of spinal nerves.

Development of the spinal cord continues by increasing the thickness of the wall of the neural tube and decreasing the size of the lumen. Three concentric layers make up the neural tube: an inner ependymal layer, a middle mantle layer, and a superficial marginal layer.

The thin *ependymal layer* of cells forms the lining of the central canal of the spinal cord and of the ventricles of the brain.

The so-called *mantle layer*, which becomes the gray matter of the spinal cord, is arranged in a longitudinal column extending the entire length of the spinal cord. In cross section this column has an H, or butterfly, shape and consists largely of nerve cell bodies, which give it the gray appearance. The dorsal branches of the H, or dorsal wings of the butterfly are called the dorsal horns; the ventral branches are called ventral horns. The dorsal horns receive processes of the afferent (sensory) nerves which enter the spinal cord. The ventral horns contain the cells of origin of the motor neurons.

The *marginal layer*, which is most superficial, consists of longitudinal nerve processes which make up the white matter of the spinal cord. The white color comes from the myelin sheaths, fatty material surrounding the nerve fibers. These fibers are grouped into more or less functional units, the dorsal, lateral, and ventral columns of white matter which are separated by the dorsal and ventral horns of gray matter.

The dorsal root ganglia are derived from the neural crest cells. Nerve cells in these ganglia give rise to some fibers which grow toward the dorsal horn of the spinal cord and other fibers which enter the spinal nerve as sensory, or afferent, fibers. The portion of these fibers which extends from the spinal nerve to the spinal cord is known as the dorsal root of the spinal nerve.

The ventral root of the spinal nerve consists largely of fibers which grow from the nerve cells located in the ventral horn of the spinal cord. The dorsal and ventral roots unite close to the intervertebral foramen to form the spinal nerve.

Development of the brain begins before the spinal cord develops, continues at a rapid pace throughout embryonic and fetal life, and extends to puberty.

The first gross subdivisions of the brain form the so-called three-vesicle stage. These subdivisions are the *prosencephalon*, or *forebrain*; *mesencephalon*, or *midbrain*; and *rhombencephalon*, or *hind-brain*.

The prosencephalon is widened by the presence of optic vesicles, which are the forerunners of the eyes. At this stage the neural tube is not completely closed, leaving a cranial opening called the *anterior neuropore* and a caudal opening called the *sinus rhomboidalis*.

To form the five-vesicle stage of development, the prosencephalon further subdivides to form the *telencephalon* and the

diencephalon; the mesencephalon does not subdivide; and the rhombencephalon divides into the *metencephalon* and the *myelencephalon*.

THE CENTRAL NERVOUS SYSTEM

Some appreciation of the complexity of the *central nervous system* (brain and spinal cord) can be gained by comparing the evolution of the nervous system with the development of electronic control mechanisms such as are used to guide missiles and rockets. From the first simple mechanical adding machine have been developed the complex electronic brains with innumerable circuits, switches, and relays.

However, the most sophisticated electronic apparatus is bulky, crude, and non-versatile when compared with the mammalian nervous system. All man-made devices are quite limited in the types of information they can receive and process. The central nervous system on the other hand not only receives but interprets and evaluates such diverse information as changes in light waves, sound waves, temperature, gravitation, pressure, and chemicals. While a $2\frac{1}{2}$-inch cable such as the transatlantic telephone cable contains 2100 pairs of wires, the pituitary stalk of the human brain, which is less than $\frac{1}{2}$ inch in diameter, contains approximately 50,000 individual nerve fibers.

THE BRAIN

The gross subdivisions of the adult brain include the cerebrum, the cerebellum, and the brain stem. The telencephalon includes the *cerebral cortex*, the *corpora striata*, and the *rhinencephalon*. It encloses the cavities of the lateral ventricles, the *interventricular foramena of Monroe*, and the rostral portion of the third ventricle.

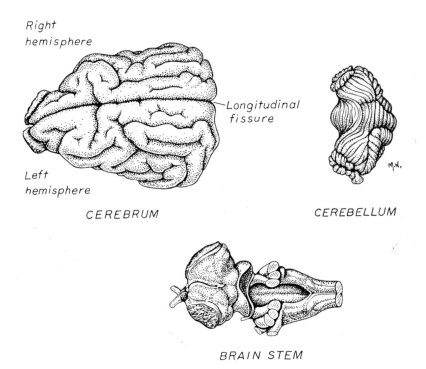

FIG. 5–5.—Gross subdivisions of the brain. (Meyer, in Miller, Christensen, and Evans, *Anatomy of the Dog*, courtesy of W. B. Saunders Co.)

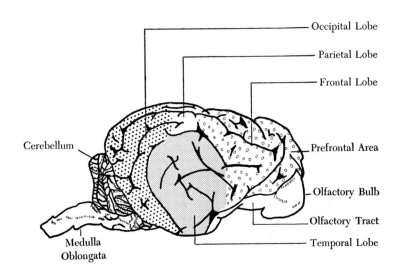

FIG. 5–6.—Diagrammatic lateral view of dog's brain. (McGrath, *Neurologic Examination of the Dog*, Lea & Febiger.)

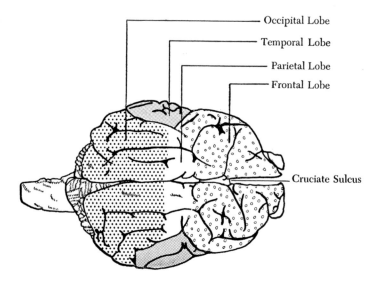

FIG. 5–7.—Diagrammatic dorsal view of dog's brain. (McGrath, *Neurologic Examination of the Dog*, Lea & Febiger.)

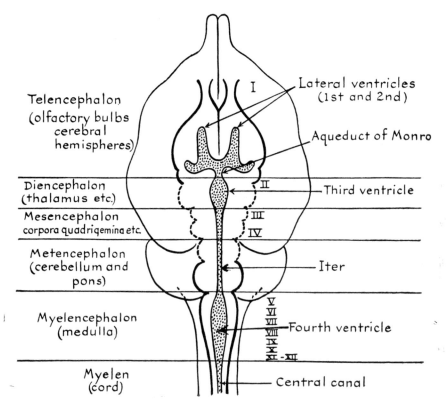

FIG. 5–8.—General plan of the mammalian brain. (Iter is cerebral aqueduct.) (Leach, *Functional Anatomy, Mammalian and Comparative*, courtesy of McGraw-Hill Book Co.)

The surface area of the *cerebrum* is increased considerably by numerous foldings to form convex ridges, called *gyri*, which are convolutions separated by furrows called *fissures*, or *sulci*. In man and some animals the cortical areas have been extensively mapped as to localization of specific sensory and motor functions. Division of the cerebrum into lobes is indicated in Figures 5–6 and 5–7. The highest types of mental activities,

corpus striatum consists, to quite an extent, of projection fibers which connect the cerebral cortex with other parts of the central nervous system and indirectly with the peripheral nervous system.

The *rhinencephalon* is, from the evolutionary standpoint, one of the oldest parts of the cerebrum. It is associated primarily with the sense of smell and is therefore sometimes called the *olfactory brain*.

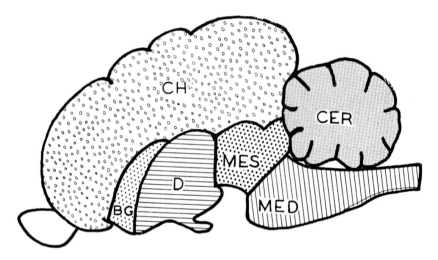

Fig. 5–9.—Schematic median section of the dog brain. *CH*, Cerebral hemisphere; *BG*, Basal ganglion, *D*, Diencephalon; *MES*, Mesencephalon; *CER*, Cerebellum; *MED*, Medulla oblongata. (McGrath; *Neurologic Examination of the Dog*, Lea & Febiger.)

such as voluntary muscle control, interpretation of sensations, and reasoning, are carried on primarily by the cells of the cerebral cortex, thus leading to the use of the term "gray matter" as synonymous with mental ability.

The *corpus striatum* of each cerebral hemisphere consists of a mixture of white and gray matter, thus giving a striated appearance, as the name implies. The gray matter of the corpus striatum is represented by a number of nuclear masses sometimes called the *basal nuclei*, or *basal ganglia*, even though the term "ganglion" usually refers to an accumulation of cell bodies outside the central nervous system. The white matter of the

The *diencephalon* is the part of the prosencephalon located next to the midbrain. The *thalamus*, the *epithalamus*, the *hypothalamus*, and most of the third ventricle are included in the diencephalon.

The *thalamus* is essentially a relay center for nerve fibers connecting the cerebral hemispheres with the brain stem and spinal cord. The *epithalamus* includes the *habenular nuclei* (associated with smell), white matter tracts, and the *pineal body*, which is sometimes considered to be an endocrine organ. The hypothalamus includes the *pituitary gland* (one of the most important endocrine glands) and the structures closely associated with it. These structures include the *tuber*

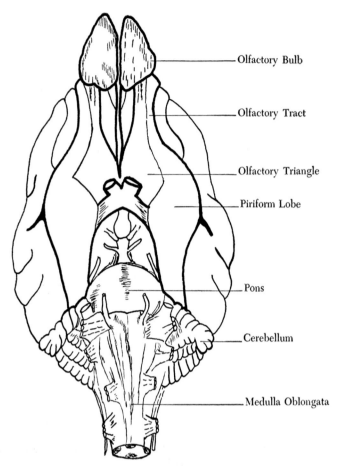

Olfactory Bulb

Olfactory Tract

Olfactory Triangle

Piriform Lobe

Pons

Cerebellum

Medulla Oblongata

FIG. 5–10.—Diagrammatic ventral view of the dog's brain. Olfactory bulb, olfactory tract, olfactory triangle, and the piriform lobe are parts of the rhinencephalon, or olfactory brain. (McGrath, *Neurologic Examination of the Dog*, Lea & Febiger.)

cinereum which attaches the stalk of the pituitary gland to the brain, the *optic chiasm*, or crossing of the optic nerves just cranial to the pituitary gland, and the *mammillary bodies* located immediately caudal to the pituitary gland.

The *mesencephalon*, or *midbrain*, is that portion of the brain that does not subdivide during the development from the embryo to the adult. As the name implies, the midbrain is located between the prosencephalon cranially and the rhombencephalon caudally. The two *cerebral peduncles* and four *quadrigeminal bodies* are the largest structures of the mesencephalon, or midbrain.

The *cerebral peduncles*, also called *crura cerebri*, are essentially the continuation of the right and left halves of the spinal cord and brain stem into the respective cerebral hemispheres. They contain fiber tracts and nuclei.

The *quadrigeminal bodies*, or *corpora quadrigemina*, consist of a right and a left anterior (cranial or superior) colliculus; and a right and left posterior (caudal or inferior) colliculus. The anterior colliculi are associated with vision; the posterior are associated with hearing.

The *rhombencephalon*, or *hindbrain*, is subdivided into the metencephalon; the myelencephalon, or *medulla oblongata* (fre-

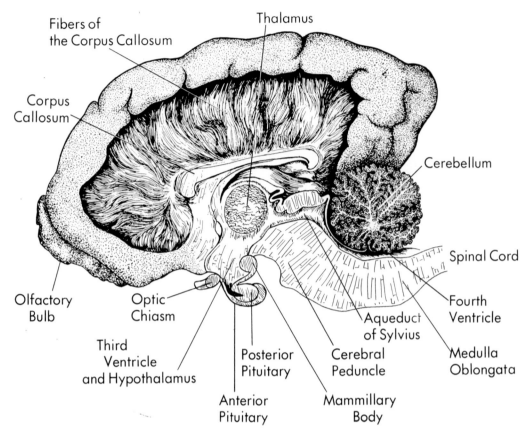

Fig. 5-11.—Sagittal section of the brain partially excavated. (After Meyer in Miller, Christensen, and Evans, *Anatomy of the Dog*, courtesy of W. B. Saunders Co.)

quently referred to as the medulla); and the fourth ventricle.

The *metencephalon* includes the *cerebellum* and the *pons*. The cerebellum consists of two lateral hemispheres and a median ridge called the *vermis*, because of its resemblance to a worm. The surface of the cerebellum consists of many lamina called *folia*. When cut on the median line, the cerebellum gives the appearance of foliage, thus leading to the ancient term "arbor vitae" or "tree of life," for this view of the cerebellum. In the cerebellum the white matter is chiefly centrally located and the gray matter peripherally located, as they are in the cerebrum.

The pons is located ventral to the cerebellum and appears to form a bridge of

fibers from one hemisphere of the cerebellum to the other. Many other fiber tracts and nuclei make up the remainder of the pons.

The fourth ventricle is located ventral to the cerebellum and dorsal to the pons and brain stem.

The myelencephalon forms the medulla oblongata. It is the cranial continuation of the spinal cord, from which it is arbitrarily separated at the foramen magnum, the largest foramen in the skull. The fourth ventricle covers much of the dorsal surface of the brain stem, giving it somewhat the appearance of the spinal cord before the neural groove was completely closed.

As well as containing many fiber tracts from the spinal cord, the brain stem is the site of nuclei for a number of *cranial nerves* including those termed *V*, *VI*, *VII*, *IX*, *X*, *XI*, and *XII*. It also contains reflex centers for the control of respiration and circulation.

VENTRICLES

The ventricles of the brain are derivatives of the embryonic neural canal. Right and left *lateral ventricles* are located within the respective cerebral hemispheres. They connect with the *third ventricle* by way of the interventricular foramina of Monro. Most of the third ventricle is surrounded by the diencephalon. A portion of the third ventricle projects into the infundibulum (the stalk) of the pituitary gland. The third ventricle connects with the fourth ventricle by way of the *aqueduct of Sylvius*, also called the *cerebral aqueduct*.

The *fourth ventricle*, located between the cerebellum above and pons and medulla below, communicates with the *subarachnoid space* through the *foramina* of *Magendie* and *Luschka*. Each of the four *choroid plexuses* of the ventricles (one plexus for each ventricle) consists of a network of blood capillaries that protrudes into the lumen of the ventricle. Each plexus is covered intimately by a layer of ependymal cells derived from the lining membrane of the ventricles.

Cerebrospinal fluid is found in the ventricles of the brain, where it is formed by the choroid plexuses, and in the subarachnoid space surrounding the brain and spinal cord. There is some question as to whether the cerebrospinal fluid is merely a transudate which passively crosses the capillary vessel wall or whether it is actively secreted by the ependymal cells.

The route of passage of cerebrospinal fluid is from the two lateral ventricles through the interventricular foramina into the third ventricle, then by way of the cerebral aqueduct into the fourth ventricle, and finally through the foramina of Luschka and Magendie into the subarachnoid space where it surrounds both the brain and spinal cord. Any obstruction in this route may cause extensive damage to the brain.

Hydrocephalus, or water on the brain, frequently results from obstruction of the interventricular foramen. If this occurs in the embryo or fetus, the cerebrum may become extremely thin due to the pressure of the fluid which cannot escape from the lateral ventricles. In extreme cases the cranium may become so enlarged that normal parturition is difficult or impossible due to the large size of the head of the fetus.

MENINGES

The coverings of the brain and spinal cord, called *meninges*, include, from without inward, the dura mater, the arachnoid mater, and the pia mater.

The *dura mater* is a tough fibrous covering of the central nervous system. In the cranial cavity the dura mater blends intimately with the inner periosteum of the cranial bones. It also forms the *falx cerebri*, a median sickle-shaped fold which partially separates the cerebral hemispheres, and another fold of dura mater, called the *tentorium cerebelli*, which runs transversely between the cerebellum and the cerebrum. The dura mater contains channels filled with blood, called the sinuses of the dura mater. These sinuses are essentially veins which carry blood from the brain back toward the heart.

The spinal dura mater surrounds the spinal cord. It is separated from the periosteum of the vertebral canal by a fat-filled space, the *epidural space*.

The next deeper membrane is the *arachnoid mater*. It is assumed to resemble a spider web, hence the name arachnoid, after arachnid—the spider. The outer layer is practically fused to the dura

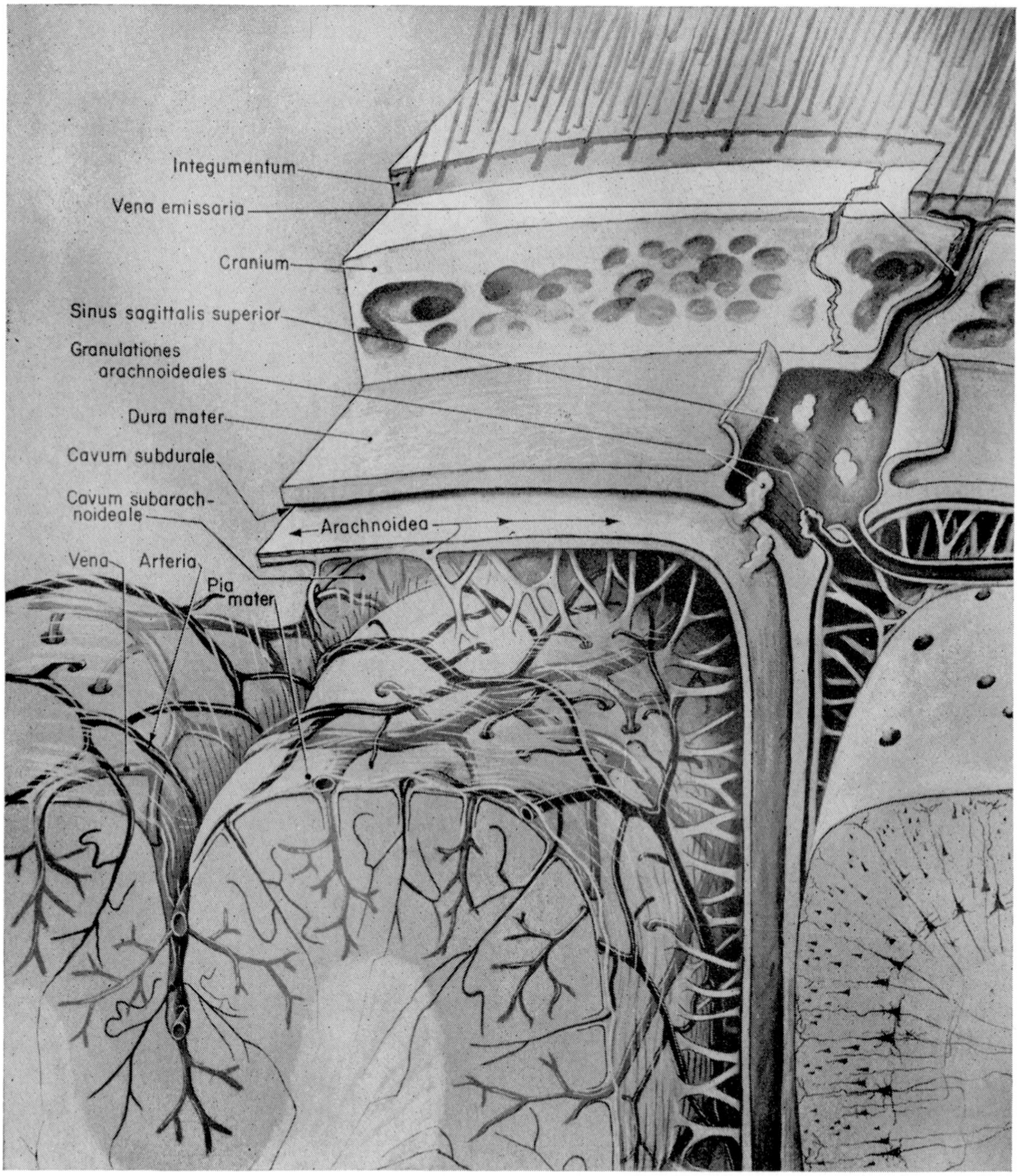

Integumentum

Vena emissaria

Cranium

Sinus sagittalis superior

Granulationes arachnoideales

Dura mater

Cavum subdurale

Cavum subarachnoideale

Arachnoidea

Vena   Arteria

Pia mater

FIG. 5–12.—Three-dimensional diagram of the meninges in the cranium. Some detailed structures shown in this diagram are not mentioned in the text. (Elias and Pauly, *Human Microanatomy*, 2nd Ed., courtesy of Da Vinci Publishing Co.)

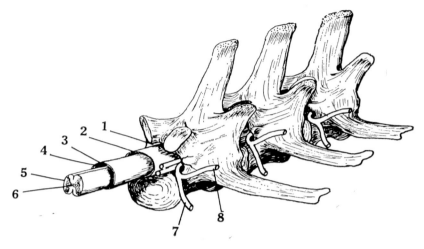

MENINGES AND SPINAL CORD

1. Epidural space   *5.* Pia mater
2. Dura mater   *6.* Grey matter of spinal cord
3. Arachnoidea   *7.* Spinal nerve—ventral branch
4. Subarachnoid space   *8.* Spinal nerve—dorsal branch

FIG. 5–13.—Three-dimensional diagram of the spinal cord and its meninges. (Foust and Getty, *Atlas and Dissection Guide for the Study of the Anatomy of Domestic Animals*, courtesy of the Iowa State College Press.)

mater, so the subdural space is almost non-existent. Spider-web-like projections of arachnoid mater extend from the outer layer of the arachnoid mater to the pia mater. This space, known as the subarachnoid space, contains cerebrospinal fluid. The cerebrospinal fluid formed in the ventricles of the brain acts as a protective cushion for the brain and spinal cord.

The *pia mater* is the deepest of the meninges. It is a delicate membrane that closely invests the brain and spinal cord. The pia mater forms a sheath around the blood vessels and follows them into the substance of the brain, forming the so-called "pial barrier," which inhibits movement of certain chemicals between the cerebral blood flow and the nervous tissue of the brain.

THE SPINAL CORD

The spinal cord is the caudal continuation of the medulla oblongata. Seg-

mentation is much more distinct in the spinal cord, with each segment giving rise to a pair of spinal nerves. The spinal cord receives sensory, or afferent, fibers by way of the dorsal roots of the spinal nerves and gives off the efferent, or motor, fibers to the ventral roots of the spinal nerves.

The central gray matter of the spinal cord consists primarily of nerve cell bodies and their processes.

Tracts of the Spinal Cord

The peripheral white matter can be roughly divided into three columns on each lateral half of the cord, a dorsal white column, a lateral white column, and a ventral white column.

The *dorsal white columns* contain afferent tracts which convey impulses or stimuli from joints, tendons, muscles, and bones. These are called proprioceptive functions because they give a sense of position of limbs or other body parts without the use of vision. The chief *tracts* in each dorsal

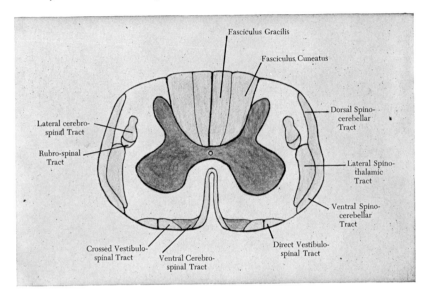

Fasciculus Gracilis

Fasciculus Cuneatus

Dorsal Spino-
cerebellar
Tract

Lateral cerebro-
spinal Tract

Rubro-spinal
Tract

Lateral Spino-
thalamic
Tract

Ventral Spino-
cerebellar
Tract

Crossed Vestibulo-
spinal Tract

Ventral Cerebro-
spinal Tract

Direct Vestibulo-
spinal Tract

Fig. 5–14.—Diagrammatic view of spinal cord in cross section to indicate location of gray and white matter. Note location of major fiber tracts. (McGrath, *Neurologic Examination of the Dog*, Lea & Febiger.)

white column are the *fasciculus gracilis*, and the *fasciculus cuneatus*.

The *fasciculus gracilis*, the more medial tract, is formed from dorsal root fibers of the lower thoracic, lumbar, sacral, and coccygeal nerves. These fibers end in the *nucleus gracilis* in the medulla.

The *fasciculus cuneatus*, lateral to the fasciculus gracilis, is found only in the cervical region, since it receives fibers only from dorsal roots of upper thoracic and cervical nerves. The fibers end in the *nucleus cuneatus*, also located in the medulla.

Many tracts are named according to the structures they connect. The lateral white columns contain the following tracts: *dorsal* and *ventral spinocerebellar*, *rubrospinal*, *lateral spinothalamic*, and *lateral corticospinal*.

The dorsal spinocerebellar tract conducts proprioceptive impulses from the spinal cord to the cerebellum to aid coordination of movements.

The rubrospinal tract connects the red nucleus in the midbrain with motor cells in the ventral gray horn of the spinal cord on the opposite side. The red

nucleus receives impulses from the cerebellum. Thus the spinocerebellar tract, the cerebellum, and the rubrospinal tracts are important in reflex control of movements, particularly those of locomotion.

The lateral spinothalamic tract conducts impulses relating to pain and temperature. It receives fibers from the dorsal gray horn of the opposite side, travels up the spinal cord, and terminates in the thalamus.

The lateral corticospinal tract carries voluntary motor impulses from the motor area of the cerebral cortex to cells in the ventral gray horn of the spinal cord. These fibers pass by way of the internal capsule, cerebral peduncle, pons, and medulla to the spinal cord. A majority of the fibers cross to the opposite side in the medulla.

Important tracts in the ventral white columns include the *direct vestibulospinal tract*; the *crossed vestibulospinal tract*; and the *ventral corticospinal tract*.

The direct vestibulospinal tract extends from the *lateral vestibular nucleus* to motor nuclei of the spinal cord. It trans-

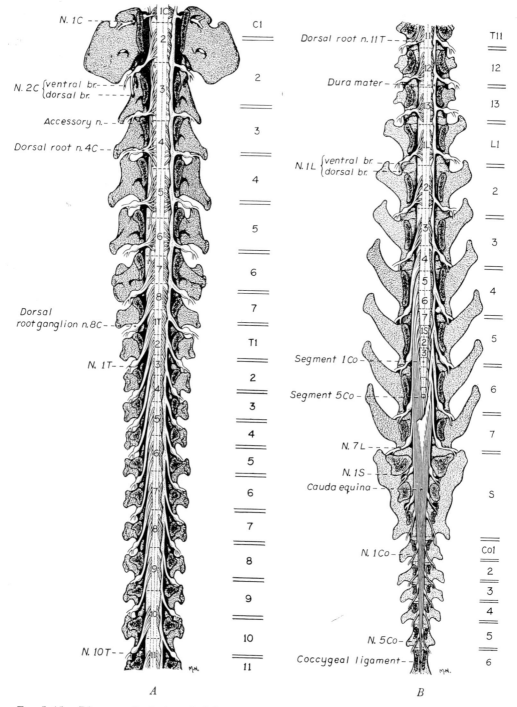

FIG. 5–15.—Diagram of spinal cord of dog exposed by removing dorsal portions of all vertebrae and most of the dura mater except on the extreme right side of the spinal cord.

    A,   Spinal cord from 1st cervical nerve to 11th thoracic nerve.

    B,   Spinal cord from 11th thoracic nerve to 5th coccygeal nerve.

    C = Cervical   *T* = Thoracic   *L* = Lumbar   *S* = Sacral   *CO* = Coccygeal.

Numbers on spinal cord indicate origin of spinal nerve of same number. Numbers to right of each drawing indicate vertebra number at that level. (McClure in Miller, Christensen, and Evans, *Anatomy of the Dog,* courtesy of W. B. Saunders Co.)

mits impulses which maintain tone of extensor muscles.

The crossed vestibulospinal tract extends from the *descending vestibular nucleus* to motor centers of the opposite side of the spinal cord. It conducts impulses which inhibit, or decrease, tone in extensor muscles.

The ventral corticospinal tract connects the motor area of the cerebral cortex with motor cells in the ventral gray horns on the same side and opposite sides of the spinal cord. The impulses are associated with voluntary motor activity.

THE PERIPHERAL NERVOUS SYSTEM

The *peripheral nervous system* provides a means of communication from the environment (both external and internal), where stimuli are received by receptor organs, to the central nervous system, and from the central nervous system to the proper effector organs in the body, muscles or glands.

By definition, the peripheral nervous system includes all nervous structures outside the brain and spinal cord. Of course this is an arbitrary division simply for convenience of description. This classification includes peripheral ganglia and spinal nerves, cranial nerves, and autonomic nerves.

SPINAL NERVES
(Somatic Components Only)

With the exception of cervical nerves and coccygeal nerves, there is a pair of spinal nerves (one right and one left) which emerge behind the vertebra of the same serial number and name. For example, the first pair of thoracic nerves emerges through the intervertebral foramina located between the first and second thoracic vertebrae; the last pair of thoracic nerves emerges through the intervertebral foramina between the last

thoracic and first lumbar vertebrae, and the second pair of lumbar nerves emerges through the foramina between the second and third lumbar vertebrae. Thus there are the same number of pairs of thoracic, lumbar, and sacral nerves as there are similar vertebrae.

The first pair of cervical nerves emerges through the foramina in the first cervical vertebra, and the second pair between the first and the second cervical vertebrae. Therefore, there are eight pair of cervical nerves although only seven cervical vertebrae.

Usually there are fewer pairs of coccygeal nerves than there are coccygeal vertebrae. The terminal part of the spinal cord, meninges, and nerves is called the *cauda equina*.

A typical spinal nerve may be compared to a tree because it has roots, the nerve proper, and various branches (see Figs. 5–16 and 5–17).

The *dorsal root* enters the dorsal portion of the spinal cord. It carries only afferent (sensory) impulses from the periphery of the animal toward the spinal cord. The nerve cell bodies of these afferent neurons are located in the dorsal root ganglion, a swelling on the dorsal root close to the point where the dorsal and ventral roots join to form the spinal nerve proper. These sensory neurons are classified as *pseudo-unipolar neurons*.

The *ventral root* emerges from the ventral portion of the spinal cord. It carries only efferent (or motor) impulses from the spinal cord to striated muscle fibers. The nerve cell bodies of these *somatic motor nerves* (derived from ventral roots) are located in the ventral horn of the spinal cord.

Near the intervertebral foramen, the dorsal root, which is sensory, meets the ventral root, which is motor, to form the main part of the spinal nerve. The spinal nerve proper thus contains both sensory and motor fibers, so it is classified as a mixed nerve.

Almost as soon as the spinal nerve

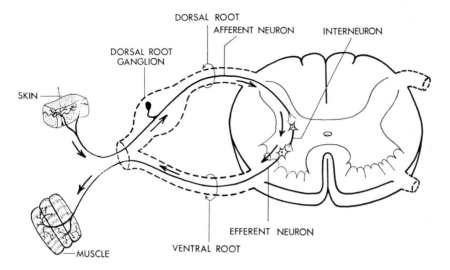

Fig. 5–16.—Diagrammatic cross-section of the spinal cord. (Kitchell in Miller, Christensen, and Evans, *Anatomy of the Dog*, courtesy of W. B. Saunders Co.)

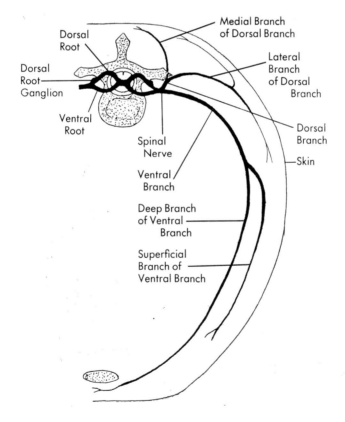

Fig. 5–17.—Diagram of a typical spinal nerve.

emerges from the vertebral canal through the intervertebral foramen, it divides into a dorsal branch and a ventral branch. Both of these branches are mixed nerves, because each contains both sensory and motor fibers.

In general, the dorsal branches of spinal nerves supply structures that are dorsal to the transverse processes of the vertebrae. The ventral branches supply structures ventral to the transverse processes and most structures of the forelimbs and hind-limbs.

The spinal nerves tend to supply sensory and motor fibers to the region of the body in the area where they emerge from the spinal cord. The appendages, however, are supplied with sensory and motor fibers by braid-like arrangements of nerves known as *plexuses*.

BRACHIAL PLEXUS

Each forelimb is supplied by a *brachial plexus*, which is a network of nerves derived from the last three or four cervical and first one or two thoracic nerves. The spinal cord shows a considerable increase

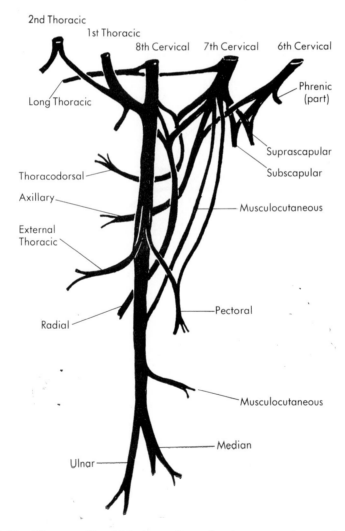

FIG. 5–18.—Diagram of brachial plexus of cow showing names of nerves involved. (After McLeod, *Bovine Anatomy*, 2nd ed., Burgess Pub. Co.)

in size in this region, known as the *cervical enlargement.*

Derivation of the Brachial Plexus

Horse: Last 3 cervical and first 2 thoracic nerves
Cow: Last 3 cervical and first thoracic nerves
Sheep: Last 3 cervical and first thoracic nerves
Pig: Last 3 cervical and first thoracic nerves
Dog: Last 3 cervical and first 2 thoracic nerves

The brachial plexus gives rise to the specific named nerves, which innervate the muscles of the forelimb and also supply sensation to the same general regions of the skin.

The following table indicates the nerves derived from the brachial plexus and the region and muscles supplied by each.

TABLE 5–1

Nerve	*Region*	*Muscles Supplied*
Pectoral	Shoulder	Superficial and deep pectorels
Suprascapular	Shoulder	Supraspinatus Infraspinatus
Subscapular	Shoulder	Subscapularis
Long Thoracic	Shoulder	Serratus ventralis
Axillary	Shoulder	Teres Major Teres Minor Deltoid Brachiocephalicus
Thoracodorsal	Shoulder	Latissimus Dorsi
External Thoracic	Shoulder	Cutaneous Trunci
Musculocutaneous	Arm	Biceps brachii Coracobrachialis Brachialis
Median	Forearm	Flexor carpi radialis Deep digital flexor (part) Superficial digital flexor (part) Pronator teres (if present) Pronator quadratus (if present)
Ulnar	Forearm Digit	Flexor carpi ulnaris Superficial digital flexor (part) Deep digital flexor (part) Many intrinsic muscles of digit (if present)

Radial	Arm
	
	Forearm
		Triceps, medial, lateral, long heads
		  (also accessory in dog)
		Anconeus
		Brachioradialis (if present)
		Extensor carpi radialis
		Common digital extensor
		Lateral digital extensor
		Medial digital extensor
		  (in cow, sheep, and pig)
		Extensor carpi ulnaris
		  (ulnaris lateralis in horse)
		Abductor pollicis longus
		  (extensor carpi obliquis)
		Supinator (if present)

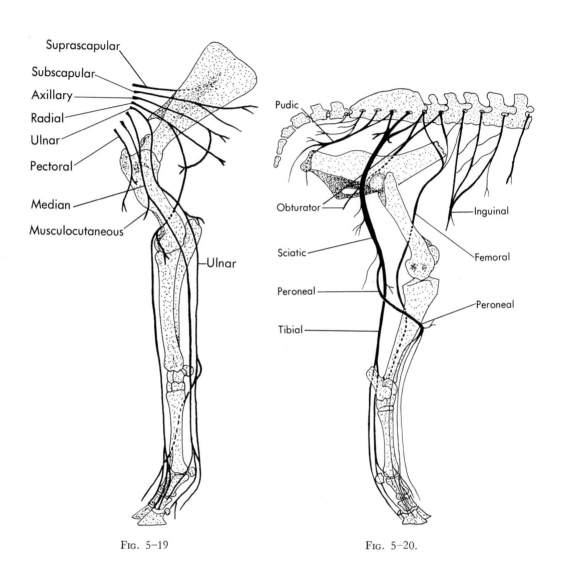

Fig. 5–19   Fig. 5–20.

Fig. 5–19.—Nerve supply of front leg of cow. (After McLeod,
Bovine Anatomy, 2nd ed., Burgess Pub. Co.)

Fig. 5–20.—Nerve supply of hind leg of cow. (After McLeod,
Bovine Anatomy, 2nd ed., Burgess Pub. Co.)

THE LUMBO-SACRAL PLEXUS

The right and the left *lumbo-sacral plexuses* supply nerves to the respective hind limb, as the corresponding brachial plexuses do to the corresponding front limb. The lumbo-sacral plexuses are made up of the ventral branches of the last few lumbar and first one or two sacral nerves as indicated below:

Derivation of the Lumbo-Sacral Plexus

Horse: Last 3 lumbar and first 2 sacral nerves
Cow: Last 3 lumbar and first 2 sacral nerves
Sheep: Last 3 lumbar and first 2 sacral nerves
Pig: Last 3 lumbar and first sacral nerves
Dog: Last 5 lumbar and first sacral nerves

TABLE 5–2

Nerve	Region	Muscles Supplied
Cranial gluteal	Rump	Middle gluteus Deep gluteus Tensor fasciae latae
Caudal gluteal	Rump	Superficial gluteus

Femoral	Thigh	Pectineus
		Sartorius
		Quadriceps femoris
		   Rectus femoris
		   Vastus lateralis
		   Vastus medialis
		   Vastus intermedius
		Psoas major and iliacus

Obturator	Thigh	Adductor Gracilis External obturator
Sciatic	Thigh	Semitendinosus Semimembranosus Biceps femoris Internal obturator Gemellus Quadratus femoris
Tibial	Leg	Gastrocnemius Superficial digital flexor Deep digital flexor Popliteus Tibialis posterior
Peroneal	Leg	Tibialis anterior Long digital extensor Medial digital extensor (cow, sheep, pig) Lateral digital extensor Peroneus tertius Peroneus longus (if present) Peroneus brevis (if present)

The nerves derived from the lumbo-sacral plexus are indicated in Table 5–2.

CRANIAL NERVES

The twelve pairs of cranial nerves in general resemble ordinary spinal nerves with the exception that they have no dorsal or ventral roots and emerge through various foramina of the skull rather than through intervertebral foramina, as do the spinal nerves. Another difference is that some cranial nerves are strictly sensory (afferent) and some are strictly motor (efferent), while spinal nerves are all mixed (containing both sensory and motor fibers). Many cranial nerves, however, are also mixed.

Cranial nerves are known by number (usually indicated by Roman numeral) and by name. The sequence of numbers is approximately in the order the nerves appear to be derived from the brain, from cranial to caudal.

The following table summarizes the general relationships of the cranial nerves.

THE AUTONOMIC NERVOUS SYSTEM

The *autonomic nervous system* is that part of the peripheral nervous system that innervates smooth muscle, cardiac muscle, and glands. In other words, the autonomic nervous system is associated with visceral structures, while the remainder of the peripheral nervous system is associated with somatic structures. Using this breakdown, we find four types of nerves in the peripheral nervous system. Visceral efferent fibers and visceral afferent fibers make up the autonomic portion, while somatic afferent (sensory) fibers and somatic efferent (motor) fibers form the remainder of the peripheral nervous system.

Some authorities disagree with such a simple concept of the peripheral nervous system. They believe that the term "somatic" should be limited to nerves supplying structures definitely known to be derived from somites.

No.	Name	Type	Distribution
I	Olfactory	Sensory	Nasal mucous membrane (sense of smell)
II	Optic	Sensory	Retina of eye (sight)
III	Oculomotor	Motor	*Most muscles of eye
IV	Trochlear	Motor	Dorsal oblique muscle of eye
V	Trigeminal	Mixed	Sensory—to eye and face / Motor—to muscles of mastication
VI	Abducens	Motor	Retractor and lateral rectus muscles of eye
VII	Facial	Mixed	*Sensory—region of ear and taste to cranial $\frac{2}{3}$ of tongue / Motor—to muscles of facial expression
VIII	Acoustic	Sensory	Cochlea (hearing) and Semicircular canals (equilibrium)
IX	Glossopharyngeal	Mixed	*Sensory—to pharynx and taste to caudal $\frac{1}{3}$ of tongue / Motor—to muscle of pharynx
X	Vagus	Mixed	*Sensory—to pharynx and larynx / Motor—to muscles of larynx
XI	Spinal Accessory	Motor	Motor—to muscles of shoulder and neck
XII	Hypoglossal	Motor	Motor—to muscles of tongue

* These nerves also contain parasympathetic fibers.

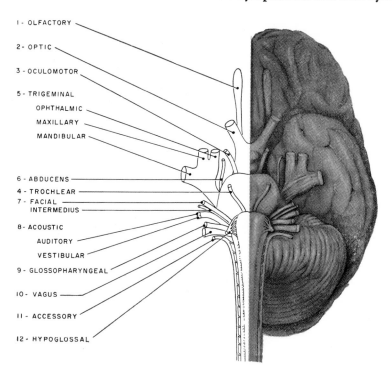

1 - OLFACTORY
2 - OPTIC
3 - OCULOMOTOR
5 - TRIGEMINAL
  OPHTHALMIC
  MAXILLARY
  MANDIBULAR
6 - ABDUCENS
4 - TROCHLEAR
7 - FACIAL
  INTERMEDIUS
8 - ACOUSTIC
  AUDITORY
  VESTIBULAR
9 - GLOSSOPHARYNGEAL
10 - VAGUS
11 - ACCESSORY
12 - HYPOGLOSSAL

FIG. 5–21.—Diagram showing the base of the human brain, the emergence of the cranial nerves, and their identification by number and name. (Grollman, *The Human Body*, courtesy of The Macmillan Co.)

THE SYMPATHETIC NERVOUS SYSTEM

The *sympathetic* portion of the autonomic nervous system is also called the *thoraco-lumbar* portion because the sympathetic outflow is mainly from thoracic and lumbar spinal nerves. The cells of origin of the visceral efferent fibers of the sympathetic nerves are located in the lateral gray column of the thoracic and lumbar segments of the spinal cord. The lateral gray column is located dorsolateral to the ventral gray horn of the spinal cord, where the cell bodies of the somatic motor nerves are located. Unlike the somatic efferent nerves, which have no cell bodies or synapses outside the central nervous system, the sympathetic nerves synapse with *secondary neurons* (post ganglionic neurons) located in sympathetic ganglia relatively close to the spinal column.

In the thoracic, lumbar, and sacral regions sympathetic ganglia, called vertebral ganglia, are located close to each intervertebral space, with a ganglion on each side of each vertebra. In addition to these vertebral ganglia located on the bodies of the vertebrae, there are other specially named paired sympathetic ganglia located ventral to the vertebral column that are called prevertebral ganglia. These include the *celiac ganglia, cranial mesenteric ganglia,* and *caudal mesenteric ganglia.* The *cranial* and *caudal cervical ganglia* are sometimes considered to be vertebral rather than prevertebral ganglia. The sympathetic ganglia contain nerve cell bodies outside the central nervous system and are also the location of synapses between preganglionic sympathetic fibers and postganglionic sympathetic fibers. The preganglionic sympathetic fibers are myelinated fibers extending from sympathetic neu-

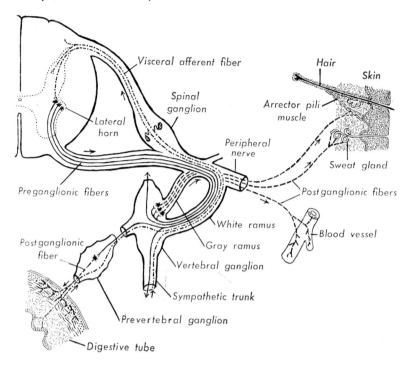

FIG. 5–22.—Diagram showing relation of sympathetic, visceral efferent, neurons to thoracic spinal cord, sympathetic trunk and visceral structures. Preganglionic fibers are shown in solid lines, postganglionic fibers in broken lines and visceral afferent fibers in dot-and-dash lines. The direction of conduction is indicated by arrows. (Bailey's *Textbook of Histology*, 12th ed. The Williams & Wilkins Co.)

rons in the lateral gray column of the spinal cord to a sympathetic vertebral or prevertebral ganglion by way of the ventral roots of the thoracic and lumbar spinal nerves, the spinal nerves proper, and the ventral branches of the spinal nerves. While each preganglionic fiber will synapse with one or more sympathetic postganglionic neurons in a ganglion, it does not necessarily synapse in the first ganglion it encounters but may continue over a considerable distance to another vertebral ganglion, or it may synapse in a prevertebral ganglion.

The cell bodies of postganglionic neurons (*secondary neurons*) are located in vertebral or prevertebral sympathetic ganglia. The processes of these secondary neurons are unmyelinated fibers called postganglionic fibers. They travel directly to the organ or structure being supplied with sympathetic fibers, usually by way of the vessels which supply blood to the structure. Thus preganglionic sympathetic fibers travel from thoracic and lumbar parts of the spinal cord to sympathetic ganglia. Postganglionic sympathetic fibers travel from sympathetic ganglia to an organ.

One exception to this general arrangement is the so-called *gray rami* which return from each sympathetic vertebral ganglion to the spinal nerve of the same serial number, to be distributed with the branchings of the spinal nerve to such structures in the skin as sweat glands and *pilomotor* fibers (smooth muscle cells in the skin that raise the hairs during fright, anger, or cold weather).

The many interconnections between various levels of ganglia (by both preganglionic fibers and postganglionic sympathetic fibers) form paired nerve trunks which pass along each side of the vertebral column from the region of the head as far back as the sacrum. The main paired trunk, the *ganglionated sympathetic trunk* of each side, receives *white rami communicantes* from the ventral branches of the thoracic and lumbar spinal nerves. These white rami are simply that portion of the myelinated preganglionic fibers extending from the ventral branch of a spinal nerve to the vertebral ganglion of the same serial number. They parallel the gray rami, which are unmyelinated postganglionic fibers returning from the sympathetic vertebral ganglion to the spinal nerve of the same serial number.

Thus the white rami communicantes which enter the ganglionated sympathetic trunk in the thoracic and lumbar regions constitute the entire efferent connection of the sympathetic system with the central nervous system. In other words, the entire outflow to the sympathetic system is from thoracic and lumbar segments of the spinal cord. The rest of the sympathetic nervous system consists of nerve trunks and ganglia associated with visceral structures of the body. The *greater* and *lesser splanchnic nerves* carry sympathetic fibers to the abdominal viscera by way of ganglia and *plexuses,* such as *cranial mesenteric, caudal mesenteric,* and *celiac.*

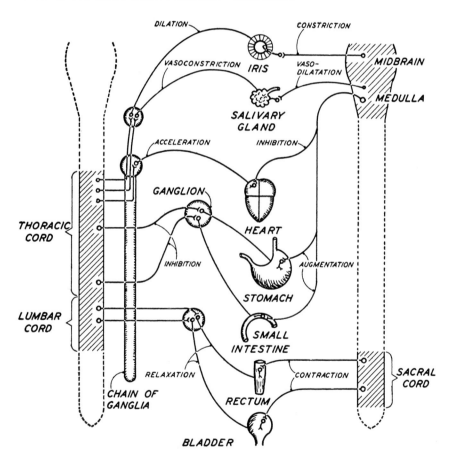

Fig. 5–23.—The autonomic (efferent) innervation of some of the viscera. The sympathetic autonomic nerves are shown on the left; the parasympathetic, on the right. Note that each organ receives a double innervation and that the action of the two nerves is opposite in each case. (Carlson, Johnson and Cavert, *The Machinery of the Body,* courtesy of University of Chicago Press.)

The head receives sympathetic fibers by way of the cervical sympathetic trunk on each side of the neck, which extends from the caudal cervical ganglion to the cranial cervical ganglion. The caudal cervical ganglion is located under cover of the first rib close to the ganglionated sympathetic trunk (to which it connects) in the region of the first thoracic vertebra. Fibers from the ganglionated sympathetic trunk pass to thoracic organs (heart and lungs) by way of the caudal cervical ganglion and the first few thoracic ganglia. Other fibers pass up the neck through the cervical sympathetic trunk to the cranial cervical ganglion and thence to smooth muscle and glands of the head by way of the *carotid plexus*, which follows branches of the carotid artery.

THE PARASYMPATHETIC NERVOUS SYSTEM

The *parasympathetic* portion of the autonomic nervous system is made up of cranial and sacral portions. Fibers of the cranial portion are distributed to visceral structures by way of four cranial *nerves*, the *oculomotor*, *facial*, *glossopharyngeal*, and *vagus*. The first three nerves mentioned above supply parasympathetic fibers to smooth muscle and glands in the region of the head, the same structures supplied by the carotid plexus of the sympathetic system.

The *vagus* nerve, one of the longest in the body, supplies parasympathetic fibers to the heart and lungs in the thorax and to nearly all abdominal viscera.

The last part of the digestive tract and most of the uro-genital system are supplied with parasympathetic fibers from the *sacral portion* of the parasympathetic nervous system.

A comparison of the sympathetic and parasympathetic nervous systems shows the following anatomical differences:

The sympathetic system is derived from thoracic and lumbar segments of the spinal cord; preganglionic fibers are relatively short, while postganglionic fibers extending from sympathetic ganglia to the organs supplied are relatively long.

The parasympathetic system is derived from cranial and sacral portions of the nervous system. The parasympathetic ganglia are located within or very close to the organs supplied. Thus the preganglionic fibers are relatively long and the postganglionic fibers are short.

CHAPTER 6

PHYSIOLOGY OF THE NERVOUS SYSTEM

Physiology of the Nerve Impulse
Reflexes
Physiology of the Autonomic Nervous System

Anesthetics
Pathology of the Nervous System

PHYSIOLOGY OF THE NERVE IMPULSE

It is convenient to compare the nervous system to various electrical systems such as a telephone exchange, with wires represented by nerve fibers. While such an analogy is useful, there are many areas in which the comparison is not valid.

In most electrical systems the electric current is supplied by an outside device such as a generator or battery, and the wires act passively to conduct the current. The efficiency of the system, therefore, depends to a large extent on the ability of the wire to conduct the current. The similar ability of a nerve fiber to conduct electricity passively is very limited. The major difference between a wire and a nerve fiber lies in the ability of the nerve fiber to propagate actively an impulse throughout its length without diminution. This is possible because of energy available from metabolism within the nerve and the special membrane properties of the nerve fiber.

A stimulus is any change in the environment of a nerve which if large enough will cause the nerve to transmit an impulse. This impulse is essentially a wave of electrical change moving along the surface of the nerve fiber.

Stimuli can be physical, chemical, or electrical in nature. In fact, any change in the environment, either internal or external, can serve as a stimulus. If the stimulus is barely strong enough to initiate an impulse in a nerve, it is called a *threshold stimulus*. In the living animal most stimuli are physical or chemical in nature and include changes in gravity, pressure, temperature, light (for vision), chemical composition of the air (for smell), and osmotic pressure. With the exception of an electric fence, electric prod, or electric eel, electrical stimuli are very rare outside of the experimental laboratory. However, because of the ease of controlling size, duration, and frequency of electrical impulses, they are the most commonly used stimuli for experimental work in the study of nerve response to stimuli and transmission of impulses.

Both irritability and conductivity of the neuron are believed to be due to the distribution of ions on each side of the membrane surrounding the neuroplasm (cytoplasm) of the nerve. The membrane of a resting nerve resists passage of sodium ions (Na^+), but potassium ions (K^+) and chloride (Cl^-) ions appear to move freely through the membrane. Outside the membrane there is a high concentration of Na^+ ions and a relatively low concentration of K^+ and Cl^- ions.

When a resting nerve is stimulated above threshold level, a depolarization wave travels away from the point of stimulation. This depolarization involves an increased permeability to Na^+ ions, with a resulting influx of Na+ ions changing the nerve from the resting condition of inside negative to an inside positive situation. The depolarization wave travels as a self-perpetuating reaction that has been compared to burning of an explosive mixture or fuse as soon as the temperature exceeds a certain critical point.

Immediately after depolarization occurs, repolarization begins. Na+ ions are actively transported from the interior of the nerve through the membrane to the interstitial fluid surrounding the nerve. It is postulated that some negative organic ion may act as a carrier, even though most organic ions are too large to

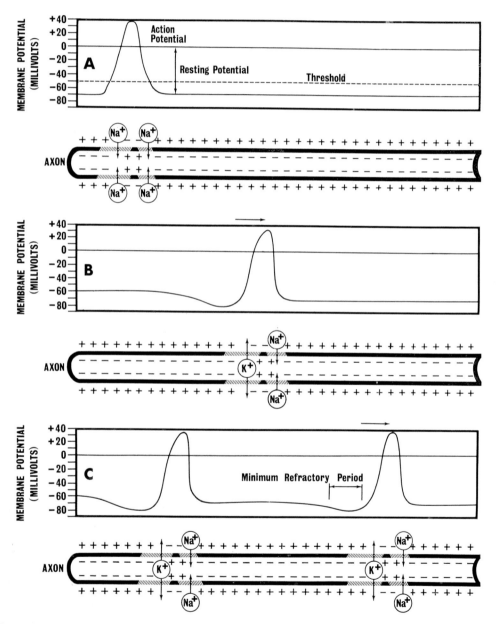

Fɪɢ. 6–1.—Schematic representation of a nerve impulse. (Kitchell, *Introduction to the Nervous System.* In Miller, Christensen, and Evans, *Anatomy of the Dog,* courtesy of W. B. Saunders Co.)

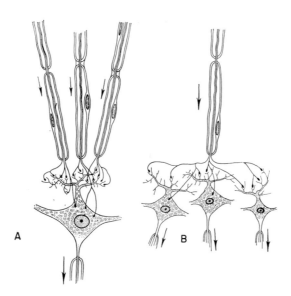

Fig. 6–2.—Convergence and divergence. *A*, Three axons are in synaptic connection with a single nerve cell body. This converging effect of axons is called convergence. *B*, A single axon makes synaptic connection with three nerve cell bodies. This spreading effect is called divergence. (After Grollman, *The Human Body*, The Macmillan Co.)

pass through the membrane. The active movement of Na$^+$ ions through the nerve membrane is referred to as the "sodium pump" and utilizes most of the metabolic energy of the nerve cell. Until repolarization is complete, the nerve is unable to transmit another impulse regardless of the size of stimulus. This short time (1/2500 second to 1/250 second) when the nerve cannot respond to stimuli is called the *refractory period*.

The resting (polarized) nerve has an electrical potential across the membrane of about 70 to 90 millivolts. This is due to the negative condition inside the membrane. In effect, this resembles a storage battery or dry cell in which there is a potential voltage between the anode (positive pole) and cathode (negative pole).

Nerve as well as striated muscle acts according to the "all or none" law. In other words, any stimulus above the threshold will trigger an impulse, but a change below threshold level will not trigger an impulse. Apparently all normal impulses over a given nerve fiber are of the same magnitude and character regardless of the stimulus which initiates them. However, the frequency of impulses can change.

Convergence of nerve impulses occurs when a number of afferent neurons send impulses to a motor neuron, the final common pathway. Thus convergence of stimuli as from the eye, ear, and skin can cause a very strong motor response.

Divergence of impulses is the opposite situation—that in which one sensory neuron affects a large number of motor neurons.

REFLEXES

A *reflex action* is an automatic, or unconscious, response of an effector organ (muscle or gland) to an appropriate stimulus. This action includes a chain of at least two neurons making up a reflex arc. The two essential neurons in a reflex arc include an afferent, sensory, or receptor, neuron and an efferent,

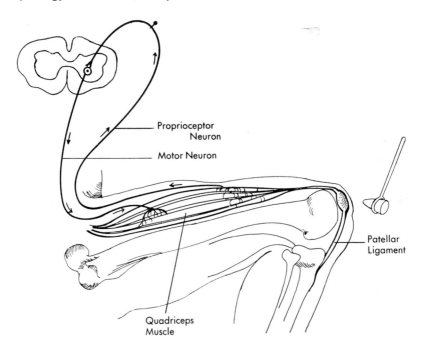

FIG. 6–3.—Diagram of stretch reflex.

motor, or effector, neuron. Usually one or more connector neurons (interneurons) are interposed between the receptor neurons and the effector neurons.

Although reflexes may involve various parts of the brain and the autonomic nervous system, the simplest reflex is the spinal reflex. A typical *spinal reflex* is the stretch reflex illustrated by tapping the patellar ligament to cause the knee, or stifle, to extend—the so-called *"knee jerk."* In this reflex action, proprioceptor neurons related to the quadriceps muscle fibers are stimulated by the sudden stretching of the muscle caused by striking the ligament at the front of the stifle. This impulse is carried to the spinal cord by way of the dorsal root of the appropriate spinal nerve. The impulse is then transmitted directly to the applicable motor neurons in the ventral gray horn of the spinal cord. The impulse then travels to the muscle fibers of the quadriceps femoris muscle of the thigh (in this case the same muscle in which the reflex originated) causing it to contract. This type of *stretch reflex* is also known as a *postural reflex* because it aids in maintaining a standing position. If the stifle suddenly flexes, this action stretches the quadriceps muscle, which initiates the reflex that causes the quadriceps to contract thus extending the stifle to support the weight of the animal. The same reflex occurs in man when the area just below the knee is struck.

The fact that reflex action does not require conscious control may be demonstrated with an animal such as a frog in which the brain has been separated from the spinal cord by cutting the cord. An animal with the spinal cord severed is called a *spinal animal*, because all activities caudal to the point of the operation must be due only to action of the spinal cord, since there is no connection with the brain.

The frog is particularly useful for demonstrating spinal reflexes because the period of spinal shock (resulting from the severing operation) in which reflex activity is absent and the animal is completely limp lasts for only a few minutes. The period of spinal shock in mammals lasts several hours or more.

After recovery from spinal shock the frog will flex (withdraw) a leg upon stimulation such as pinching the toe, applying a weak acid, or applying an electric shock. Interconnection from one side of the spinal cord to the other and from one level (cervical, thoracic, lumbar) to another can be demonstrated by using stronger stimuli and restraining the stimulated extremities. If the stimulated leg is prevented from flexing upon stimulation, the opposite leg will flex, thus showing the presence of connections from one side of the spinal cord to the opposite side. If both hind legs are restrained from flexing upon strong stimulation, the front legs will flex; or if a strong stimulus is applied to the ventral aspect of the body, all four legs will flex, thus showing connections between various levels of the spinal cord.

Reflexes may be of a somatic nature as the ones first described, in which the effector organ consists of striated muscle. Reflexes of importance to the regulation of visceral functions are mediated by the autonomic nervous system. In these, effector organs are either smooth muscle, cardiac muscle, or glands.

The classic example of a visceral reflex is the production of gastric secretions by a dog when he is shown food. Both salivary and gastric glands secrete in preparation for ingestion of the food. Some of the most famous work on reflexes was performed by Pavlov, who found he could condition a dog to secrete upon the ringing of a bell, if the bell had been rung at the time food was offered to the dog for a number of times. This is the well-known example of a conditioned reflex into which one stimulus is substitute for another to produce the same response.

Reflex centers are located throughout the central nervous system. Those associated with the spinal cord are the simplest and may involve only one side of the cord, both sides, or different levels of the cord, as illustrated by reactions of a spinal animal.

More complex reflexes are mediated through reflex centers found in the brain. The medulla oblongata contains reflex centers for control of heart action, vessel size, respiration, swallowing, vomiting, coughing, and sneezing.

The cerebellum contains most of the reflex centers associated with locomotion and posture. Many of these reflexes are inborn, as shown by a new-born foal running after its mother. However, they are subject to considerable modification during learning processes. For example, the complicated movements of a well-trained gaited horse are largely reflex in nature but have been modified considerably by education. This is true of most skilled physical activities, whether of man or lower animals.

The hypothalamus of the diencephalon contains reflex centers associated with temperature regulation and water balance. They control such functions as shivering, vasomotor activity in peripheral vessels, sweating, and urine excretion, as well as erection of hairs and feathers.

The cerebrum may be involved in such reflexes as the pupillary reflex, in which light striking the retina causes constriction of the pupil, and a general startle reaction to loud noises or frightening objects.

Either the absence or exaggeration of reflexes indicates some abnormality of the reflex pathway. Reflexes are used extensively in human medicine and to a lesser degree in veterinary medicine in diagnosis of pathological conditions. Reflex activity decreases markedly under the influence of anesthetics. The presence or absence of specific reflexes is of considerable value in determining the depth of

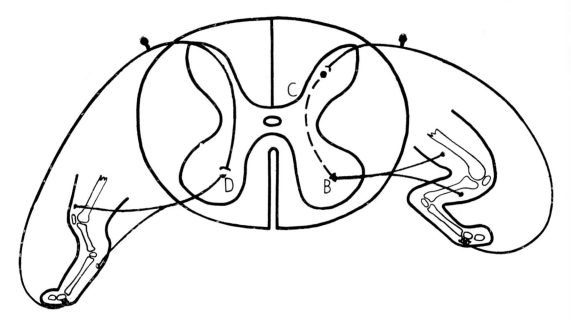

Fig. 6–4.—Simple spinal reflexes.

Left: extensor thrust: Light pressure on the sole activates a two-neuron arc, resulting in extension and support of the body. A similar effect is produced if a muscle is slightly stretched by flexion of the joint—the stretch reflex.

Right: flexor reflex: Noxious stimulus of the limb activates a three-neuron arc resulting in sharp flexion and withdrawal from the stimulus; at the same time, the opposite limb is extended to provide compensating support.

A two-neuron extensor reflex has little facility for spread and may be classified as intrasegmental or local. The flexor reflex, with its extra rank of neurons, can spread widely to affect the motor neurons for many muscles and is intersegmental. (Elliot, *Textbook of Neuroanatomy*, courtesy of J. B. Lippincott Co.)

anesthesia in a patient, whether animal or man.

McGrath (1960) describes certain reflexes in the dog. *Spinal reflexes* include *flexor reflex*, in which the limb is withdrawn when the footpad or toe is pinched; *knee jerk*, in which extension of the knee results from tapping the patellar ligament; *extensor thrust reflex*, in which extension of the limb occurs when the foot is pushed toward the body as would occur in normal body support; and *spinal visceral reflexes* controlling micturition and defecation.

Attitudinal and postural reactions include the *tonic neck reflexes*, in which passively extending the neck (raising the head) increases tone of extensor muscles of the forelimbs and decreases tone of extensor muscles of the hind limbs. This could be a partial explana-

tion for the value of raising a horse's head to prevent kicking. Conversely, when a horse gets his head down, he is much more likely to kick or buck. Tonic eye reflexes keep the eyes looking in the original direction when the head is moved.

The *extensor postural thrust* enables the limbs to support the weight of the body without conscious thought on the part of the animal. Righting, placing, and hopping reactions are associated with regaining a normal standing position following some imposed deviation in position on the animal's body or limbs.

Reflexes associated with the cranial nerves include the *corneal reflex*, in which the eyelids close in response to stimulation of the cornea of the eye, the *pupillary reflex*, in which the size of the pupil varies with light intensity, the *pharyngeal reflexes* for swallowing or vomiting, and *auditory reflexes* in which the animal turns the head toward a sound.

PHYSIOLOGY OF THE AUTONOMIC NERVOUS SYSTEM

The chief role of the autonomic nervous system is to maintain a stable internal environment of the body. The term *homeostasis* is sometimes used to describe this condition.

Most organs of the body receive both sympathetic and parasympathetic innervation. In general, the effect of sympathetic stimulation is opposite that of parasympathetic stimulation of a given organ. Thus the two systems are antagonistic. Both are needed for adequate control, and paralysis of either one has essentially the same effect as excessive stimulation of the opposite. For example, blocking of the parasympathetic nerve supply to the eye with atropine paralyzes the circular smooth muscle fibers of the iris which constrict the pupil. This permits the radial smooth muscle fibers which are supplied by sympathetic nerves to dilate the pupil.

It is impossible to state correctly that one system stimulates and the other depresses unless a specific organ or function is being discussed. A more accurate generalization is the concept of "fight or flight" activity produced by the sympathetic system as opposed to the quiet relaxed type of activity favored by the parasympathetic system.

The "fight or flight" mechanism can be visualized by imagining what changes would favor muscular activity either fighting or running, depending on the size of the opponent. Factors favorable to this type of activity, which result from sympathetic stimulation, include: increased heart rate, higher blood pressure, dilation of the bronchi, dilation of the pupil, and decreased activity of the digestive tract.

Parasympathetic stimulation produces the opposite actions, including: slower heart rate, lower blood pressure, constriction of the bronchi and pupil, and increased activity of the digestive tract. In fact, drugs with a parasympathetic action are sometimes used as laxatives or cathartics.

TABLE 6–1.— ACTIONS OF AUTONOMIC STIMULATION

Organ	Sympathetic Portion Causes	Parasympathetic Portion Causes
Sweat glands	Secretion	No effect
Salivary glands	Mucous secretion	Serous secretion
Digestive glands	Inhibition of secretion	Secretion
Muscles of hair follicles	Contraction (erection of hair)	No effect
Muscles of digestive tract	Inhibition of peristalsis Contraction of sphincters	Peristalsis Relaxation of sphincters
Muscles of bronchi	Relaxation (dilation of bronchi)	Contraction (constriction of bronchi)
Muscles of bladder	Contraction of sphincter (relaxation of wall)	Relaxation of sphincter (contraction of wall—urination)
Muscles of uterus	Contraction	Inhibition of contraction
Muscles of blood vessels	Vasoconstriction	Vasodilation
Muscles of eye		
Iris	Contraction of radial muscles (dilation of pupil)	Contraction of circular muscles (constriction of pupil)
Ciliary muscle	Relaxation (accommodation for distant vision)	Contraction (accommodation for near vision)

From the anatomical and functional viewpoints, the autonomic nervous system can be divided rather definitely into sympathetic and parasympathetic portions. However, when the type of chemical released at the nerve endings is considered, the two autonomic divisions and the somatic nervous system show a considerable amount of overlapping.

In general, the parasympathetic fibers release acetylcholine at postganglionic nerve endings as well as at synapses between preganglionic and postganglionic neurons. *Acetylcholine* is also released (1) at synapses in sympathetic ganglia, (2) at motor end plates at the junction of somatic motor nerve endings and striated muscle fibers, and (3) by postganglionic sympathetic fibers to sweat glands and the uterus. All fibers that release acetylcholine are said to be *cholinergic*.

The enzyme *cholinesterase* apparently present in tissues, inactivates acetylcholine shortly after it is formed at the nerve endings.

Most postganglionic sympathetic fibers release the substance *norepinephrine*, also called *noradrenaline*, *sympathin*, or *arterenol*, which is very similar to *epinephrine* (*adrenaline*) produced by the medullary portion of the adrenal glands. In fact, the medulla of the adrenal gland resembles a sympathetic ganglion in that it contains similar nerve cells and receives a number of sympathetic fibers, and the action of epinephrine closely resembles the effect of sympathetic stimulation. Fibers that produce norepinephrine are called *adrenergic* because of the resemblance of norepinephrine to adrenalin.

Oxidase enzymes rapidly inactivate sympathin in the same manner that cholinesterase inactivates acetylcholine.

Although Langley originally described the autonomic nervous system as being entirely efferent, it seems reasonable to include visceral afferent fibers as a part of the autonomic nervous system.

The receptive nerve endings of visceral afferent nerves are located in most of the structures supplied by autonomic nerves. The afferent nerves travel with the postganglionic and preganglionic autonomic nerves through the plexuses and ganglia but do not synapse until they reach the central nervous system. The cell bodies of these visceral afferent nerves are located in the dorsal root ganglia, and their processes reach the spinal cord by way of the dorsal root of the spinal nerve, just as somatic afferent nerves do. Most of the impulses carried by visceral afferent fibers never reach conscious level, but they form the afferent side of many autonomic reflexes which control such functions as blood pressure, heart rate, and activity of the digestive and urogenital systems.

In man, and presumably in animals, most visceral sensations are rather ill defined and poorly localized. Stimuli that can cause pain in viscera include: stretching or distention, strong contractions, loss of blood supply, and chemical substances.

Referred pain is a condition in which visceral stimuli are interpreted as coming from a somatic body area. This is well established in man, but since it is largely a subjective phenomenon, it is difficult to establish in animals. An example might be the high degree of sensitivity in the region of the sternum that some cows with traumatic gastritis (a wire or nail perforating the wall of the fore stomachs) exhibit.

ANESTHETICS

Chemicals or drugs which inhibit or completely block passage of nerve impulses are called *anesthetics*. *Local anesthetics* are used in restricted areas of the peripheral nervous system, as in blocking a horse's leg for firing or blocking the nerves to the horn of a cow for dehorning.

General anesthetics affect the central nervous system and cause unconsciousness if used in sufficient quantities. An excess of anesthetic can cause death by depressing vital reflex centers in the brain.

Sedatives and *hypnotics* reduce nerve irritability and tend to induce sleep.

PATHOLOGY OF THE NERVOUS SYSTEM

Injury to the cell body and injury to nerve processes are the two general types of damages that may occur in the nervous system.

The first, if serious enough to cause death of the cell, is irreparable, as seen in paralytic poliomyelitis in man and some nervous forms of distemper in dogs. Since the adult animal and probably the newborn animal already have all the neurons that can be formed, death of any nerve cells may be quite serious. There is general agreement among neurologists that nerve cells cannot be replaced.

Injury to nerve processes, most common in peripheral nerves, may or may not be permanent. It can vary from as transient a condition as a limb's going to sleep due to pressure on a nerve trunk, through crushing of a nerve, as sometimes occurs during difficult parturition, to actual cutting of a nerve by barbed wire, a mower, or some other means.

Frequently a nerve will recover spontaneously in a relatively short time following damage from light pressure or crushing. However, when a nerve is cut, the distal portion undergoes a process known as *Wallerian degeneration*, in which the axon becomes fragmented, the myelin sheath breaks down, and the neurolemma may undergo some changes.

Retrograde degeneration refers to somewhat similar changes that sometimes affect the proximal segment of a cut nerve and may eventually involve the cell body, causing its death.

If the cell body and proximal segment remain healthy, regeneration of the nerve process may occur, particularly if the neurolemma of the distal segment is brought into close proximity to the cut end of the proximal segment. Apparently, the neurolemma is necessary for nerve regeneration to occur.

Peripheral nerve injuries result in loss of sensation or muscle activity or both in a restricted area supplied by the particular nerve or nerves involved.

Central nervous system damage may be caused by many different factors such as trauma (injury), tumors, infections, or toxins (poisons). Usually the symptoms of damage to the central nervous system are much more general than in peripheral nerve injuries. These symptoms may range from partial or complete paralysis, as is often seen in spinal cord lesions, to spasms or convulsions which result from uncontrolled muscular contraction. Because of the crossing of most fiber tracts from one side of the brain to the opposite side of the spinal cord, a lesion on one side of the brain will result in impaired functioning of the opposite side of the body. Vision, hearing, and cutaneous sensations as well as motor activity may be impaired by disorders of the central nervous system.

CHAPTER 7

SENSE ORGANS

GENERAL SENSATIONS

SENSATIONS generally are the result of afferent impulses from stimuli that eventually reach a conscious level in the cerebral cortex. However, some afferent impulses may function in *somatic reflexes* without ever reaching the level of consciousness. This can be illustrated by producing reflex activity in decerebrate animals.

Special senses include smell, sight, taste, hearing, and equilibrium. Organic sensations include, among others, hunger, thirst, the sensation of bladder fullness, and sexual sensations. Other sensations not classified above include touch, pressure, cold, heat, pain, proprioception, and visceral sensations.

The sensation of touch is believed to be received by specialized nerve endings known as *Meissner's corpuscles*, by those known as *Merkel's discs*, and by naked nerve endings near hair follicles.

Meissner's corpuscles are located just deep to the epidermis in connective tissue papillae of the dermis. Merkel's discs are found in sensitive epithelium such as the tongue, where each disc is attached to a modified epithelial cell. Naked nerve endings surround hair follicles, particularly those of tactile hairs, such as are found in the muzzles of many animals.

Deep pressure sensation is produced by stimulation of receptors called *Vater-*

Pacinian corpuscles located in subcutaneous connective tissue, in connective tissue around joints, in the external genitalia of both males and females, and in relation to both serous membranes and mucous membranes. These corpuscles resemble an onion, with many concentric layers of connective tissue surrounding the expanded termination of the nerve.

The difference between touch receptors and deep pressure receptors may account for the fact that a horse often resents a light touch that tickles but stands for a moderately heavy slap without objection.

Special receptors for heat, termed *corpuscles of Ruffini*, and receptors for cold, termed *Krause end-bulbs*, are believed to exist mainly in connective tissue of several areas of the body.

Pain is received by naked terminal branches of sensory neurons. These branches intermingle in many areas of the skin and connective tissues as well as in the cornea of the eye. These nerve endings respond to all intense stimuli, including chemical, thermal, and mechanical stimuli.

Proprioception, also called *muscle sense*, indicates to the animal relative positions of various parts of the body without its using the eyes. This sense of position is important in physical activities such as walking, running, fighting, and grazing.

Nerve endings for muscle sense are ar-

(102)

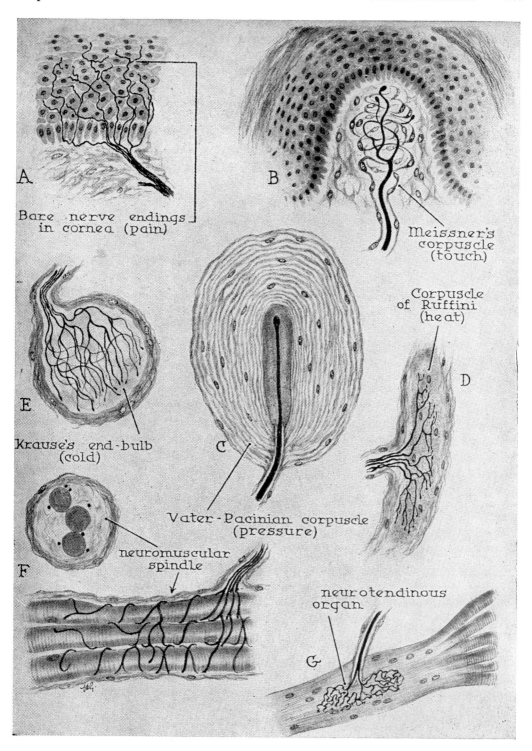

A. Bare nerve endings in cornea (pain)

B. Meissner's corpuscle (touch)

Corpuscle of Ruffini (heat)

D.

E. Krause's end-bulb (cold)

C. Vater-Pacinian corpuscle (pressure)

F. neuromuscular spindle

G. neurotendinous organ

FIG. 7–1.—Diagrams of the various types of nerve endings concerned in cutaneous and deep sensibility. (Ham and Leeson, *Histology*, courtesy of J. B. Lippincott Co.)

ranged around some muscle fibers as *neuromuscular spindles,* or at the junction of muscles and tendons as *neurotendinous organs.* Any change in muscle length or tension of muscles and tendons stimulates these receptors, which immediately transmit the information to the central nervous system. These afferent nerves form the afferent side of *stretch reflexes* (described in Chapter 6, p. 96) also called *postural reflexes.*

In general, proprioceptive fibers are heavily myelinated, touch fibers have medium myelination, and pain fibers are unmyelinated. The cell bodies of peripheral sensory nerves are located in the dorsal root ganglia of spinal nerves and in comparable ganglia of certain cranial nerves.

There is a tendency for nerve fibers carrying impulses of each sensory modality (touch, pain, heat, cold) to be grouped in specific tracts of the spinal cord. For example, light touch impulses are carried in the lateral spinothalamic tract. Each impulse carried by a peripheral sensory nerve may have one or more of several possible destinations. It may function only in the afferent side of a reflex arc, such as proprioceptive impulses in normal walking. It may reach a conscious level (*cerebral cortex*) without being involved in reflex actions, as in minor temperature and pressure changes. Or an impulse may result in both reflex action and conscious perception; for instance, in touching a hot object, the finger is withdrawn automatically (reflexly) and pain is also felt.

Visceral sensations involve structures within the body cavities. During surgery visceral organs may be handled, burned, cut, or crushed without causing apparent pain as long as the body wall is not involved and no traction is applied to the peritoneum. This, of course, is in animals under local anesthetics rather than general anesthetics. Painful stimuli to visceral organs include lack of blood supply,

sudden distention, sudden contraction, and chemical irritants. These pain impulses are carried largely by visceral afferent fibers accompanying or within the sympathetic nerves. However, the afferent limbs of vital visceral reflexes are found in parasympathetic nerves. These reflexes include cardiac reflexes, aortic reflexes, *Hering-Brewer reflexes,* and reflexes for micturition.

So-called organic sensations such as hunger, thirst, sexual sensations, and sensation of bladder fullness are carried by visceral afferent nerves. These organic sensations indicate a need and tend to lead to activity that satisfies the need.

TASTE

Taste buds, the end organs for the sense of taste, consist of fusiform gustatory cells intermingled with sustentacular (supporting) cells arranged in somewhat barrel-shaped groups. Hair-like processes of the gustatory cells project through a pore at the superficial portion of the taste bud. Nerve fibers terminate around the gustatory cells.

Circumvallate and *fungiform papillae* of the tongue contain the most taste buds, although some are also found on the palate, pharynx, and larynx. The sensation of taste is supplied to the anterior two-thirds of the tongue by the *chorda tympani* branch of the facial nerve, which

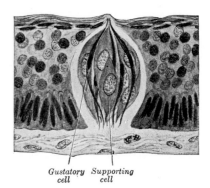

Gustatory   Supporting
 cell   cell

FIG. 7–2.—Taste bud. (Gray's *Anatomy,* Lea & Febiger.)

accompanies the *lingual branch* of the *trigeminal nerve*. The posterior one-third of the tongue receives taste by way of the lingual branch of the *glossopharyngeal nerve*. Other sensations (heat, cold, touch, pain) to the tongue are supplied by the lingual branch of the trigeminal nerve. Probably the taste buds located on areas other than the tongue are supplied by the *vagus nerve*.

In man, the four specific taste modalities include sweet, salt, bitter, and sour (acid). Other taste sensations involve mixtures of these basic tastes or combinations of tastes and smell. The base of the tongue is sensitive to bitter taste, the lateral sides of the tongue respond primarily to sour stimuli but also to salt, and the tip of the tongue is sensitive to all four modalities but is more sensitive to sweet and salt.

Taste appears to be an important factor in the ability of an animal to select food containing elements or factors in which the animal is deficient. For example, vitamin-deficient rats will select foods high in the particular vitamin they need. Rats with the adrenal glands removed prefer saline solutions to pure water to replace the salt that has been lost. If the parathyroid glands are removed, the rats prefer solutions containing calcium. This ability to correct dietary deficiencies is lost if the sensory nerves for taste are cut.

SMELL

The *olfactory system* is associated with the sense of smell. The sense of smell is mediated by the *olfactory (I cranial)* nerve. Olfactory nerve cells are scattered among columnar supporting cells throughout the olfactory mucous membrane in the dorso-caudal part of the nasal cavity. The nucleus of each olfactory cell is located near the basement membrane of the mucous membrane. A peripheral process extends between supporting cells to the surface, where it bears a tuft of several fine hair-like projections which are assumed to be the actual receptors for the sense of smell. Since these processes normally are covered by moist mucus, the material to be smelled probably must go into solution before it can reach the sensory cells. However, some authorities believe that very fine particles of some substances may be perceived without actually dissolving. The central process of each olfactory nerve cell passes through a foramen in the *cribriform plate* of the *ethmoid bone* to the olfactory bulb of the brain, where it synapses with cells whose central processes make up the olfactory tract of the brain. Some nerve fibers in each olfactory tract cross to the opposite side of the brain by way of the anterior commissure. The remainder of the nerve fibers pass caudally to various areas of the brain. A great many connections and interconnections are postulated, but there is little general agreement about terminations of the olfactory tract, even though the *rhinencephalon (olfactory cortex)* is one of the oldest parts of the brain. Development of the olfactory system varies considerably from one species to another. The sense of smell is very well developed in the dog, but poorly developed in man. Conclusive experiments in this field are difficult to design, and attempts to transfer conclusions from man to animals and animals to man are particularly hazardous.

HEARING AND BALANCE

The ear can be divided into three main parts, the external ear, the middle ear, and the inner ear. The external ear extends from the exterior as far as the tympanic membrane. The middle ear extends from the tympanic membrane into the air-filled excavation within the *petrous temporal bone*. The inner ear is also excavated in the petrous temporal bone but is filled with fluid. The basis of the external

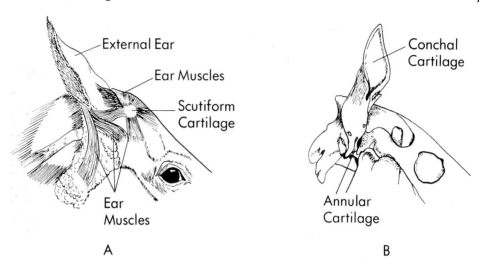

FIG. 7-3.—The external ear. (After Ellenberger, *An Atlas of Animal Anatomy for Artists*, courtesy of Dover Publications, Inc.)

ear consists of three cartilages. The *conchal cartilage* is the largest of the three. It is a seashell-shaped cartilage which acts to funnel sound waves into the ear canal.

The *scutiform cartilage* is a shield-shaped cartilage that acts as a *sesamoid* bone for some of the ear muscles. The third cartilage is the *annular cartilage*, which is shaped like a tube and connects the conchal cartilage with the external osseous auditory canal.

The conchal cartilage is an elastic cartilage that is somewhat funnel-shaped. It is lined on the inside with relatively hairless skin. On the outside it is protected with a layer of skin that in most animals is covered with a generous amount of hair.

The external ear can be pointed in any desired direction, particularly in the horse. The ear can be rotated on a longitudinal axis and it can be tilted forward, tilted backward, and tilted laterally. The mobility of the ear is of value in localizing sounds and in picking up sounds. The funnel-shaped cartilage concentrates sound waves and directs them toward the tympanic membrane.

The scutiform cartilage is located on the superficial surface of the temporal muscle and attaches to a number of the extrinsic ear muscles. Some muscles attach directly to the conchal cartilage and some attach indirectly by way of the scutiform cartilage. The extrinsic muscles of the ear are supplied by the *facial* (*VII cranial*) nerve. The external ear receives sensation from the trigeminal (V cranial) nerve, facial (VII cranial), and from the vagus (X cranial) nerve.

The middle ear is a cavity in the petrous temporal bone which communicates with the pharynx by way of the Eustachian tube (auditory tube). It is separated from the external ear by the tympanic membrane and is separated from the inner ear by the membranes which close the oval window and the round window. The three *auditory ossicles* are found in the middle ear. From without inward they are the *malleus* (hammer), *incus* (anvil), and *stapes* (stirrup). These ossicles provide a mechanical linkage from the tympanic membrane to the membrane closing the oval window. There are also two striated muscles found within the middle ear, the *tensor tympani*

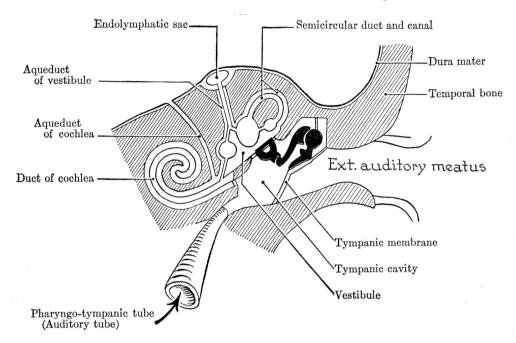

Endolymphatic sac

Semicircular duct and canal

Dura mater

Aqueduct
of vestibule

Temporal bone

Aqueduct
of cochlea

Ext. auditory meatus

Duct of cochlea

Tympanic membrane

Tympanic cavity

Vestibule

Pharyngo-tympanic tube
(Auditory tube)

FIG. 7–4.—A diagram of the parts of the ear. (Grant, *An Atlas of Anatomy*,
courtesy of The Williams & Wilkins Co.)

muscle and the *stapedius muscle.* The tensor tympani muscle originates on the upper wall of the Eustachian tube and inserts on the malleus. It receives its nerve supply from the mandibular division of the trigeminal nerve. The stapedius muscle inserts on the stapes and is supplied by the facial nerve. These two small muscles probably function in dampening excessively loud noises and may also function to increase the acuity of hearing.

The inner ear is likewise an excavation within the petrous temporal bone. The excavation is known as the *osseous labyrinth.* Within the osseous labyrinth is a completely closed connective tissue structure almost co-extensive with it, but somewhat smaller, called the *membranous labyrinth,* which contains *endolymph* and does not communicate with any other cavity. Between the osseous labyrinth and the membranous labyrinth is a fluid, the *perilymph.* The perilymph is continuous with the cerebrospinal fluid by way

of a small canal called the *aqueduct of cochlea.*

The inner ear may also be divided into two parts according to function. The *cochlear portion* receives the cochlear branch of the *auditory (VIII cranial)* nerve. This portion is sensory for sound. The *vestibular part* functions mainly for the mediation of balance and is supplied by the vestibular branch of the auditory nerve. The vestibular portion of the inner ear is housed in the parts of the osseous labyrinth known as the vestibule and the three semicircular canals. Each semicircular canal both leaves and returns to the vestibule. The three semicircular canals are arranged so that each is in a different plane, one approximately horizontal, one approximately frontal, and one approximately sagittal in direction (see Fig. 7–5).

The membranous labyrinth also includes three semicircular canals, one in each of the osseous semicircular canals. Two membranous sacs, the *utricle* and *saccule,* also are part of the membranous labyrinth and are located within the vestibule. Both ends of each semicircular canal open into the utricle. The utricle also communicates with the saccule through the *endolymphatic duct*. The saccule, in turn, communicates with the *membranous cochlea*.

Neuroepithelial areas specialized for reception of stimuli relating to balance and movement are found in the vestibular part of the membranous labyrinth. They are made up of sustentacular (supporting) cells intermingled with hair cells. The hair cells present non-motile cilia on the free surface, and each cell is related to non-myelinated nerve endings of the vestibular part of the auditory nerve.

The sensitive areas of the saccule and utricle, known as *maculae acusticae*, have been shown to be associated with static equilibrium (position of the head in space). The surface of each macula (one in the saccule and one in the utricle) is covered with a gelatinous membrane, the *otolithic membrane*, which contains a large number of crystals of calcium carbonate called otoliths. Stimulation of the hair cells of the maculae appears to be due to the effect of gravity on the otolithic membranes.

One end of each semicircular canal is expanded to form the ampulla. Within each ampulla is a receptor organ, the *crista*, which consists of a ridge of neuroepithelium at right angles to the plane of the respective semicircular canal. The crista resembles a macula of the saccule or utricle, except that it is surmounted by a tall, rounded mass called the *cupula* instead of being covered by an otolithic membrane as found in the macula. Between the sustentacular cells of the crista are the hair cells, around which terminate naked endings of the auditory nerve (vestibular part). The cristae reflect changes in movement (kinetic sense) because of displacement of the cupula over the cilia of the hair cells. This dis-placement results from pressure changes of the endolymph within the semicircular canals due to sudden movements of the head in or near the plane of the affected semicircular canal.

Impulses carried by the vestibular part of the auditory nerve are responsible for reflex movements of the eyes, head, and other parts of the body and also may produce vertigo (dizziness), as seen in motion sickness. Of course, the sense of position and equilibrium is due largely to these impulses.

The cochlear portion of the osseous labyrinth resembles a short, broad metal screw (made of bone) surrounded by a loose-fitting congruent female screw (also made of bone). This produces in effect a spiral tube hollowed out of the petrous temporal bone. The inner male screw-like portion is called the *modiolus*, and it transmits the cochlear portion of the auditory nerve to the *organ of Corti* within the membranous labyrinth. The membranous labyrinth extends from the bony thread (the spiral lamina) of the modiolus across the lumen of the osseous labyrinth to the connective tissue lining the outer wall of the osseous labyrinth. Thus the cavity of the osseous labyrinth which contains the perilymph is completely divided into two spiral tubes by the membranous labyrinth. However, at the apex of the spiral the *scala vestibuli* communicates with the *scala tympani* through a small opening, the *helicotrema*. The upper tube (assuming the base is horizontal and the apex is above the base) is the scala vestibuli, which opens into the vestibule so that the perilymph in both cavities (cochlear and vestibular) is continuous. The lower tube, the scala tympani, opens into the area of the round window.

The aqueduct of cochlea is a small duct through which perilymph from the cochlea communicates with cerebrospinal fluid in the *subarachnoid space*. A small tube, the *endolymphatic duct*, leads from

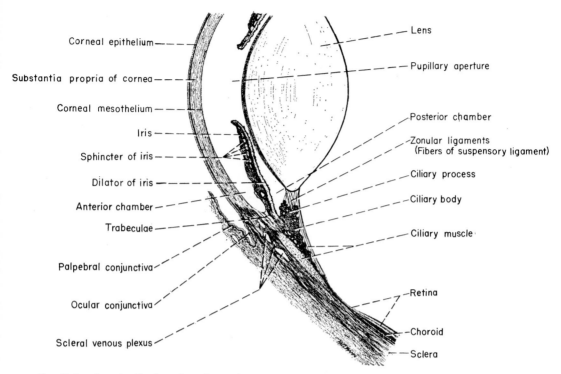

Corneal epithelium

Substantia propria of cornea

Corneal mesothelium

Iris

Sphincter of iris

Dilator of iris

Anterior chamber

Trabeculae

Palpebral conjunctiva

Ocular conjunctiva

Scleral venous plexus

Lens

Pupillary aperture

Posterior chamber

Zonular ligaments
(Fibers of suspensory ligament)

Ciliary process

Ciliary body

Ciliary muscle

Retina

Choroid

Sclera

FIG. 7–8.—Longitudinal section of anterior part of eye showing attachments of cornea, iris, and lens. (Getty, *The Sense Organs*, in Miller, Christensen, Evans, *Anatomy of the Dog*, courtesy of W. B. Saunders Co.)

The *iris* is the pigmented structure of the eye that forms a curtain to control the amount of light entering the eye. The *pupil* of the eye is an opening approximately in the center of the iris. The size of the pupil is determined by two sets of smooth muscles. One set of muscles of the iris consists of circular fibers which circumscribe the pupil to form a sphincter. The *circular fibers* (sphincter pupillae) are supplied by the *parasympathetic* portion of the *oculomotor nerve*. These circular fibers decrease the size of the pupil when reflexly stimulated by an increased amount of light. The other set of fibers, the *radial fibers*, is supplied by the sympathetic nerves from the *cranial cervical ganglion* of the *cervical sympathetic trunk* by way of the *carotid plexus*. The pupil of the eye is reflexly dilated whenever the level of light is decreased. A solution of *atropine* instilled into the eye paralyzes the parasympathetic nerve fibers which supply the constrictor muscles of the iris, thus permitting the sympathetic nerves to take over and produce a dilation of the pupil of the eye.

The portion of the eye between the cornea and the lens is incompletely divided into two parts by the iris. That portion between the cornea and the iris is known as the *anterior chamber* and that portion between the iris and the lens is known as the *posterior chamber* of the eye. The fluid within these two chambers is called the *aqueous humor*. It communicates freely from one chamber to the other through the pupil of the iris.

PHYSIOLOGY OF SIGHT

A convex glass lens causes transmitted light rays to converge and focus at a point behind the lens called the principal focus. The refractive surfaces of the eye act like a convex lens. The chief refractive surfaces of the eye are the anterior surface of the cornea, the anterior surface of the lens, and the posterior surface of the lens.

Light rays from an object more than 20 feet away are assumed to enter the eye in a nearly parallel manner and focus on the retina of the relaxed eye to produce an inverted image similar to the image seen on the ground glass of a view camera. To view objects closer than 20 feet, some accommodation is necessary to focus the image on the retina.

The retina contains two types of receptors for light. Because the central area of the retina (known as the *fovea centralis* in man and *macula lutea* in animals) contains only cones, it is specialized for detailed vision and the differentiation of colors. These functions require a high level of illumination. Rods predominate in the peripheral areas of the retina, making it more useful for vision under conditions of low illumination.

Rhodopsin (visual purple) is the pigment involved in the photochemical change that translates light waves to nerve impulses in the rods, which are extremely sensitive to small quantities of light in night vision. The rhodopsin is synthesized in the relative absence of light, from *retinene* (a pigment related to *carotene*) and a protein molecule. Retinene in turn is reduced to vitamin A by an enzyme, *alcohol dehydrogenase*. The following equation illustrates the reversible synthesis and reduction of rhodopsin.

The presence of light causes the below equation to move to the right, a condition called *light adaptation*. A short exposure to bright light produces more retinene than vitamin A. Subsequent dark adaptation, a move to the left in the equation, is faster in this instance than following long exposure to weak light which produces more vitamin A, requiring more time for resynthesis to rhodopsin because two steps are necessary.

Light adaptation occurs when the eye is exposed to a bright light. At first, the light is dazzling, but the eye adapts quickly by constriction of the pupil and bleaching of the rhodopsin. A high level of illumination brings the cones into function, with the resulting greater acuity of vision and ability to differentiate color. A somewhat similar pigment has been postulated in the cones, but the equation has not been worked out.

The difference in receptivity of rods compared with cones depending on the amount of light available may well be the basis for the old saying that "at night all cats are gray."

The eye may be compared with a closed circuit television system with the following somewhat analogous parts:

Closed Circuit T.V.	Eye
Light tight camera box	Sclera
Lens cap	Eyelid
Diaphragm	Iris
Lens (focus by moving)	Lens (focus by changing shape)
Light sensitive cell	Retina
Cable from camera to monitor	Optic nerve and tract
T.V. monitor	Visual area of brain

Rhodopsin	light	Retinene + protein	light	Vitamin A + protein
(visual	$\xrightleftharpoons{}$	(visual yellow)	$\xrightleftharpoons{}$	(visual white)
purple)	dark		dark	

EYE MUSCLES

The eyeball is held in place by a group of extrinsic muscles which hold the eyeball in the orbit against a pad of *retro-ocular fat*. These muscles include the *dorsal (superior) rectus* and *ventral (inferior) rectus* muscles which rotate the eyeball around a horizontal axis extending from the medial canthus (corner) of the eye to the lateral canthus of the eye. The *lateral (external) rectus* and *medial (internal) rectus* muscles rotate the eyeball around a vertical axis. There are two oblique muscles. The *dorsal (superior) oblique* muscle originates with the other ocular

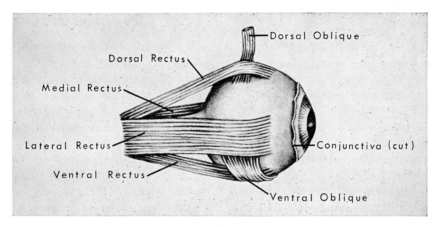

FIG. 7–9.—Extrinsic muscles of the right human eye, lateral view. The eye of a domestic animal would also show the retractor oculi muscle with its fibers filling in the spaces between the four recti muscles and running in the same direction as the recti. Only the insertion of the superior (dorsal) oblique muscle is shown. (Francis, *Introduction to Human Anatomy*, courtesy of the C. V. Mosby Co.)

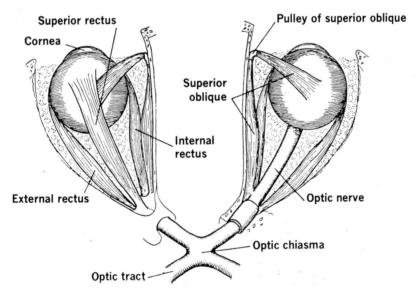

FIG. 7–10.—Diagram showing the eyeballs from above. On the right the superior rectus has been removed to show the insertion of the superior oblique behind the equator of the eyeball. (From W. D. Zoethout: *Introduction to Human Physiology*, St. Louis, The C. V. Mosby Co.)

muscles near the apex of the orbit, passes forward around a pulley of cartilage, the *trochlea*, on the medial wall of the orbit and inserts on the sclera at the dorsum of the eye. This muscle rotates the top of the eye medially. The *ventral (inferior) oblique* muscle originates in the ventral part of the medial side of the orbit and inserts on the ventral part of the sclera. It rotates the ventral part of the eye medially. Thus, the two oblique muscles rotate the eye around a horizontal axis extending from the anterior to the posterior poles of the eye. A series of muscles alternates with the rectus muscles just deep to them, inserting on the sclera a little posterior to the insertion of the recti. These deeper muscles, not present in man, are called collectively the *retractor oculi* muscles.

Another group of muscles associated with the eye are the muscles of the eyelid. These include the *levator palpebrae superioris proprius*, which originates near the apex of the orbit and inserts into the tissue of the eyelid between the conjunctiva and the skin of the upper eyelid. It serves as one of the major muscles to raise the upper eyelid. Circular muscle fibers in the eyelid are known as the *orbicularis oculi* muscle. These muscle fibers serve as a sphincter to close the eyelids. The *retractor of the lateral canthus, corrugator supercilii*, and *malaris* muscles also affect the upper and lower eyelids. The muscles of the eyelid and the eyebrow with the exception of the levator palpebrae superioris proprius can be considered as muscles of facial expression and are supplied by the facial nerve. The dorsal oblique muscle passes around a trochlea. Its nerve supply is the *trochlear (IV cranial) nerve*. The lateral rectus muscle causes the eye to rotate laterally (abduct). It is supplied by the *abducens (VI cranial) nerve* along with the retractor oculi muscle. All the other muscles of the eye are supplied by the *oculomotor (III cranial) nerve*. These mus-

cles include the dorsal rectus, medial rectus, ventral rectus, ventral oblique, and levator palpebrae superioris proprius muscle.

Sensation to the eye and associated structures with the exception of the sensation of vision is all supplied by branches of the trigeminal (V cranial) nerve.

CONJUNCTIVA

The lining of the eyelids and covering of the eyeball is known as the conjunctiva. That portion lining the eyelids is the *palpebral conjunctiva*, and that covering the eyeball is the *bulbar conjunctiva*. Both are parts of a membrane containing blood vessels, except for that portion forming the superficial layer of the cornea, which contains no blood vessels. The conjunctiva is of considerable value in examining animals because the blood vessels are very close to the surface in this particular area. The color of the blood and general condition of the vascular system can be discovered by examining the conjunctiva. Conditions such as *jaundice* and *conjunctivitis* can be seen, particularly when the upper and lower eyelids are everted.

THE LACRIMAL APPARATUS

The lacrimal apparatus includes the *lacrimal gland*, ducts of the lacrimal gland leading into the *conjunctival sac*, and a means of withdrawing the tears (lacrimal secretion) from the surface of the eye. The lacrimal gland, located within the orbit dorsal to the eyeball, empties the lacrimal secretion (tears) into the space between the palpebral conjunctiva and bulbar conjunctiva. The ducts from the lacrimal gland enter the dorsal fornix at the junction of the conjunctiva of the upper eyelid and the bulbar conjunctiva. This secretion washes out foreign particles that may get into the eye and also lubricates the eyelid in relation to the

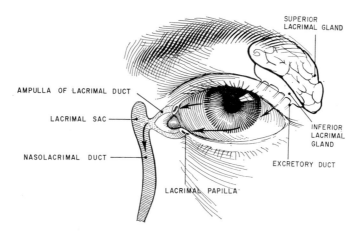

SUPERIOR
LACRIMAL GLAND

AMPULLA OF LACRIMAL DUCT

LACRIMAL SAC

NASOLACRIMAL DUCT

INFERIOR
LACRIMAL
GLAND

EXCRETORY DUCT

LACRIMAL PAPILLA

FIG. 7–11.—Lacrimal apparatus of man. (Grollman, *The Human Body*, courtesy of The Macmillan Co.)

eyeball; a moist cornea is necessary for proper refraction of light. The fluid passes from the eye by way of two *puncta lacrimalia* (small openings, one in the upper lid near the medial canthus and one in the lower lid near the medial canthus). Leading from each punctum lacrimale is a small duct that goes to the *lacrimal sac* located in a fossa of the orbit in the *lacrimal bone*. From the lacrimal sac is a duct leading into the nasal cavity, passing along the wall of the maxilla in the *osseous nasolacrimal canal* and emptying into the lower part of the nasal cavity. In the horse, the nasolacrimal duct opens on the floor of the nasal cavity close to the junction of skin and mucous membrane. Obstruction of any of the excretory portion of the lacrimal apparatus may result in tears overflowing the margin of the eyelids.

THE EYELIDS

The eyelids consist of an upper and a lower fold of skin lined with mucous membrane, the conjunctiva. The margin of each lid has a number of sebaceous glands, the *Meibomian glands*, which produce a waxy substance that helps prevent tears from overflowing onto the face.

In domestic animals a plate of cartilage is located along the medial side of the eyeball. It is partially covered by conjunctiva and partially embedded in the retro-ocular fat. This cartilage is the third eyelid, sometimes called the *nictitating membrane*. It is a remnant of the complete third eyelid of lower animal forms, including the chicken. No muscles attach to the third eyelid, so its movement is entirely passive. The third eyelid is extruded whenever the extrinsic muscles of the eye contract, putting additional pressure on the retro-ocular fat. Protrusion of the third eyelid is a prominent symptom of conditions in which all striated muscles of the body contract, such as in *strychnine poisoning* and *tetanus* (lockjaw).

CHAPTER 8

THE SKELETAL SYSTEM

GENERAL

THE study of the bones which collectively make up the skeleton or framework of the body is called osteology.

The skeleton of a living animal is made up of bones which are themselves living structures. They have blood vessels, lymphatic vessels, and nerves; are subject to disease; repair themselves; and adjust to changes in stress.

About one-third of the weight of bone consists of an organic framework of fibrous tissue and cells. This organic matter gives resilience and toughness to bones. The remaining two-thirds of the weight of bone consists of inorganic salts (largely calcium and phosphorus) deposited within the organic framework. These salts give hardness and rigidity to bones and make them resist the passage of x-rays. If the inorganic salts are removed by soaking a bone in dilute acid, the resulting decalcified bone will retain its original form but will be flexible enough to be tied in a knot. On the other hand, if the organic matter is removed by charring in a furnace so that only the inorganic salts remain, the bone will be extremely brittle and will break unless handled with extreme care.

TERMINOLOGY

Certain terms routinely used in reference to bones, particularly long bones, include the following:

Compact (dense) bone refers to the hard layer of bone which covers most bones and forms almost the entire shaft of long bones.

Cancellous (spongy) bone is composed of plates (*spicules*) arranged to form a porous network. The spaces are usually filled with bone marrow.

Cortex denotes the compact bone forming the shaft of a long bone.

Medullary cavity (marrow cavity) is the space surrounded by the cortex of a long bone. In young animals it is filled with red bone marrow which gradually changes to fatty yellow marrow in old animals.

Epiphysis refers to either extremity of a long bone. The end closest to the body is called the proximal epiphysis and the end farthest from the body is the distal epiphysis.

Diaphysis is the cylindrical shaft of a long bone situated between the two epiphyses.

Epiphyseal cartilage is a layer of *hyaline cartilage* which separates the diaphysis and epiphysis of an immature bone. This is the only area in which a bone can increase in length.

Articular cartilage is a thin layer of hyaline cartilage which covers the articular surface of a bone.

Periosteum is a fibrous membrane which covers the surface of a bone except where articular cartilage is located. It is responsible for increase in diameter of

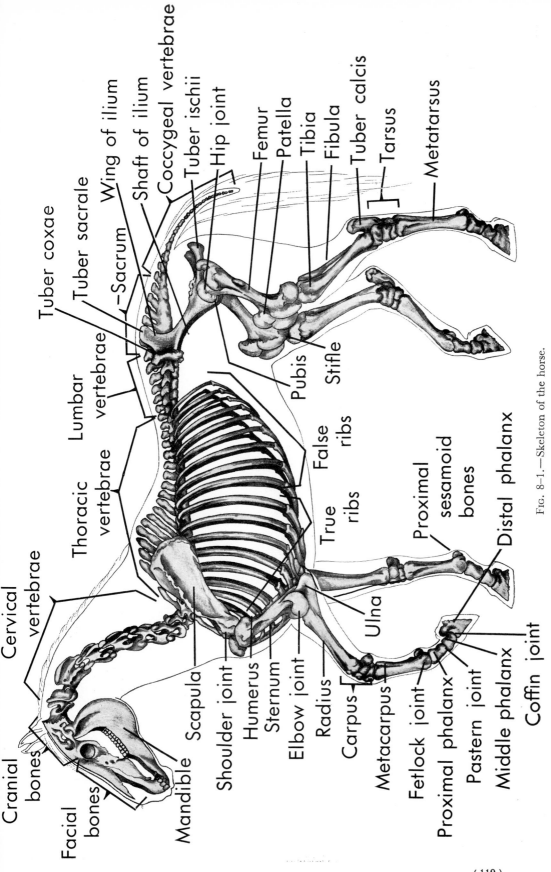

Cranial bones

Facial bones

Cervical vertebrae

Tuber coxae

Tuber sacrale

Wing of ilium

Shaft of ilium

Coccygeal vertebrae

Tuber ischii

Hip joint

Femur

Patella

Tibia

Fibula

Tuber calcis

Tarsus

Metatarsus

Sacrum

Thoracic vertebrae

Lumbar vertebrae

Pubis

Stifle

True ribs

False ribs

Proximal sesamoid bones

Distal phalanx

Mandible

Scapula

Shoulder joint

Humerus

Sternum

Elbow joint

Radius

Carpus

Metacarpus

Ulna

Fetlock joint

Proximal phalanx

Pastern joint

Middle phalanx

Coffin joint

Fig. 8–1.—Skeleton of the horse.

(119)

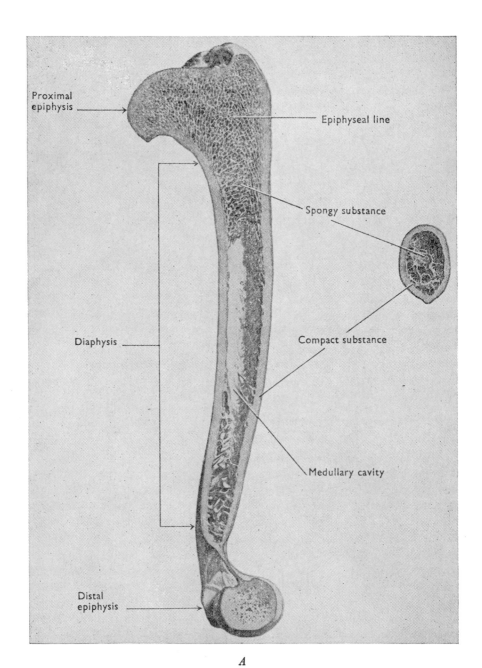

A

Fig. 8–2.—*A*, Longitudinal section of the humerus of a young dog.

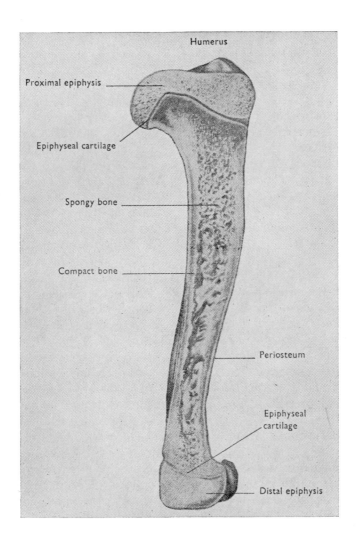

B

Fig. 8–2.—*B*, A longitudinal section of the humerus of a mature dog. (Taylor, *Regional Applied and Anatomy of the Domestic Animals,* courtesy of J. B. Lippincott Co.)

bones and functions in healing of fractures.

Endosteum is a fibrous membrane that lines the marrow cavity of a bone.

Many of the projections from bones and depressions in bones have general names which depend to some extent on their size and function. Both projections and depressions may be articular or non-articular. If they are articular, they form an integral part of a joint and are covered with articular cartilage. Non-articular projections and depressions are located outside of joints. Many of them provide areas for attachment of muscle tendons or of ligaments.

Articular projections include the following:

A *head* is a spherical articular projection such as the head of the femur.

A *condyle* is a more or less cylindrical articular mass such as the condyles on the distal end of the humerus.

A *trochlea* is a pully-like articular mass at the distal end of the femur, on which the patella slides.

A *facet* is a relatively flat articular surface as found between adjacent carpal bones.

Non-articular projections include the following:

A *process* is a general term for a bony projection such as the spinous process or transverse processes of a vertebra.

A *tuberosity* is a relatively large non-articular projection such as the lateral tuberosity on the proximal end of the humerus.

A *tubercle* is a smaller projection.

A *spine* may be a pointed projection such as the spine at the proximal end of the tibia, or spine may refer to a ridge such as the spine of the scapula. (Spine is sometimes used as a synonym for the vertebral column.)

A *crest* is a term for a sharp ridge.

A *neck* is a cylindrical part of bone to which a head is attached. For example, the neck of the femur is located between the head of the femur and the proximal end of the femur.

A *line* is a small ridge or mark on a bone, often caused by the pull of a muscle. The gluteal lines on the ilium are caused by pull of the gluteal muscles.

Articular depressions include the following:

A *glenoid cavity* is a shallow articular concavity as is found on the articular surface of the scapula.

A *cotyloid cavity* is a deep articular concavity such as the acetabulum of the hip joint.

A *notch* may be an articular indentation such as the semilunar notch of the ulna, which articulates with the condyles of the humerus, or it may be a non-articular indentation in the margin of a bone.

Non-articular depressions include the following:

A *fossa* is a large non-articular depression such as the atlantal fossa located ventral to the wing of the atlas.

A *fovea* is a small non-articular depression such as the fovea capitis on the head of the femur.

A *foramen* is a circumscribed hole in a bone. The foramen magnum at the base of the skull through which the spinal cord passes is an example of a foramen.

A *canal* is a tunnel through one or more bones, such as the vertebral canal, through which the spinal cord passes along the length of the vertebral column.

CLASSIFICATION OF BONES ACCORDING TO GROSS APPEARANCE

Any bone may be classified in one of the following groups: long, short, flat, sesamoid, pneumatic, or irregular.

Long bones are greater in one dimension than any other. Each consists of a rela-

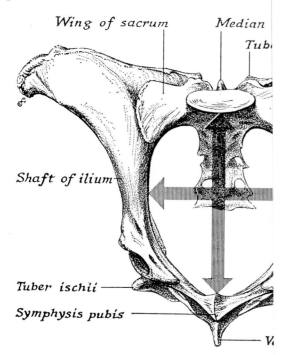

Wing of sacrum   *Median*

Tub

Shaft of ilium

Tuber ischii

Symphysis pubis

V

FIG. 8–7.—The pelvic bones of the cow (viewed from in
the calf must pass at birth. The arrows indicate the greates
the pelvic girdle. (*In* Salisbury and VanDenmark, *Physiolo
Cattle*, courtesy of W. H. Freeman & Co., copyright 1961.)

fossa, which is caudal and below the spine.

The medial (deep) side of the scapula gives attachment to many of the muscles which connect the limb to the body. It also has a depression known as the *subscapular fossa*.

The humerus (arm bone) is a typical long bone that varies only in minor de-

tails from one animal to another. It has a shaft and two extremities. The proximal (upper) end joins the articular angle of the scapula to form the shoulder joint. The prominence produced by this end of the humerus is called the *point of the shoulder*. The upper end of the humerus has a number of irregular prominences (tuberosities) resulting from the

form two irregular bones, the *os coxae*. Each os coxae, or *pelvic bone* of one side, is firmly attached to its fellow at the *symphysis* ventrally to form the *ossa coxarum (pelvis)* and is joined to the axial skeleton dorsally by a very strong joint on each side, the right and left sacro-iliac articulations. The bones entering into the formation of the os coxae are the ilium, the ischium, and the pubis. These bones unite at the acetabulum (socket) of the hip joint.

The *ilium* is the largest and most dorsal of the bones. It is irregularly triangular in shape, with the apex at the acetabulum and the base projecting craniodorsally. The medial angle is called the *tuber sacrale* and is very close to the sacro-iliac joint near the midline. The lateral angle is called the tuber coxae and is known as the *point of the hip*, or *hook bone*. The broad, flat portion between

the *tu*
the *w*
dorsal
ilium.
down
wing
latera

The
ventra
much
ischiu
promi
called

The
bones
floor
into th
meets
symph
the bo
the bo

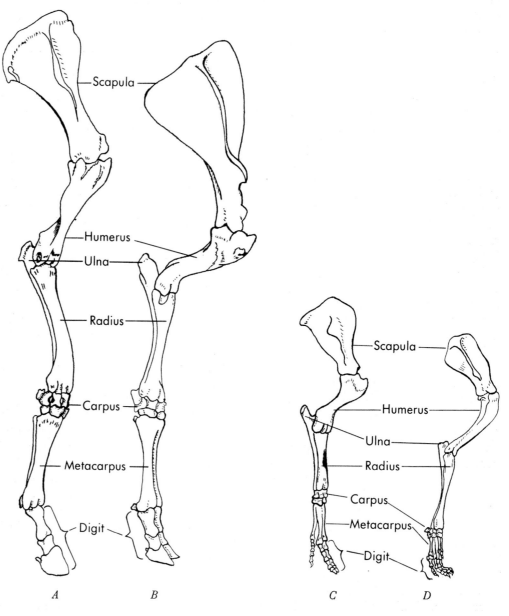

FIG. 8-6.—Forelimb skeletons of domestic animals. *A*, Horse; *B*, cow; *C*, pig; *D*, dog.

9

pull of the strong muscles which attach here. The distal end of the humerus forms the elbow joint with the proximal ends of the radius and ulna.

The *radius* is the larger of the two forearm bones, and the *ulna* is the smaller. The radius is well developed in all species. It enters into the elbow joint proximally and the carpus (knee joint) distally. The radius is a long bone located on the medial side of the forearm, where it can be felt immediately beneath the skin. "Radial" is a term frequently used as an adjective meaning medial in relation to the front limb.

The ulna varies in the amount of development from species to species. The *olecranon process (point of the elbow)* is found in all animals, where it projects above and behind the elbow joint. This process forms a lever for attachment of muscles which extend the elbow. In the horse the proximal portion of the shaft of the ulna is well developed but fused to the radius. The cow, sheep, and pig each have a complete ulna but with very restricted or no movement between the ulna and radius. The cat and dog have considerably more movement between these bones, but not nearly as much as man.

The *carpus* in all animals is a very complex region made up of two rows of small bones. Those in the proximal row are called (from medial to lateral) *radial*, *intermediate*, and *ulnar*, while those in the distal row are numbered 1, 2, 3, and 4. In addition, an accessory carpal bone projects backward from the lateral side of the carpus. The *metacarpal* or *(cannon)* region is immediately distal to the carpus. In the horse it consists of one *large metacarpal (cannon)* bone, representing the base for the third digit or middle finger, and two small metacarpal (splint) bones. The second metacarpal bone is on the medial side, and the fourth is on the lateral side. Fusion of these small bones to the cannon bone with excess bone

The *femur (thigh bone)* extends from the hip joint to the *stifle* (the joint corresponding to the human knee). When seen in cross section in round steaks, the femur is known as the round bone. The proximal end of the femur presents a nearly spherical head which articulates with the acetabulum of the os coxae to form the hip joint. There are also several roughened prominences known as trochanters for the attachment of heavy thigh and hip muscles. The shaft of the femur is nearly circular on cross section and of considerable length. The distal end has two condyles for articulation with the tibia and a trochlea for articulation with the *patella*, which is the largest sesamoid bone in the body.

The *tibia* and *fibula* correspond to the radius and ulna in the forelimb, with the tibia being the larger and located medially. The fibula is much smaller and is located on the lateral side of the leg.

The tibia has an expanded proximal end that enters into the stifle joint. The shaft is elongated but triangular in cross section. The distal end of the tibia has two sagittal concave depressions that form the hinge joint of the hock with the *tibial tarsal bone (talus)*.

In the dog, pig, and man the fibula is a long, thin bone extending from the proximal end of the tibia to the lateral side of the tarsus (hock). Both the proximal end and shaft are present in the horse, but only a vestige of the proximal end of the fibula is present in the cow and sheep.

The *tarsus (hock)* is composed of small bones much like the carpus (knee) in the front limb. The proximal row of tarsal bones consists of two large bones. The tibial tarsal bone dorsally presents two spool-like ridges for articulation with the tibia. The *fibular tarsal* bone (calcaneus), projects upward and backward to form the point of the hock. The calcaneus acts as a lever for the muscles extending the hock, and corresponds to the human heel.

In the horse the central row of tarsal bones is represented by one bone, the central tarsal. The bones of the distal row are again numbered from medial to lateral, 1, 2, 3, and 4. These bones of the hock are bound tightly together by short strong ligaments. The 4th tarsal and central tarsal bones are fused in ruminants and swine.

The metatarsus and digits of the hind limb are similar to those of the forelimb.

when subjected to stress but return to its original shape when the stress is removed. Bone is relatively inelastic. A rod of bone can be elongated only about 1/200 part of its length before breaking. However, even this much deformity is not perfectly elastic; the deformity is permanent and the bone will not return completely to its original length if stretched near its breaking point. This characteristic of deforming under stress without returning to the original shape is exaggerated in bone diseases such as *rickets*.

In addition to tension (stretching), bone is subjected to compression, shearing and bending, and torsion (twisting) stresses. Steindler (1955) cites resistance of bone to tension as 10 kg/mm.^{2}, and to compression as 16.86 kg/mm.^{2} Other types of stress are more difficult to measure. A bone will support considerably more weight in a static situation (supporting weight without moving) than under a dynamic load. A dynamic load results from impact of the bone against an object or an object against a bone. For example, the leg bones of a horse bear a static load when the horse is standing quietly, but bear a dynamic load when the horse is running, jumping, or kicking. Compression, bending, and shearing stresses of the leg bones are all involved in this type of activity. When a horse or other animal pivots with one or more feet bearing weight in contact with the ground, torsion or twisting is added to the other stresses. This is seen particularly well in the action of cutting horses.

Muscles and tendons that run parallel to a bone tend to act like guy wires and reduce stresses of all types, particularly bending and shearing stresses.

FRACTURES AND FRACTURE HEALING

A fracture of bone is simply a break in the continuity of a bone.

Among the many types of fractures described are the following:

A *simple fracture* is one in which the skin over the fracture site is unbroken.

A *compound fracture* is one in which a wound from the exterior contacts the bone at the point of the fracture. This may be caused by a broken end of bone perforating the skin or by a penetrating object such as a bullet causing the fracture.

A *greenstick fracture* is one in which one side of the bone is broken or splintered and the other side only bent. This type of fracture usually is found only in young animals.

A *complete fracture* is one in which the bone is broken entirely across.

An *epiphyseal fracture* is one that occurs at the junction of an epiphysis and the diaphysis of a bone. This type of fracture also is limited to young animals.

A *comminuted fracture* is one in which a number of small fragments are formed due to the bone being splintered or crushed.

If the broken ends of a fractured bone are brought into apposition (touch) and are immobilized (prevented from moving), the normal process of healing will take place. At the time the fracture occurs, some blood vessels are ruptured, pouring blood around the broken ends of the bone. This forms a clot that is invaded by connective tissue cells forming granulation tissue and new blood capillaries. The osteoblasts from the surface of the bone, from the periosteum, from the endosteum, and from the linings of the Haversian canals divide rapidly and produce a massive amount of osteoid tissue called a *callus*. This osteoid tissue fills the gap between the broken ends of the bone, fills the marrow cavity for a distance, and completely encircles the broken ends of the bone, forming an effective splint which usually prevents movement between the segments. As

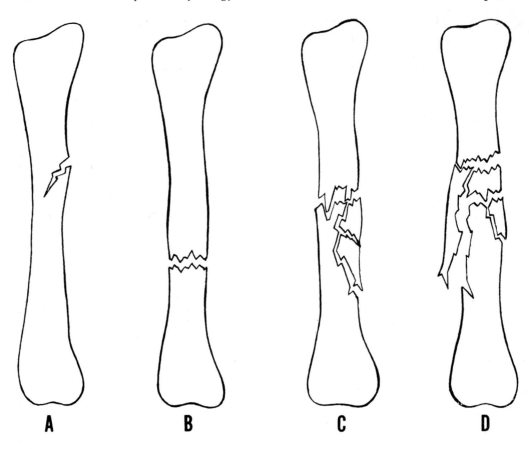

Fig. 9–3.—Types of fractures shown diagrammatically. *A*, Green stick; *B*, complete; *C*, comminuted and *D*, compound (if fragment punctured skin). (After Kahn, *Man in Structure and Function*, courtesy of Alfred A. Knopf.)

soon as the callus becomes calcified, it has changed into true bone. The healing process is then completed by reorganization of the callus to form a typical bone shaft with a marrow cavity. Misalignment of the fractured bone will be corrected to some extent by the action of osteoclasts, which also will remove excessive internal and external callus. As soon as the bone is put to use, functional orientation of the callus begins with a tendency to straighten imperfections in the alignment of the bone. The callus will increase in size on the concave side where stress is greatest and tend to erode on the convex side, thus tending to correct any deformity.

The amount of spontaneous correction possible in fractures depends on a number of factors, including age of the animal, blood supply to the bone, degree of correction necessary, presence or absence of infection, and amount of damage to surrounding tissues.

Excessive separation of fragments, which may be caused by too much traction or incomplete immobilization of a fracture, may result in non-union, with fibrous tissue filling the gap between fragments.

Quickest fracture healing occurs in young animals, particularly if the fracture site has a good blood supply and is completely immobilized with the ends of

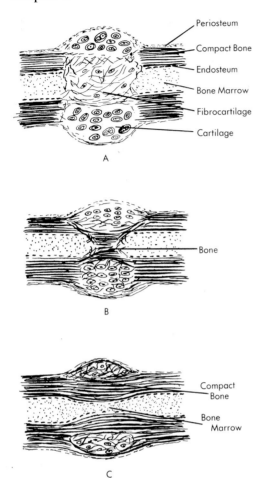

Periosteum
Compact Bone
Endosteum
Bone Marrow
Fibrocartilage
Cartilage

A

Bone

B

Compact Bone

Bone Marrow

C

Fig. 9–4.—Some stages in healing of a fracture of a long bone. *A*, Early soft callus—replaces blood clot; *B*, intermediate callus; *C*, nearly healed hard callus.

the fragments in apposition. In man, a fracture may heal completely within one month in an infant, but a similar fracture in a person past middle age may require six months or longer to heal.

Occasionally bone is repaired by grafting another piece of bone into the area. If the bone is from the same species and particularly from the same animal, the portion of the bone in contact with tissue fluid may survive and the osteoblasts become active. At the same time osteoclasts remove the dead portions of the graft, which are replaced by healthy bone

if the graft is functional and subjected to the proper amount of stress. If the graft is taken from an animal of a different species, all osteoblasts in the graft will die because every body resists the introduction of any foreign protein.

Other Pathological Conditions

Other pathological conditions of bones may be caused by infections, tumors, endocrine disturbances, or nutritional imbalances.

Tuberculosis of bone and *osteomyelitis*, which means inflammation of the bone and bone marrow, are two infections sometimes seen in bone. In man, osteomyelitis usually is caused by staphylococcus or streptococcus bacteria which may gain access to the bone by way of the blood stream, as a general infection, or by way of a wound, in which case the infection may remain localized.

Bone tumors are named according to the cells of the bone from which they originate. A tumor of bone tissue itself is called an *osteoma*, but most bony growths from the surface of a bone are called *exostoses* and are simply due to the response of the bone to irritation. A *fibroma* of bone grows from the outer layer of the periosteum.

A *chondroma* may develop from the epiphyseal cartilage or from unabsorbed islands of cartilage which preceded the developing bone. Giant cell tumor is a tumor of the osteoclasts and is sometimes called an *osteoclastoma*.

The preceding tumors are considered to be benign; that is, they are slow growing and not likely to cause death. Malignant tumors grow very rapidly and will kill the individual if not stopped. Malignant tumors include *osteogenic sarcoma* of the bone proper and *multiple myeloma* of the bone marrow.

Most endocrine disturbances that affect bone involve the parathyroid glands. *Osteitis fibrosis*, also called *von Reckling-*

hausen's disease, is believed to be caused by malfunction of the parathyroid glands (excess secretion).

Rickets and *osteomalacia* usually are due to lack of vitamin D, with the resultant failure to lay down calcium in the bones. Although rickets usually is due to lack of vitamin D, it may be caused by an imbalance or lack of calcium and/or phosphorus in the ration. Rickets is essentially a disease of young bones that chiefly affects the growing areas.

Osteomalacia, sometimes called adult rickets, affects the entire bone, since there are no rapidly growing areas in adult bone. *Achondroplasia* is a hereditary condition in which the epiphyses fuse early in life but the bones continue to increase in diameter. An animal affected with the disease is called an *achondroplastic* dwarf. The Dachshund is a breed of dogs selectively bred for this condition. Dwarfism in cattle closely resembles achondroplasia.

CHAPTER 10

JOINTS

GENERAL

ARTHROLOGY is the study of the articulations (unions) between bones, which are commonly called joints. These articulations may be immovable, slightly movable, or freely movable, and are known respectively as synarthroses, amphiarthroses, and diarthroses.

Synarthroses, or immovable joints, may be further subdivided according to the uniting medium:

1. *Suture* refers to the junction between bones of the skull which are united by fibrous tissue early in life but may ossify after maturity.

2. *Gomphosis* refers to the articulation of teeth in their sockets in the mandible and *maxillae*.

3. *Synchondrosis* refers to an immovable joint in which the uniting medium is cartilage. The union of the *diaphysis* and *epiphysis* of an immature bone is an example of synchondrosis.

4. *Synostosis* refers to a joint in which the uniting medium is bone. This type of joint may be a pathological or normal development from other types of joints. The normal ossification of the *epiphyseal cartilage* of a long bone produces a synostosis.

Amphiarthroses (slightly movable joints) include *symphyses* and *syndesmoses*.

Symphyses (certain median-line joints) are united by flattened discs of *fibro-*

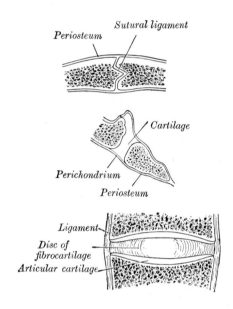

FIG. 10–1.—Types of synarthrodial joints. (Gray's *Anatomy*. Lea & Febiger.)

cartilage as found between adjacent pelvic bones, and between the bodies of adjacent vertebrae.

Syndesmoses refer to joints with a fibrous-tissue uniting medium which permit slight movement. The normal union of the shafts of the *splint bones* and *cannon bone* of the horse is an example of syndesmosis.

Diarthroses are freely movable (true joints). They are also called synovial joints and are the most important from the standpoint of movement.

(143)

DIARTHRODIAL JOINTS

The general structure of most diarthrodial joints is quite similar and includes the following structures: articular surfaces, articular cartilages, joint capsule, and ligaments.

The *articular surfaces* are specialized layers of compact bone on the surfaces which articulate with other bones.

The *articular cartilage* is a layer of *hyaline cartilage* covering the articular surface. *Periosteum* covers the remainder of the bone.

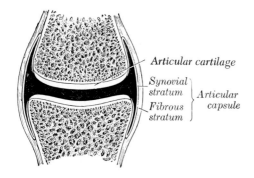

Fig. 10–2.—Diagrammatic section of a diarthrodial joint. (*Gray's Anatomy*, Lea & Febiger.)

The *joint capsule* consists of two layers.

The deeper layer is the *synovial membrane*, which is a delicate sleeve-like layer of specialized connective tissue extending from the edges of the articular cartilages of the adjacent bones, but does not cover either articular cartilage. This membrane secretes the *synovial fluid* (joint oil) which lubricates the normal joint.

The superficial layer is the *capsular ligament* (capsular thickening) which is a heavier fibrous sleeve covering the synovial membrane. This capsular ligament may be thickened in certain areas to form the extracapsular (or periarticular) ligaments which connect adjacent bones and help stabilize the joint.

Ligaments are connective tissue bands which extend from bone to bone. They are named according to their location in relation to the joint.

Intra-articular ligaments are found within joints and are surrounded by the joint capsule. Examples include the *cruciate ligaments* of the stifle and the ligaments that hold adjacent carpal or tarsal bones together.

Peri-articular ligaments are outside the joint capsule and include the following:

Collateral ligaments are located on the medial and lateral sides of a joint.

Anterior and *posterior ligaments* are located in front of and behind the joint.

Annular ligaments surround the joint, and the fibers generally run in a circular fashion around the joint to strengthen and protect the joint capsule.

CLASSIFICATION OF DIARTHRODIAL JOINTS

Diarthrodial joints are classified according to the type of joint surface and movements possible. The types of diarthrodial joints commonly found in domestic animals include: ginglymus, arthrodial, trochoid, and enarthrodial.

Ginglymus (hinge) joints move only in the sagittal plane. The movements possible in this type of joint are flexion, extension, and in some joints hyperextension. The fetlock joint is a good example of a ginglymus joint.

Arthrodial (plane) joints have only a slight gliding movement between relatively flat opposed surfaces. These surfaces are called *facets*. The joints between adjacent carpal bones are examples of arthrodial joints.

A *trochoid (pivot) joint* is one in which rotary movement occurs around one axis. The *atlanto-axial joint* is the only good example of a trochoid joint in domestic animals.

Enarthrodial (ball and socket) joints permit movement in nearly any direction. A spherical head on one bone fits into a cup-shaped depression in the other segment of the joint. Flexion, extension, adduction, abduction, rotation, and circumduction are all possible movements in enarthrodial joints. The *coxo-femoral (hip) joint* is the best example of an enarthrodial joint.

MOVEMENT OF JOINTS

Diarthrodial (true) joints may exhibit one or more of the following movements:

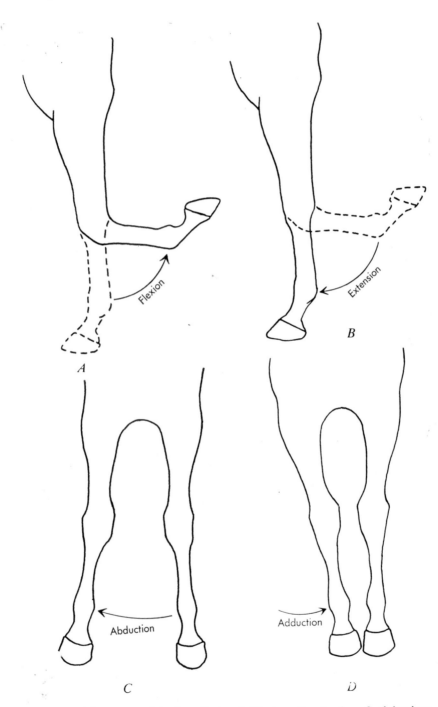

Fɪɢ. 10–3.—Movements of the front limb. *A*, Flexion; *B*, extension; *C*, abduction; and *D*, adduction.

flexion, extension, hyperextension, rotation, adduction, abduction, and circumduction.

Flexion refers to movement in the sagittal plane which tends to decrease the angle between segments making up a joint. The carpus (knee) must be flexed when a horse's front foot is picked up.

Extension is the reverse of flexion and refers to movement in the sagittal plane which tends to increase the angle between segments forming the joint.

Hyperextension refers to movement in which the angle between segments is increased beyond 180° or a straight line. In some instances hyperextension is also called *dorsal flexion*. The fetlock joint of the horse is hyperextended in the normal standing position.

Rotation consists of a twisting movement of a segment around its own axis. Turning the head from side to side as in indicating "no" is perhaps the best example of rotation.

Adduction refers to movement of an extremity toward the median plane.

Abduction refers to movement of an extremity away from the median plane.

Circumduction results from a combination of the preceding movements and may be defined as a movement in which an extremity describes a cone and the distal end of the extremity describes a circle. A horse that "paddles" exhibits circumduction.

Pronation is a movement that tends to rotate an extremity so that the dorsum is up.

Supination is a movement that tends to rotate an extremity so that the volar or plantar aspect of the limb is up.

Pronation and supination are rarely seen to any extent in domestic animals.

JOINTS OF THE AXIAL SKELETON

The joints of the skull are chiefly of the *suture* type, with adjacent bones united by fibrous tissue. In old age these ossify,

becoming solid bone. The *fontanel* (soft spot) in a baby's head is an example of the fibrous tissue connecting adjacent bones.

Exceptions to the suture type of joint in the skull are the symphysis of the *mandible* and the *synchondrosis* at the junction of the sphenoid bone and occipital bone at the base of the skull.

The first movable joint in the axial skeleton is the *temporo-mandibular joint* between the *mandible* (jaw bone) and the *temporal bone* of the skull. This joint consists of two articular surfaces, one on the skull and one on the mandible, with a plate of cartilage between. The temporo-mandibular joint acts as a *ginglymus* (*hinge*) *joint* when the mouth is opened and closed and as an *arthrodial*, or sliding-gliding, *joint* when the jaw is moved from side to side and forward and back as in grinding food.

The *atlanto-occipital* joint between the skull and first cervical (neck) vertebra is strictly a ginglymus (hinge type) of joint. Two *condyles* (convex ridges) of bone on the skull fit into corresponding depressions in the *atlas* (first cervical vertebra). The only movements possible are flexion and extension in the sagittal plane as in nodding the head "yes."

Rotation of the head occurs almost entirely between the atlas and axis. The *dens*, a tooth-like projection from the anterior extremity of the *axis* (second cervical vertebra) projects into the *vertebral foramen* of the atlas, where it is held by a strong *annular ligament* that permits considerable rotary movement. This is the best example of a pivot joint in which one segment rotates around the long axis of another.

The *amphiarthrodial joints* between adjacent vertebrae throughout the rest of the vertebral column exhibit relatively little motion. The bodies of adjacent vertebrae are united by a heavy disc of fibro-cartilage which is flexible enough to permit some bending in any direction, or even twisting. This fibrocartilage has a soft center known as the *nucleus pulposus* which may abnormally protrude into the spinal canal and cause pressure on the spinal cord. The resulting condition is called a ruptured *intervertebral disc* and may cause paralysis of the body caudal to the involved disc. The articular processes of adjacent vertebrae have flat surfaces which are apposed to form an *arthrodial* (sliding) *joint*. These surfaces are larger; and the movements, more extensive toward the head, decrease in the thoracic region and are more extensive again in the lumbar region. The joints between sacral vertebrae disappear completely, and the *sacrum* becomes a single fused bone.

The *ribs* are attached to the vertebral column by two separate joints: one joint is between the head of the rib and a depression located between the bodies of two adjacent thoracic vertebrae; and one joint is between an articular facet a short distance from the head of the rib and a facet on the transverse process of the vertebra of the same series as the rib. The first joint is of the pivot type, and the second is of the arthrodial type.

The ventral ends of the first few ribs are directly attached to the *sternum* by bars of cartilage known as *costal cartilages*. The cartilages of the ribs behind these are attached to the costal cartilages of the *sternal ribs* and are called *asternal ribs*. *Floating ribs* have no sternal attachment either directly or indirectly. Whenever any animal has an extra pair of ribs the last pair is likely to be floating.

JOINTS OF THE APPENDICULAR SKELETON

Joints of the Front Limb

The *scapula* (or shoulder blade) has no true bony connection with the *bony thorax*. It is held in place by a number of

10

muscles and ligaments. This type of joint is called a *synsarcosis*.

The *shoulder joint* proper (*scapulo-humeral joint*) is an *enarthrodial* (ball and socket) *joint*. Movements in all directions including rotation are possible. However, in our domestic animals the arrangement of shoulder muscles practically limits movement to a hinge type of action in the sagittal plane. Thus extension and flexion are the chief movements. The head of the *humerus* is a segment of a very large sphere much more extensive than the comparable cavity of the scapula. The joint capsule is very extensive, with poorly developed ligaments. The muscles surrounding the shoulder joint on all sides act rather effectively as ligaments, with the added advantage of being able to contract or relax, thus giving greater movement to the joint.

The *elbow joint* is a true *ginglymus* (hinge) *joint* formed by the *condyles* (spool-like distal end of the humerus) uniting with the proximal ends of the *radius* and *ulna*. The proximal end of the radius is slightly concave and expanded to give an extensive surface for support. Combined with the *semilunar notch* of the ulna, the radius forms a half circle embracing the humeral condyles. Movement in the elbow is limited to flexion and extension in the horse. In man and to a lesser degree in the dog the joint between the radius and ulna permits rotation, specifically supination and pronation.

The *carpus* (knee) is a very complex joint which not only permits flexion and extension between the radius and proximal row of carpal bones, but also between the proximal and distal rows of carpal bones. The entire joint absorbs considerable shock because of the many small *arthrodial joints* formed by adjacent carpal bones connected by short ligaments. The joint between the distal row of carpal bones and the *metacarpus* (*cannon bones*) is almost entirely arthrodial, with little movement except sliding and gliding.

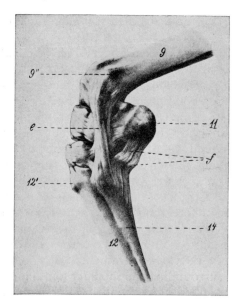

Fig. 10–4.—Lateral view of the carpus of the horse.

9. Distal end of radius
9″ Lateral tuberosity of radius
11. Accessory carpal
12. Third (large) metacarpal
12′ Tuberosity of third metacarpal
14. Fourth (small) metacarpal
e. Lateral ligament of carpus
f. Ligaments of accessory carpal
(Ellenberger, *An Atlas of Animal Anatomy for Artists*, courtesy of Dover Publications, Inc.)

The fibrous layer of the *joint capsule* of the carpus is very extensive, being a long sleeve extending from the radius to the metacarpus, and enclosing the carpal bones. The *synovial membrane*, however, forms three separate sacs; a *radiocarpal sac*, an *intercarpal sac*, and a *carpometacarpal sac*.

In the horse there is normally very little movement between the large metacarpal (cannon) bone and the small metacarpal (splint) bones. If very much movement occurs, inflammation will follow, resulting in a *"splint,"* which is a painful swelling where the shafts of the great and small metacarpal bones meet. Later this swelling may ossify and form a bony prominence which may not cause any lameness at all.

In the cow and sheep the third and fourth metacarpal bones are fused to form the single cannon bone, so the only true joint present in this area is an arthrodial joint between the carpus and metacarpus.

In the dog and pig, the metacarpal bones are of more nearly equal size, so arthrodial joints are present between adjacent metacarpals as well as between the metacarpals and carpus.

The *fetlock (metacarpo-phalangeal) joint* is formed by the distal end of the *metacarpus*, the proximal end of the *first phalanx*, or *long pastern bone*, and the two *proximal sesamoid bones*. It is a ginglymus joint that in the standing position is hyperextended, or in dorsal flexion.

The *pastern joint (proximal inter-phalangeal joint)* is a ginglymus joint between the first and second phalanges (the long and the short pastern bones). Although it is a ginglymus joint, it is rather limited in motion.

The *coffin joint (distal inter-phalangeal joint)* is formed by the second and third phalanges and the *distal sesamoid (navicular) bone*. The coffin joint is largely encased within the hoof and is essentially a ginglymus joint.

Joints of the Hind Limb

The *hip joint (coxo-femoral joint)* is the best example of an *enarthrodial* (ball-and-socket) *joint*. The head of the *femur* is about two-thirds of a sphere which fits into the less extensive *cotyloid cavity (acetabulum)* of the *os coxae*. The margin of the acetabulum is reinforced and deepened by a marginal cartilage, which increases the depth of the cavity.

The *joint capsule* is quite extensive, but not so extensive as that of the shoulder. The *round ligament* of the femur connects the head of the femur with a non-articular area in the acetabulum. Movements in all directions are possible in the hip joint, but, as in the shoulder joint, extension and flexion are the movements chiefly employed. Dislocation of the hip of the dog is fairly common, particularly when the dog has been struck by a car.

The *sacro-iliac* joint is the only bony connection between the axial and appendicular skeletons. The sacro-iliac is a true joint in which the articular *surface* of the sacrum is held tightly in apposition with the wing of the *ilium* by a number of short, strong ligaments. Movement in this joint is normally very limited but may become more extensive just preceding parturition, when the ligaments stretch under the influence of the hormone *relaxin*.

Excessive movement of the sacro-iliac joint can be very painful if some of the nerves in the area are injured by pressure. Ligaments in this area include dorsal and ventral *sacro-iliac* and *sacro-sciatic ligaments*. The latter is a strong, wide band in the cow, sheep, and horse, which helps form the lateral wall of the pelvis.

The *stifle joint* corresponds to the human knee. The stifle joint is made up of the *condyles* of the distal end of the femur, separated from the proximal end of the *tibia* by two *semilunar cartilages (menisci)*. Each meniscus is a half-moon-shaped disc that is flattened on the lower side to conform to the surface of the tibia and con-

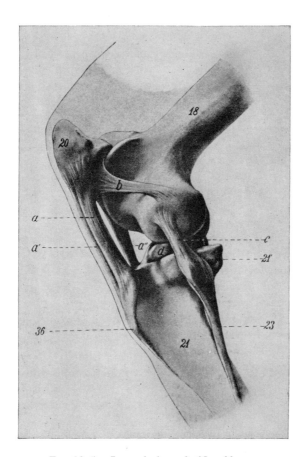

FIG. 10–5.—Lateral view of stifle of horse.

18, Distal end of femur; *20*, patella; *21*, tibia; *21′*, lateral condyle of tibia; *23*, fibula; *a*, lateral patellar ligament; *a′* middle patellar ligament; *a″*, medial patellar ligament; *b*, lateral femero-patellar ligament; *c*, lateral femero-tibial ligament; *d*, lateral meniscus. (Ellenberger, *An Atlas of Animal Anatomy for Artists*, courtesy of Dover Publications, Inc.)

cave on the upper surface to fit the respective condyle of the femur. These menisci help keep the joint in apposition and also absorb shock. The stifle joint is held in apposition by a *medial* and a *lateral collateral ligament* on either side and by two *intra-articular cruciate* (X-shaped) *ligaments* that extend from the tibia to the femur in the middle of the joint. Also associated with the stifle joint is the *patella* (*knee cap*) the largest *sesamoid* bone in the body. The patella rides on the *trochlea* of the femur, helps reduce fric-

tion, and changes the direction of pull of the *quadriceps femoris* muscle which is the large *extensor muscle* of the stifle, located on the front of the *thigh*.

The *tarsus* (*hock joint*), like the carpus, is a complex joint. The *ginglymus* portion is formed between the distal end of the tibia and the *tibial tarsal bone* (*talus*). This portion of the joint is held together by the strong medial and lateral collateral ligaments of the hock.

The *fibular tarsal bone* (*calcaneuus*) projects upward and backward to form a lever for attachment of the *tendon of Achilles* and hence the extensor muscles of the *hock*. The calcaneuus is firmly attached to the remaining tarsal bones by many short, strong ligaments. The ligaments are less extensive over the craniomedial aspect of the hock, where, in the horse, the joint capsule may bulge, producing a condition known as *bog spavin*. In the horse and dog movement between adjacent tarsal bones is extremely limited and then is only of the *arthrodial* type. However, in the cow, sheep, and pig the *proximal intertarsal joint* has some hinge movement.

Below the hock the joints are similar to those of the fore limb.

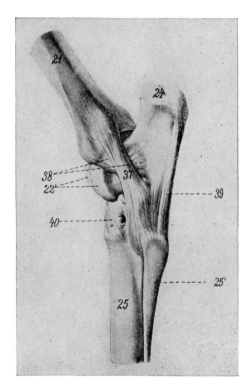

FIG. 10–6.—Lateral view of hock of horse.

21. Tibia
22. Tibial tarsal
24. Tuber calcis (point of hock)
25. Third (large) metatarsal
25' Fourth (small) metatarsal
37. Lateral long ligament of hock
38. Lateral short ligament of hock
39. Plantar ligament of hock
40. Dorsal ligament of hock

(Ellenberger, *An Atlas of Animal Anatomy for Artists,* courtesy of Dover Publications, Inc.)

PATHOLOGY OF JOINTS AND RELATED STRUCTURES

Since diarthrodial joints depend on free movement for effective functioning, anything that interferes with their mobility can be quite serious. Conditions affecting joints may be due to injuries, infections, or inflammations.

Injuries to joints include dislocations, fractures, sprains, cuts, and puncture wounds. A *dislocation*, also known as a *luxation*, of a joint refers to a condition in which one or more segments of the joint are out of place. Dislocation of a joint nearly always involves stretching or tearing of *ligaments*, and if the dislocation is severe enough, the *joint capsule* also may be torn. The usual treatment for dislocation consists of replacing the joint into its normal position, frequently followed by the application of a splint or cast. Replacement may be extremely difficult unless the animal is put completely to sleep so all muscles will be relaxed. Early treatment is very important to prevent the joint cavity from filling with connective tissue. Because of the excessive stretching or tearing of ligaments, recovery from a dislocation may be less satisfactory and take longer than recovery from a properly treated fracture.

Occasionally a fairly functional joint, called a *false joint*, may develop, even though the dislocated joint has never been replaced. In a false joint the fibrous connective tissue which grows around the end of the bone permits considerable movement even though no joint capsule or cartilage develop as in true joints. False joints may also form at a fracture site if the ends of the bone are not immobilized.

Fractures, or breaks of bones, may involve one or more of the segments making up a joint. In young animals the fracture may be simply a separation of the *epiphysis* of the bone from the *diaphysis* close to or within the joint. Bone fractures within or very close to a joint are difficult to *reduce* (bring segments into proper alignment) and to immobilize after reduction because of the short length of at least one of the segments.

A *sprain* of a joint is a condition in which the ligaments are stretched but the joint does not remain dislocated. The term "*strain*" is sometimes used in place of "sprain." "Strain" is more frequently used to denote excessive stretching of a muscle or tendon. Although a considerable amount of swelling may follow a sprain, the affected joint usually will recover spontaneously if rested adequately.

Cuts such as barbed wire cuts may enter a joint cavity, with subsequent loss of *synovial fluid*. A condition of this nature, called an open joint, may be quite serious and difficult to treat successfully. The danger is not from loss of synovial fluid, but from infection of the joint cavity. Synovial fluid is a good medium for bacterial growth, and the many recesses of most joint capsules make drainage and treatment of an infected joint difficult. There is always the danger of permanent damage to the articular cartilage from infection.

Puncture wounds involving joints may result from penetration by sharp objects such as nails, wire, or thorns. Since the object causing the puncture rarely is sterile, a puncture wound of a joint resembles an infected cut. However, the puncture wound is more insidious because it may not be discovered for several days and there usually is little chance for drainage. Cuts and puncture wounds may involve *bursae* and tendon *synovial sheaths*, with results similar to those involving joints.

Infections of joints may result from cuts or punctures as mentioned above, or the infection may reach the joint by way of blood or lymph stream. *Erysipelas* of swine and *joint ill* of foals are two diseases that frequently result in joint infections. In conditions of this nature, the disease must be treated systemically rather than treating only the affected joint.

Inflammation of a joint, involving swelling and pain, usually accompanies each of the conditions previously mentioned. In addition, injury from kicks, blows, and falls may result in inflammation of a joint without any infection being present. If no complications develop, this type of injury should recover quite readily.

Some specific conditions (usually in horses) involving joints or related structures include:

Name of Condition	*Involvement*
Arthritis	Inflammation of any joint from any cause
Bicipital bursitis	Inflammation of the bursa between the biceps brachii tendon and the humerus near the point of the shoulder
Bog spavin	Distension of the joint capsule of the hock—swelling on the cranio-medial side of the hock
Bone spavin (jack)	Exostosis (extra bone formation) of tarsal bones
Bowed tendon (tendinitis)	Stretching (possibly with tearing) and inflammation of the superficial and deep digital flexor tendons and their synovial sheaths in the area of the cannon—usually front leg
Bursitis	Inflammation of any bursa from any cause
Capped elbow	Inflammation of the superficial or deep bursa over the olecranon process of the ulna (the point of the elbow)
Capped hock	Inflammation of the bursa over the tuber calcis (point of the hock)
Carpitis (popped knee)	Inflammation of the carpal joint capsule and/or carpal bones and ligaments
Curb (curby hocks)	Thickening of the plantar ligament of the hock at the caudal surface of the hock
Dislocation	Out of joint—one or more segments of a joint out of proper position
Fistulous withers	Inflammation and infection of the supraspinous bursa between the ligamentum nuchae and thoracic vertebrae
Herniated intervertebral disc	Prolapse of intervertebral fibrocartilage into the vertebral canal—may cause pressure on the spinal cord resulting in pain and/or paralysis
Laminitis	Inflammation of the sensitive laminae which are located between the distal phalanx and the hoof wall
Navicular disease	Inflammation of navicular bursa, deep digital flexor tendon, and/or navicular bone (distal sesamoid bone) in the region of the coffin joint.
Osselets	Inflammation of proximal end of proximal phalanx and/or distal end of third metacarpal
Poll evil	Inflammation (usually with infection) of the bursa between the ligamentum nuchae and atlas
Popped ankle (wind gall)	Inflammation of fetlock joint, capsule or other synovial structure in the area
Ring bone	Exostosis of the phalanges (usually the proximal and middle phalanges)
Side bone	Ossification of the collateral cartilages of the distal phalanx
Splints	Ossification and exostosis of the joint between the shaft of a splint bone and the cannon bone—(usually the second and third metacarpal bones are involved)
Sprain	Stretching of the ligaments of any joint
Stifling (upward fixation of the patella)	Locking of the patella over the medial ridge of the trochlea of the femur—keeps the stifle extended and indirectly extends the hock
Subluxation	Partial dislocation of any joint
Synovitis	Inflammation of any tendon synovial sheath
Thoroughpin	Swelling of the synovial sheath of the deep digital flexor tendon above the hock.
Trochanteric bursitis	Inflammation of the bursa between the tendon of the middle glutea muscle and the greater trochanter of the femur

THE MUSCULAR SYSTEM

GENERAL

THE three types of muscle tissue found in the body are smooth, involuntary striated and voluntary striated.

Smooth (involuntary unstriated) muscle is found in the systems which are chiefly automatic in their functioning. Smooth muscle is found in the wall of the digestive tract, where it moves food from the stomach into the intestines and through the intestines without any conscious control. The walls of the urogenital system contain a considerable amount of smooth muscle. The diameter of blood vessels and consequently the quantity of blood flowing to a given area is controlled rather extensively by the smooth muscle within the vessel walls. Contraction of smooth muscles is stimulated by the *autonomic nervous system* as well as by certain drugs. The individual muscle cells are spindle-shaped, with a centrally located nucleus. The cells are usually arranged in sheets, bundles, or a network, although occasionally individual smooth muscle cells are scattered through a tissue, as the smooth muscle fibers within the skin that raise the hair.

Involuntary striated muscle is also known as *cardiac muscle*, since it is found within the heart. These cardiac muscle cells are arranged in the form of a network. They are automatically controlled within the heart itself, as well as being regulated by the autonomic nervous system. There is no conscious control of the heart muscle. The cells are striated, and the nuclei are centrally located.

We are familiar with voluntary striated (*skeletal*) muscle as the flesh (meat) of our domestic animals. The individual cells, as the name implies, appear striated (striped) when viewed under a microscope. The nuclei are located near the surface of the cells. Each muscle cell (fiber) is covered by a cell membrane (sheath) known as the sarcolemma. This covering acts as a connecting link between muscle fibers and tendons and gives elasticity to the muscle fiber. It is composed of the plasma membrane and the so-called basement membrane of related connective tissue.

Each muscle fiber is insulated from all other muscle fibers, is controlled directly by a branch from a *voluntary nerve (motor neuron)*, and usually is under conscious control. The functional unit of voluntary striated muscle, called a *motor unit*, consists of a motor neuron and all the muscle fibers it supplies.

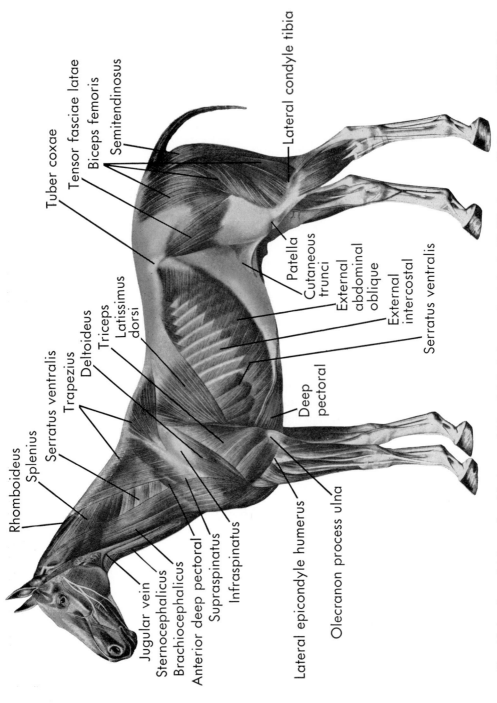

Fig. 11–1.—Superficial muscles of the horse. (*Atlas of Animal Anatomy for Artists* by W. Ellenberger, H. Baum, and H. Dittrich, reprinted with permission of Dover Publications, Inc., New York 14, N. Y.)

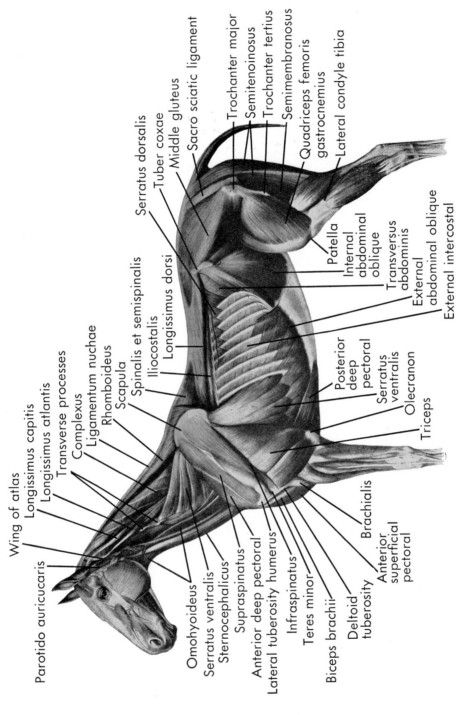

Parotido auricucaris
Wing of atlas
Longissimus capitis
Longissimus atlantis
Transverse processes
Complexus
Ligamentum nuchae
Rhomboideus
Scapula
Spinalis et semispinalis
Iliocostalis
Longissimus dorsi

Serratus dorsalis
Tuber coxae
Middle gluteus
Sacro sciatic ligament
Trochanter major
Semitenoinosus
Trochanter tertius
Semimembranosus
Quadriceps femoris
gastrocnemius
Lateral condyle tibia

Patella
Internal abdominal oblique
Transversus abdominis
External abdominal oblique
External intercostal

Posterior deep pectoral
Serratus ventralis
Olecranon
Triceps

Omohyoideus
Serratus ventralis
Sternocephalicus
Supraspinatus
Anterior deep pectoral
Lateral tuberosity humerus
Infraspinatus
Teres minor
Biceps brachii
Deltoid tuberosity
Anterior superficial pectoral
Brachialis

FIG. 11–2.—Deeper muscles of the horse. (*Atlas of Animal Anatomy for Artists* by W. Ellenberger, H. Baum, and H. Dittrich, reprinted with permission of Dover Publications, Inc., New York 14, N. Y.)

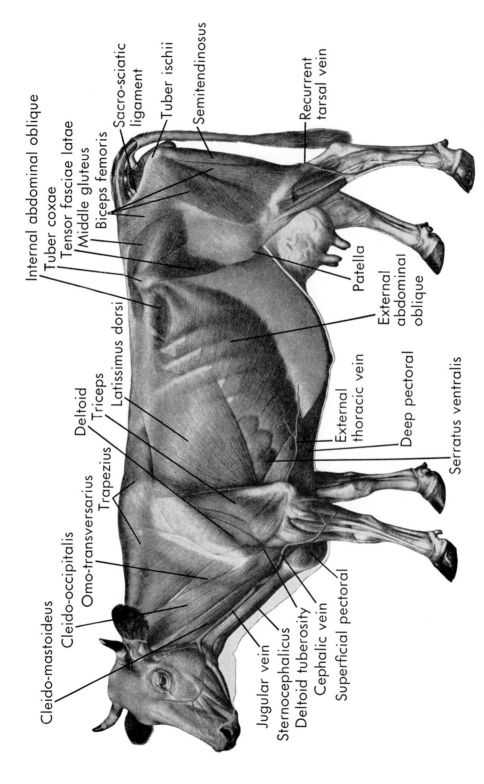

FIG. 11-3.—Superficial muscles of the cow after removal of the cutaneous muscle. (*Atlas of Animal Anatomy for Artists* by W. Ellenberger, H. Baum, and H. Dittrich, reprinted with permission of Dover Publications, Inc., New York 14, N. Y.)

STRIATED MUSCLES

Muscle fibers are arranged in bundles surrounded by fibrous connective tissue. The connective tissue between individual muscle fibers is called *endomysium*. The sheath surrounding bundles of muscle fibers is called *perimysium*, and the connective tissue around an entire muscle is known as *epimysium*.

(fat interspersed between muscle bundles) largely account for the relative toughness or tenderness of a cut of meat. Thus a cut from the rump or loin of an animal will be more tender than a shank end, where all the connective tissue is concentrated to form the tendon of Achilles.

Muscle fibers may be arranged in a parallel manner in sheets, as in the abdominal muscles, or bands as in the

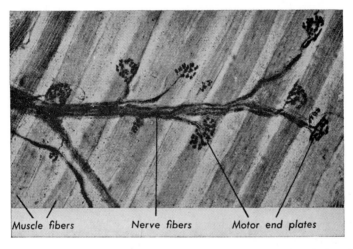

Muscle fibers   Nerve fibers   Motor end plates

FIG. 11–4.—Photomicrograph of motor nerve ending in intercostal muscle. Gold chloride method. X 215. Copenhaver, *Bailey's Textbook of Histology*, courtesy of Williams & Wilkins Co.)

The maximum amount a muscle fiber can contract is to about one-half its resting length. In man, the *strength of muscle contraction* is believed to be somewhere between 35 pounds and 150 pounds per square inch of cross sectional area. Whenever a muscle fiber receives a sufficiently strong nervous impulse to stimulate it to contract, that fiber will contract to the maximum of its ability. Thus any increase in strength of contraction of a muscle is due to a greater number of fibers contracting, since each fiber contracts to its maximum when properly stimulated. This property of maximal contraction upon stimulation is referred to as the "*all or none principle.*"

The proportion of connective tissue to muscle tissue and the amount of *marbling*

sartorius muscle located on the medial side of the thigh. Other arrangements of muscle fibers include spindle-shaped muscles and various *penniform* (feather-like) arrangements. In the penniform arrangements, a tendon represents the quill, and the muscle fibers attaching to the tendon at an angle represent the vane of the feather. If the fibers come from only one side, the arrangement is called unipennate; from two sides, bipennate; and from three or more sides, multipennate.

A parallel arrangement of muscle fibers gives the greatest distance of shortening but is a relatively weak arrangement, while the pennate arrangement increases the power of a muscle but at the expense of distance of contraction.

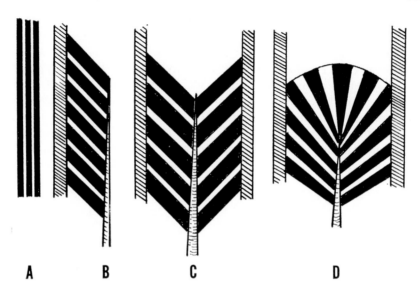

A   B   C   D

FIG. 11–5.—Arrangements of muscle fibers. *A*, Parallel; *B*, unipennate; *C*, bipennate; and *D*, multi-pennate. (After Grant, *A Method of Anatomy*, 4th ed., Williams & Wilkins Co.)

Muscle Attachments

If a muscle appears to come directly from the bone, it is said to have a *fleshy attachment*. The muscles attaching to the *scapula* (blade bone) have fleshy attachments. If these muscles are peeled from the bone as in boning beef, the *periosteum* is stripped from the bone and stays with the muscle. In reality the muscle fibers attach to very short tendons, which in turn attach to the periosteum of the bone or may even penetrate the surface of the bone for a short distance.

Tendons proper are composed of dense regular connective tissue. The fibers are arranged in parallel bundles. Most tendons are cords or bands and attach spindle-shaped or pennate muscles to bones. Other tendons, however, are flat sheets known as *aponeuroses* and usually are associated with flat muscles. The heavy fibrous sheets found covering the muscles of the loin are good examples of aponeuroses.

Most muscles have attachments to two different bones. The least movable at-tachment is called the *origin* and the more movable attachment is called the *insertion*. As an example, the *biceps brachii* muscle extends from the scapula to the *radius*. The scapula usually moves less than the radius, so the origin of the biceps is its attachment to the scapula, and the insertion is its attachment to the radius. In the extremities the origin usually is proximal and the insertion distal. Since the only thing a muscle can actively do (when stimulated) is to con-tract, it will nearly always tend to bring its origin and insertion closer together, thereby causing one or both of the bones to move.

Functional Grouping of Muscles

If a muscle is located on the side of the limb toward which the joint bends in de-creasing the angle between the segments, it will be a *flexor* of that joint. If the muscle is located on the opposite side it will be an *extensor*. The biceps brachii being on the front of the limb flexes the elbow toward the front. The *triceps brachii* (usually called simply "triceps"), located at the back of the elbow takes origin from the scapula and humerus and inserts on the ulna. Thus the triceps is an extensor of the elbow.

Muscles which tend to pull a limb toward the median plane are classed as *adductors*, while those that tend to move the limb away from the median plane are *abductors*. Muscles which pass over more than one joint often have different classifications depending on the joint on which they are acting. The *gastrocnemius* (the large muscle in the calf of the leg) is a flexor of the stifle and an extensor of the hock.

Muscles which surround an opening, whether they are striated or smooth, are called *sphincters*. The smooth muscle surrounding the opening from the stomach to the intestine forms the *pyloric sphincter*, which controls passage of food from the stomach. The *orbicularis oculi* muscle is composed of striated muscle fibers in the eyelids, which closes the eyelids. This is an example of a striated sphincter.

Cutaneous muscles are developed in the superficial fascia between the skin and the deep fascia covering the chief skeletal muscles. These cutaneous muscles attach to the skin and are responsible for movement of the skin. When a fly rests on a horse, the *cutaneous trunci muscle* enables the horse to shake the skin in order to dislodge the fly.

The muscles involved in a specific action such as extension of the elbow may be classified according to the part each plays in the action. The *agonists* (prime movers) are the muscles directly responsible for producing the desired action. The *antagonists* are muscles which may oppose the desired action. They have an action directly opposite that of the agonists. *Synergists* are muscles that oppose any undesired action of the agonists. In our example (extension of the elbow) the triceps brachii and *anconeus* are the agonists because they ex-

tend the elbow. The biceps brachii and *brachialis* are antagonists because they produce the opposite action, flexion of the elbow. Since the long head of the triceps can flex the shoulder joint as well as extend the elbow, any muscle that opposes flexion of the shoulder joint is a synergist. The *supraspinatus* and *brachiocephalicus* muscles are synergists for this particular action. The term *"fixators"* is sometimes used in place of synergists since these muscles usually stabilize one or more bones.

Whether a given muscle will be classified as an agonist, as an antagonist, or as a synergist, depends entirely on the specific action being considered. It is obvious that if flexion of the elbow is the action (instead of extension), the biceps brachii and brachialis muscles become agonists while the triceps brachii and anconeus muscles become antagonists.

Synovial Structures

Synovial structures of the body include *joint capsules, bursae,* and *synovial sheaths.* The inner layer of each consists of a connective tissue membrane which produces synovial fluid for the purpose of reducing friction.

As described in Chapter 10, p. 144 the inner (synovial) layer of the joint capsule normally produces just enough *synovial fluid* to keep the apposed joint surfaces well lubricated. Inflammation of the joint (*arthritis*) may result in production of excess synovial fluid with resultant swelling and pain in the affected joint.

A bursa is simply a synovial sac located between two structures which tend to rub against each other. Examples of bursae are superficial bursae between the skin and *olecranan process* of the ulna at the point of the elbow and between the skin and *superficial digital flexor* tendon at the point of the hock; the *bicipital bursa* between the biceps brachii tendon and the proximal end of the humerus; the *atlantal bursa* between the *ligamentum nuchae* and *atlas*; and the *supraspinous bursa* between the ligamentum nuchae and the spinous process of the seventh thoracic vertebra. Normally a bursa contains only enough fluid to reduce friction between adjacent parts. Excess fluid is produced by the lining of a bursa, producing swelling in cases of inflammation of the bursa, called *bursitis*.

A bursa gives adequate protection to structures which move only a short distance in relation to each other. However, tendons which must travel a long distance (sometimes as much as several inches) over a bone or other structure require protection for the entire length of the tendon that moves. This protection is afforded by a synovial sheath.

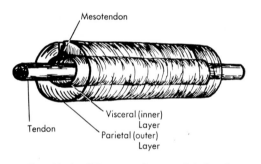

FIG. 11–6.—Diagram of a synovial sheath.

A synovial sheath resembles an elongated bursa placed between the tendon and underlying tissue, with the edges of the bursa (sheath) reflected around the tendon till they meet. This results in an inner layer of synovial membrane surrounding the tendon and a superficial layer of the synovial membrane outside the tendon, forming a closed sac which contains enough synovial fluid to reduce friction between the tendon and adjacent structures. The double fold of membrane formed where the edges of the synovial sheath meet is called the *mesotendon*. Synovial sheaths are also called *vaginal sheaths*, so inflammation of a synovial sheath is called *synovitis* or

vaginitis (not to be confused with inflammation of the genital tract). If the tendon is involved as well as the synovial membrane, the condition is called *tendo-synovitis* or *tendo-vaginitis*.

MUSCLES OF THE FRONT LIMB

Muscles Acting on the Shoulder Girdle

The *scapula* is subject to a number of complex movements in man, but in the domestic animals the chief movement is a pendulum-like swing forward and backward of the articular (ventral) angle. The pivot point is about the middle of the junction of the dorsal one-fourth and the ventral three-fourths of the scapula. The muscles which hold the scapula in place contribute to this swinging movement. From superficial to deep, these muscles include the following:

The *trapezius* is a triangular flat muscle that takes origin along the dorsal mid-line from the head as far back as the lumbar vertebrae. The trapezius inserts chiefly on the spine of the scapula. That portion taking origin cranial to the scapula will help swing the scapula forward, that attaching behind will swing it back. The entire trapezius also aids in holding the scapula against the body.

The *rhomboideus* is a heavier muscle just deep to the trapezius. The rhomboideus also takes origin from the dorsal mid-line both cranial and caudal to the scapula. The rhomboideus inserts on the deep (medial) face of the dorsal end of the scapula.

The *serratus ventralis* (also called the serratus anterior) is the largest and most important muscle attaching the front limb to the trunk. It is a large fan-shaped muscle. The origin of the serratus ventralis is the widest part and extends from the transverse processes of the cervical vertebrae and ribs along a curved line just above the *sternum* as far back as the

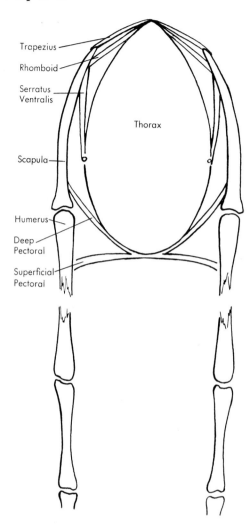

Trapezius

Rhomboid

Serratus
Ventralis

Thorax

Scapula

Humerus

Deep
Pectoral

Superficial
Pectoral

Fig. 11–7.—Diagram of a cross section through the thorax and forelegs showing muscles that attach the forelegs to the trunk.

tenth costal cartilage. The insertion is on the medial side of the dorsal portion of the scapula. The serratus ventralis muscles from each side form a sling which supports the trunk between the front legs. Each muscle also acts to swing the scapula; and the cranial (cervical) portion, on contraction, tends to swing the lower part of the scapula backward, while the caudal (thoracic) portion swings it forward.

The *omo-transversarius* is a muscle found in most domestic species except the horse. It takes origin from the transverse processes of the cervical vertebrae and inserts on the lower part of the spine of the scapula. With these attachments the omo-transversarius usually will pull the lower part of the scapula forward, although with the animal in the standing position, it would assist lateral flexion of the neck.

Muscles Acting on the Shoulder Joint

The *brachiocephalicus*, as the name implies, extends from the arm to the head. The origin is from the *occipital bone* of the skull and transverse processes of the cervical vertebrae. It inserts on the lateral side of the proximal part of the *humerus* above the *deltoid tuberosity*. The brachiocephalicus is the heavy muscle covering the cranial aspect of the point of the shoulder. It is very effective in raising the shoulder and pulling it forward. The brachiocephalicus is the principal extensor of the shoulder and also acts as a lateral flexor of the neck. In the horse the brachiocephalicus is a single muscle, while in the dog, cow, and sheep it can be divided into three parts which all meet at the *clavicular tendon* (area representing the *clavicle*). The parts extending up the neck from the clavicular area are the *cleido-mastoideus*, which takes origin from the *mastoid process* of the *temporal bone*, and the *cleido-occipitalis*, which takes origin from the cranial part of the dorsal mid-line of the neck and occipital bone. The *cleido-brachialis* is the remaining portion which extends from the clavicular tendon to the humerus and is comparable to the *anterior deltoid* of man.

The *supraspinatus muscle* takes origin from the *supraspinous fossa* of the *scapula* in front of the spine on the lateral side. It inserts on the lateral *tuberosity* (both lateral and medial in the horse) of the humerus. The supraspinatus may assist in extending the shoulder but acts chiefly as a ligament of the shoulder joint. This is one of the muscles that atrophies or shrinks in the condition known as *sweeny* in horses, in which the *suprascapular nerve* is paralyzed.

The *infraspinatus muscle* originates from the *infraspinous fossa* just behind and below the spine of the scapula. It inserts into the caudal part of the lateral (greater) tuberosity of the humerus. The infraspinatus also acts as a very strong ligament of the shoulder joint and may serve to abduct and flex the shoulder. This muscle also atrophies in cases of sweeny.

The *subscapularis* is another muscle holding the shoulder joint in close apposition. It takes origin from the *subscapular fossa* on the medial side of the scapula below the attachments of the *rhomboideus* and *serratus ventralis muscles*. It inserts on the *medial tuberosity* of the humerus and may serve as an adductor of the shoulder joint.

The *teres major* takes origin from the upper part of the axillary border of the scapula and inserts on the *teres tuberosity* on the medial side of the shaft of the humerus. It is a strong flexor of the shoulder joint.

The *latissimus dorsi* is a wide trangular muscle that takes origin from the spinous processes of the thoracic and lumbar vertebrae by means of a wide aponeurosis, the *lumbo-dorsal fascia*. It inserts with the teres major on the medial side of the humerus and is a strong flexor of the shoulder. Also, it pulls the front limb backward, or, if the limb is fixed, advances the trunk.

The *pectoral muscles* form the substance of the brisket. They originate from the *sternum* and insert on the proximal part of the humerus. Commonly they are divided into the superficial pectoral muscle and the deep pectoral muscle. These pectoral muscles are very effective adductors of the fore-limb and also serve to advance the trunk when the limb is fixed.

The *coraco-brachialis* is a small muscle

extending from the *coracoid process* of the medial side of the scapula to the medial side of the shaft of the humerus. It has little function except to hold the joint in apposition.

The *deltoid muscle* extends from the spine of the scapula to the deltoid tuberosity of the humerus. It is an abductor and flexor of the shoulder joint. In man, the deltoid is one of the most important muscles of the arm, being the only one that can effectively abduct the arm.

Muscles Acting on the Elbow

Since the elbow is a hinge joint, the muscles acting on it are either flexors or extensors. Those in front of the elbow are flexors and those behind are extensors. In quadripeds the extensors are stronger than the flexors because they support the weight of the body by maintaining the limbs in an extended position.

Extensors of the Elbow

The *triceps* has three heads. The long head takes origin from the axillary (caudo-ventral) border of the scapula, while the medial and lateral heads originate from the respective sides of the *humerus*. In the dog there is an accessory head that also takes origin from the humerus between the medial and lateral heads. All heads insert on the *olecranon process* of the *ulna* (point of the elbow). The triceps is the strongest extensor of the elbow. The long head may also act to flex the shoulder.

The *anconeus*, located deep to the triceps, is a rather small muscle which covers the back of the joint capsule of the elbow. It also takes origin on the humerus, inserts on the ulna, and extends the elbow.

Flexors of the Elbow

The *biceps brachii* originates on the *scapular tuberosity* just above and in front of the articular surface of the scapula. It inserts on the *radial tuberosity* of the *radius* at the front of the proximal end of the radius. The biceps assists in holding the shoulder joint in apposition and may extend it to some extent. However, the chief action of the biceps is flexion of the elbow. In addition, in animals with a separate radius and ulna, it tends to supinate the forearm (rotate it outward).

The *brachialis* is strictly a flexor of the elbow, since it takes origin on the humerus and inserts on the front of the ulna.

Extensor muscles of the carpus and digit which originate on the *lateral epicondyle* of the humerus may assist in flexion of the elbow as a secondary function.

Muscles Acting on the Carpus

The *carpus*, like the elbow, acts essentially as a hinge joint. However, the muscles acting on it are extensors in front and flexors behind.

Extensors of the Carpus.—The *extensor carpi radialis* is the largest extensor of the carpus. It extends from the *lateral epicondyle* of the *humerus* to the proximal end of the *metacarpal region*. The exact snsertion varies with the species. In the dog it inserts on the dorsal (cranial) surface of the proximal ends of the second and third *metacarpal bones*. (Remember the term dorsal here refers to the front of the fore-limb.) In the horse it attaches only to the dorsal surface of the proximal end of the third metacarpal (*cannon*) bone. This is the most prominent muscle on the front of the forearm. It is the most medial muscle of the group. As the name implies the extensor carpi radialis acts primarily as an extensor of the carpus.

The *extensor carpi ulnaris* (*ulnaris lateralis*) is the most lateral of the extensor group of muscles. It also takes origin from the lateral epicondyle of the humerus but passes downward over the lateral side of the carpus to insert on the most lateral

metacarpal bone. In most domestic animals this muscle flexes the carpus, although by origin and nerve supply it belongs with the extensor group.

In addition, the extensor muscles of the digits whose tendons pass over the dorsal surface of the carpus may act secondarily as extensors of the carpus.

Flexors of the Carpus.—Starting from the medial side of the volar surface of the forearm, the *flexor carpi radialis* is the first muscle encountered. It takes origin from the *medial (flexor) epicondyle* of the humerus and inserts on the volar aspect of the proximal end of the metacarpus (medial side).

On the lateral side the flexor carpi ulnaris gains considerable leverage as a flexor of the carpus by inserting on the *accessory carpal bone* which projects in a volar direction from the lateral side of the carpus.

These muscles are, of course, primarily flexors of the carpus but may act slightly in extending the elbow.

Muscles Acting on the Digit

Extensors of the Digit.—The *common digital extensor* is the longest extensor muscle in the fore-limb. It takes origin from the lateral epicondyle of the humerus close to the *extensor carpi radialis*. The insertion is on the extensor process of the third phalanx. The tendon is single in the horse, double in the cow and sheep, and split into four separate tendons in the pig, dog, and cat, where it inserts on the second through the fifth digits. This muscle is an extensor of all joints of the digit including the *fetlock joint*. It may also assist in extending the *carpus*, and even in flexing the *elbow*.

The *lateral digital extensor* is found in all species. Its origin is just lateral to the common digital extensor, and the insertion varies according to the number of digits present. In the dog and cat, it inserts on the fifth digit; in two-toed

11

animals, on the fourth digit; and in the horse, on the first phalanx of the third (and only) digit.

The *medial digital extensor* goes to the third digit of two-toed animals, and to the second digit in the dog and cat, where it is called the *extensor indicus proprius* (extensor of the index finger). It is absent in the horse.

The extensor and abductor of the thumb or first digit is known as the *abductor pollicis longus* in the dog. It takes origin from the distal portion of the dorsal surface of the *radius*, and its tendon crosses obliquely over the tendon of the extensor carpi radialis. In the dog, it inserts on the first metacarpal bone. In animals without a first metacarpal bone, this muscle inserts on the most medial metacarpal bone, which is the second in the horse and the third in the cow and sheep. In these animals it is known as the *extensor carpi obliquis*.

Flexors of the Digit.—In all animals the principal digital flexors are the superficial and the deep digital flexors.

The *deep digital flexor* lies the closest to the metacarpal bones. It takes origin from the humerus, *radius*, and *ulna*. The long tendon extends distally through the *carpal canal* then along the volar side of the metacarpus to insert on the volar surface of the third phalanx. As with the common digital extensor tendon, the number of tendons and insertions depends on the number of digits. If the tendon is cut, the respective toe cannot be held against the ground, but will point up whenever weight is placed on the foot. The deep digital flexor is the only muscle that flexes the *distal interphalangeal joint*. Secondarily, it will also flex the more proximal joints of the digit and the carpus. The deep digital flexor also is important in supporting the *fetlock*.

The *superficial digital flexor* is similar to the deep digital flexor, but it inserts on the base of the second phalanx of each

digit except the first. In the horse the superficial digital flexor tendon inserts on the volar aspect of the proximal end of the second phalanx and the volar aspect of the distal end of the first phalanx. Tendons of both the superficial digital flexor and deep digital flexor can be palpated (felt) at the back of the cannon region. *Bowed tendons* of horses involve one or both of these tendons in the cannon region.

Interosseous muscles are present as muscles between the *metacarpal* bones of the dog. In the larger animals most of the muscle tissue has disappeared, and these structures are known as the *suspensory ligaments*. They support the *proximal sesamoids* and hence the fetlock, and a band extends dorsally on each side of the digit to attach to the common digital extensor tendon.

MUSCLES OF THE HIND LIMB

The *hip joint* is a ball-and-socket joint, and as such can move in nearly any direction. However, the chief movements are extension, or backward movement, of the femur, and flexion, or forward movement, of the femur. Adduction and abduction are also fairly common movements.

Muscles Acting on the Hip Joint

The chief extensor muscles of the hip are the so-called *hamstring muscles* which pass behind the hip joint from the *tuber ischii* (*pin bones*) to the proximal end of the *tibia* or *fibula*. They include the *biceps femoris*, the most lateral of the posterior muscles of the thigh, the *semitendinosus*, the middle muscle of the posterior group, and the *semimembranosus*, the medial muscle of this group. The divisions between these muscles can be seen as vertical grooves in animals that are not too fat. In the horse, the biceps femoris and semintendinosus extend dorsally over the rump to attach to the *sacral* and *coccygeal vertebral spines*. In many other animals the hamstring muscles take origin only from the tuber ischii.

The *middle gluteus muscle* is another strong extensor of the hip. It takes origin from the wing of the *ilium* and inserts on the *trochanter major* of the femur, which is a lever projecting above the hip joint.

Flexors of the hip are located cranial to the femur. The most important are the *iliacus* and *psoas major*, which insert on the *trochanter minor* on the medial side of the femur. The iliacus takes origin from the ventral surface of the wing of the ilium. The psoas major takes origin from the ventral surfaces of the lumbar transverse processes. The psoas major and minor make up the *tenderloin*. The *sartorius* is a thin strap-like muscle that extends from the *tuber coxae* to the tibia, diagonally crossing the medial surface of the *thigh*.

Abductors of the hip extend laterally over the hip joint so that either a lever or pulley-type action moves the leg away from the median plane. The *deep gluteus* extends from the spine of the ischium laterally over the proximal part of the *hip joint* to insert on the trochanter major. The top of the femur, when pulled medially, moves the rest of the limb laterally. The *superficial gluteus* extends from the sacral vertebral spines to the *trochanter tertius* just below the trochanter major. The *tensor fascia latae* extends from the tuber coxae to the *lateral femoral fascia*, which attaches to the patella. In addition to abducting the hip joint this latter muscle also flexes the hip joint and extends the *stifle*.

Adductors of the hip joint pull the limb toward the median plane. They are all located on the medial side of the thigh and extend from the *os coxae* to either the femur or the tibia. The *gracilis* is the most medial muscle extending from the *symphysis of the pelvis* to the tibia. It has the best angle of pull of any of the adductors.

The *pectineus*, a small spindle-shaped muscle under cover of (lateral to) the gracilis, is both an adductor and flexor of the hip.

The *adductor muscle* is the largest muscle on the medial side of the thigh. It extends from the ventral aspect of the *pelvis* to the medial side of the femur and tibia. It is a strong adductor but may also help extend the hip.

The *quadratus femoris* is an adductor and outward rotator of the thigh. There are several other small muscles extending from the area of the *obturator foramen* which are outward rotators of the thigh. They include the *obturator externis*, the *obturator internis* and the *cranial* and *caudal gemelli*.

Muscles Acting on the Stifle

The stifle is essentially a hinge joint, so the muscles acting on it are either extensors or flexors.

Extensor of the Stifle.—One large muscle, the *quadriceps femoris* does most of the extending of the stifle. This muscle has four heads. The longest head, the *rectus femoris*, takes origin from the *ilium* just above the *acetabulum*. The other three heads, *vastus medialis*, *vastus intermedius*, and *vastus lateralis* take origin from the respective areas of the shaft of the *femur*. All four heads insert on the *patella* (knee cap). The patella, being fastened to the front of the *tibia* by the patellar ligaments, extends the stifle when it is pulled proximally by the quadriceps femoris. The *tensor fascia latae* may also pull on the patella, thus helping extend the stifle.

Flexors of the Stifle.—The chief flexors of the stifle are the *hamstring muscles* which also extend the hip. In addition, those extensor muscles of the *hock* which take origin from the posterior surface of the distal end of the femur may also flex the stifle. These muscles include the *gastrocnemius* and the *superficial digital* *flexor*. The *popliteus* is a relatively small muscle located behind the stifle. Its chief action is flexion of the stifle, although it may slightly rotate the leg (tibia and *fibula*) inward.

Muscles Acting on the Hock

The principal actions in the *hock* are extension and flexion.

Extensors of the hock primarily attach to the *tuber calcis* (*point of the hock*) by way of the *tendon of Achilles*. The *gastrocnemius* and *superficial digital flexor* take origin from the distal end of the posterior surface of the femur and make up the bulk of the tendon of Achilles. They are joined in part by a portion of the *biceps femoris* and *semitendinosus*, which also enter into the tendon of Achilles and assist in extending the hock, as well as extending the hip and flexing the *stifle*. The *deep digital flexor* also extends the hock.

Flexors of the hock include the *tibialis anterior* and the *peroneus muscles*, whose tendons pass over the anterior surface of the hock to insert on the *tarsus* and *metatarsus*. The *peroneus tertius* is the only peroneal muscle named in the horse. The *peroneus longus* is found on the cow, sheep, pig, and dog. The digital extensors also flex the hock.

Muscles Acting on the Digit

Muscles acting on the hind digits are quite similar to those of the digits of the front limb.

The Extensors of the Digit.—The *long digital extensor* takes origin from the distal end of the *femur* and passes down the limb to insert on the extensor process of the third phalanx. As with the common extensor in the fore-limb, the tendon is single in the horse, double in the cow and sheep, and has four parts in the pig, dog, and cat.

The *lateral digital extensor* tendon of the horse joins the long digital extensor

about the middle of the *cannon* (*metacarpus*).

Flexors of the Digit.—The superficial and deep flexors are arranged in the hind limb as they are in the front. However, the tendon of the superficial flexor also attaches to the tuber calcis in the hind limb.

MUSCLES OF THE TRUNK, NECK, AND HEAD

Extensor Muscles of the Trunk, Neck, and Head

The group of muscles located dorsal to the transverse processes of the vertebrae on either side of the spinous processes make up the loin muscles and continue forward to the head. In man they are called the *erector spinei* (*sacrospinalis*) muscles and are essential for maintaining an erect posture. In our domestic animals the largest of these loin muscles is known as the *longissimus dorsi*. It is composed of innumerable small bundles of muscle fibers which extend from vertebral transverse processes to spinous processes, from transverse processes to transverse processes, or from spinous processes to spinous processes. As these attachments may extend from one vertebra to the next or overlap one or more vertebrae, there are many possibilities for naming individual muscles and many chances for individual muscle actions. However, in our domestic animals these muscles are responsible for extension and lateral flexion of the *spinal column*. They may also cause slight rotation (twisting) of the spinal column, as seen when a bucking horse throws his front feet to one side and his hind feet to the opposite side.

The same general arrangement of muscles is continued into the neck and head, where much greater flexibility is evidenced. The dorsal neck muscles which extend (raise) the head and neck are well developed because of the added load due to the mechanical disadvantage resulting from the head's being located at the end of the neck, which acts as a long lever. The large extensor muscles of the head take origin from the vertebrae in the region of the *withers* and insert on the *occipital bone* of the skull. The most superficial of these muscles (other than the trapezius, which does not take origin from the vertebrae) is the *splenius* and deep to it is the *complexus*. Other muscles that actively extend the head and neck include the *rhomboideus*, the *longissimus capitis et atlantis*, and the *dorsal oblique* and *dorsal straight muscles* of the head. Deeper muscles of the neck which extend from one vertebra to the next also aid in movements of the neck. In addition to these muscles, a heavy elastic band, the *ligamentum nuchae*, reaches from the withers to the *skull*. This ligamentum nuchae gives considerable aid to the muscles which extend (raise) the head and neck.

Flexor Muscles of the Head and Neck

Gravity is the most powerful force involved in flexing or lowering the neck and head of domestic animals. The ventral muscles of the neck which aid in flexing the head and neck include the *sterno-cephalicus*, which extends from the sternum to the *mandible* in the horse and to the mandible and *mastoid process* of the skull in the cow. In addition, the *sterno-thyro-hyoideus, longus coli*, and *ventral straight muscles* of the head are flexors.

Abdominal Muscles

The muscles which form the bulk of the abdominal wall have a number of functions. They support the organs of digestion and many of the reproductive organs, particularly in the female during gestation. The abdominal muscles may act to flex the *vertebral column* (arch the back). If contracting on one side only they flex it laterally, or even twist the vertebral column. These muscles are very important in emptying the contents of the digestive tract (*defecation*), urinary tract (*micturition* or *urination*), and female reproductive tract at the time of giving birth to the young (*parturition*). The abdominal muscles are used in *regurgitation* and *vomiting* and serve as strong muscles for active expiration of air from the lungs, as seen during coughing or sneezing. The horse rarely if ever vomits.

The abdominal muscles are arranged in layers much like plywood with the muscle fibers fanning in different directions. Most of these muscles have broad aponeurotic insertions that meet at the mid-ventral line at an area known as the *linea alba* (white line).

The *external abdominal oblique* muscle is the most superficial. The fibers of this muscle are directed obliquely downward and backward. Its origin is from the last few *ribs* and *lumbo-dorsal fascia* over the back and loins. The insertion is by means of a broad flat tendon (aponeurosis) that meets the insertion of the muscle from the opposite side at the linea alba. Caudally, the muscle is continued by an aponeurosis (fascia) and the *inguinal ligament*. This aponeurotic ligament forms the superficial wall of the *inguinal canal* for the passage of the *spermatic cord* of the male. It contains a slit, the *external inguinal ring*, through which the spermatic cord passes from the inguinal canal into the scrotum.

The *internal abdominal oblique muscle* is immediately deep to the external abdominal oblique. It takes origin from a deeper layer of the lumbo-dorsal fascia and the inguinal ligament. The fibers pass obliquely downward and forward, and the muscle also inserts on the linea alba by means of an aponeurosis. In most animals this muscle forms the deep wall of the inguinal canal and also of the *internal inguinal ring*. The most caudal group of fibers from the internal abdominal oblique passes through the inguinal canal with the spermatic cord and attaches to the outer covering of the *testicle* (tunica vaginalis communis). This muscle mass is called the *external cremaster muscle* and functions in pulling the testicle toward the inguinal canal. In some animals, such as rodents and elephants, the testicle is retracted into the abdominal cavity except during breeding seasons.

The *transversus abdominis muscle* is the deepest of the abdominal muscles. It takes origin from the deepest fascia of the back, and the fibers are directed straight downward to insert on the linea alba.

The *rectus abdominis* forms the muscular floor of the abdomen. It takes origin from the cartilages of the ribs and the *sternum*. The fibers run directly caudally in a frontal plane (horizontally) to attach to the pubis by means of a strong tendon, the *prepubic tendon*.

Muscles of Respiration

The muscles of respiration are either expiratory, forcing air out of the lungs by decreasing the size of the *thorax* (*chest*) or they are inspiratory and cause air to enter the lungs by increasing the size of the thorax.

Inspiratory Muscles.—The *diaphragm* is the chief muscle of inspiration. It is a dome-shaped sheet of muscle separating the thoracic and abdominal cavities. It projects into the thorax. Contraction of the fibers of the diaphragm tend to straighten the curvature of the diaphragm and force the abdominal viscera out of the thorax and into the abdomen. This in effect increases the size of the thorax and creates a partial vacuum in the thorax, causing air to enter the *lungs*.

The *external intercostal muscles* extend from each rib to the next rib behind. The fibers are directed downward and backward in a direction similar to those of the external abdominal oblique muscle. When these muscles contract, they tend to rotate the ribs upward and forward, thereby increasing the size of the thorax.

Muscles of Expiration.—As mentioned previously, the abdominal muscles may act as muscles of expiration by forcing the abdominal viscera against the diaphragm, thus decreasing the size of the thorax. In addition to these muscles, the *internal intercostals*, which lie deep to the external intercostals, are said to rotate the ribs backward, thus decreasing the size of the thorax. They run from each rib to the next one in front, and the fibers are directed downward and forward.

Some authorities believe that both the external intercostal muscles and the internal intercostal muscles may function in both inspiration and expiration.

CHAPTER 12

MICROANATOMY AND PHYSIOLOGY
OF MUSCLE

GENERAL

MUSCLE cells are highly specialized for the function of contraction. Many responses of vertebrate organisms to environmental change depend on muscle contraction. These responses include such diverse activities as walking; breathing; ingestion, transport, and elimination of food; blood circulation; and most activities associated with reproduction.

Connective tissue is closely associated with all muscle cells or fibers to form a sort of harness, so the pull extended by muscle contraction can be usefully applied. The connective tissue between muscle cells also serves as a path for the vessels and nerves of the muscle.

Muscle fibers appear either striated or smooth (non-striated) and are voluntary or involuntary, depending on the type of nerve supply. Involuntary muscle receives autonomic nerves and is not under conscious control. Voluntary muscle is supplied chiefly by somatic nerves and can be consciously controlled.

The three types of muscle usually described are involuntary smooth muscle, involuntary striated muscle, and voluntary striated muscle.

SMOOTH MUSCLE

Smooth muscle is also called *involuntary, unstriped, visceral,* or *plain muscle.* The terms are synonymous.

As the term "visceral" implies, smooth muscle is largely found in visceral structures associated with the digestive system, urogenital system, respiratory system, vascular system, and eye. In addition, smooth-muscle fibers in the skin erect the hairs and also cause wrinkling of the skin of the scrotum.

Structure of Smooth Muscle Fibers

The smooth muscle cell appears to be simply a fusiform (spindle-shaped) contractile unit with a centrally located nucleus. Size of smooth muscle fibers varies considerably. Most cells range between 50 and 250μ in length and from 5 to 10μ in greatest diameter. No cross striations, myofibrils, or *sarcolemma* are visible. The major portion of the cell consists of *sarcoplasm*.

The increase in size of the uterine wall during pregnancy to several times its non-pregnant volume is due in a considerable measure to an increase in the amount of smooth muscle in the wall.

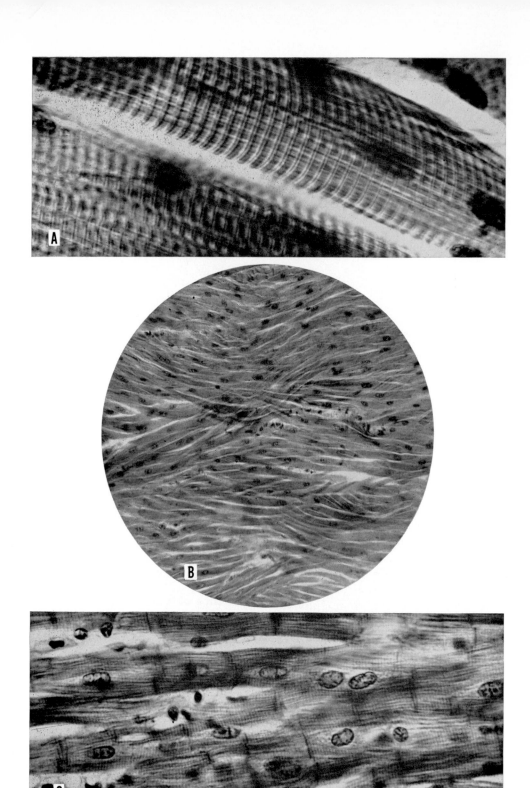

Fig. 12–1.—*A*, Striated voluntary muscle; *B*, smooth (involuntary) muscle; and *C*, cardiac (involuntary striated) muscle. (Turtox Biological Supplies, 65 Catalogue, courtesy of General Biological Supply House, Inc.)

(170)

There are three ways in which this increase may occur. Individual muscle fibers may increase in size, as is seen in voluntary striated muscle. Smooth muscle cells may divide mitotically to increase the number of cells. Finally, smooth muscle cells may form from undifferentiated mesenchymal cells.

Smooth muscle cells are believed to be surrounded always by connective tissue, even though it may be only a small amount of reticular tissue. These reticular fibers join the larger *collagenous* and elastic fibers which make up the major part of the connective tissue associated with smooth muscle.

Smooth muscle cells in the walls of hollow organs are arranged so that only a fraction of the cells are supplied directly by nerves. Although only an occasional smooth muscle cell receives a direct nerve supply in most arrangements, the impulse for contraction appears to spread from one muscle fiber to another. Some authorities believe protoplasmic processes connect adjacent cells and conduct the impulse for contraction. Others believe the stimulus for contraction is transmitted from the innervated cell to others that are not innervated by chemical means (acetylcholine) or mechanical means (stretching).

Contraction of Smooth Muscle

Smooth muscle can be made to contract by nerve impulses, chemicals, hormones, sudden stretching, or electric current. A stronger electric current is required to stimulate smooth muscle than striated muscle.

Under normal conditions in the body, smooth muscle cells usually either respond to *norepinephrine* released by sympathetic nerves or they respond to *acetylcholine* released by parasympathetic nerves, but a given cell will not react to both sympathetic and parasympathetic stimulation. If a specific smooth muscle cell is caused to contract by sympathetic stimulation, either it will not respond at all to parasympathetic stimulation or it will relax.

In some situations each smooth muscle cell appears to receive a definite nerve supply. These areas include the *pilomotor* smooth muscle cells in the skin and the smooth muscle cells in the iris and ciliary body of the eye.

The characteristic slow sustained contractions of smooth muscle are undoubtedly associated with the large amount of sarcoplasm and the apparent absence of myofibrils, striations, and Z discs in smooth muscle cells. Contractions of smooth muscle are often rhythmic in nature, as seen in peristalsis in the intestine. Gradual stretching of smooth muscle is possible without much change in tension, as occurs when the bladder fills with urine. Sudden stretching, however, increases the tension considerably and usually stimulates contraction of smooth muscle.

CARDIAC MUSCLE

Cardiac muscle (involuntary striated muscle) has many characteristics that are similar to voluntary striated muscle fibers. Both consist largely of sarcoplasm, myofibrils, nuclei, and a sarcolemma. The most striking difference is the tendency for cardiac muscle fibers to join, forming a network. Work with the electron microscope has indicated that the heart does **not** consist of one large multinuclear cell (*syncytium*) as some have believed, but is made up of cells which are separate entities.

Unique structures found in cardiac muscle are the intercalated discs. These discs are interposed between segments of muscle 50 to 120μ in length. They may cross the fiber in an irregular manner. Usually each segment contains only one nucleus. There is now general agreement that these discs represent apposed cell membranes. This has been proved by evidence obtained with the electron microscope.

Blood vessels and lymphatic vessels are both plentiful in cardiac muscle. A generous blood supply is essential, because cardiac muscle undergoes rhythmic contraction from early fetal life continuously until death of the animal.

Hypertrophy (increase in cell size) occurs in cardiac muscle when the heart has excessive work to do. In man this condition is sometimes called athlete's heart. Living in high altitudes may also cause hypertrophy of the heart. *Brisket disease* (*high-mountain disease*) of cattle involves enlargement of the heart as well as edema of the brisket.

VOLUNTARY STRIATED MUSCLE

Structure of Striated-muscle Fibers

Voluntary striated muscle is also called *somatic* or *skeletal muscle*.

The *voluntary muscle* fiber is actually a multinucleated cell with cross striations. It consists of the sarcolemma (a thin translucent envelope), numerous nuclei immediately deep to the sarcolemma, a large number of myofibrils (tiny fibers arranged parallel to the long axis of the fiber), and the sarcoplasm (intervening protoplasmic material).

The sarcolemma appears to be a thin membrane very closely related to the *endomysium*, the deepest connective tissue which surrounds individual muscle fibers. The sarcolemma is a major factor in the elasticity of muscle and acts as the connection from the muscle fiber to the tendinous part of the muscle or tendon. It is a combination of plasma membrane and connective tissue basement membrane.

Long muscle fibers may contain several hundred *nuclei*. In the adult they are ovoid, dark-staining structures located just deep to the sarcolemma. In the fetus, however, nuclei of voluntary muscle fibers may be located near the center of the fiber.

On casual examination with a light microscope, the cross striations of voluntary muscle appear to be discs throughout the entire fiber. However, work with the electron microscope has confirmed the concept that the striations appear only in the myofibrils and not in the sarcoplasm. The alternate light and dark bands of all fibrils appear at the corresponding places in the fiber. The fact that corresponding bands of adjacent myofibrils are in register makes these bands seem to extend completely across the whole fiber. Numerous designations have been given the bands. Usually letters are used to designate the different bands. The dark areas are called A (*anisotrophic*), and the light areas I (*isotrophic*) *bands*. In addition, a dark line in the middle of the I band is called the Z *disc*. The section from one Z disc to the next is called a *sarcomere*. H, N, and M bands are also described by some investigators.

Sarcoplasm is essentially the undifferentiated protoplasm of the muscle cell. Delicate filaments within the sarcoplasm have been described as an *endoplasmic* (or *sarcoplasmic*) *reticulum* which may function in metabolism of the fiber and also in conduction of the impulse causing contraction. A *Golgi apparatus* and *mitochondria* as well as glycogen and fat inclusions also are found in muscle fibers.

Voluntary muscle fibers range in diameter from about 10 to 100μ. In general, the large fibers appear to be longer and tend to be found in large rather than small muscles. Animals on full feed are reported to have larger fibers than animals on restricted feed. It is generally accepted that males have larger muscle fibers than females. Length of voluntary muscle fibers is extremely variable, depending on the length of the muscle and arrangement of muscle fibers (parallel or pennate). Probably some fibers in parallel muscles extend the entire length of the muscle.

Although Murry (1960) states that there is a substantial potential for regenerative growth in mature mammalian skeletal muscle, it is quite generally believed that voluntary muscle fibers are such specialized cells that little if any multiplication of fibers or formation of new fibers occurs after birth. All increase in size of muscles at any stage in life following birth is due to hypertrophy (increase in size) of individual muscle fibers. It is well known that exercise can cause increased muscular development, such as is seen in weight-lifters. This, of course, is accomplished by increase in size of existing individual muscle fibers. If the nerve supply to a muscle is destroyed, the muscle fibers decrease to practically

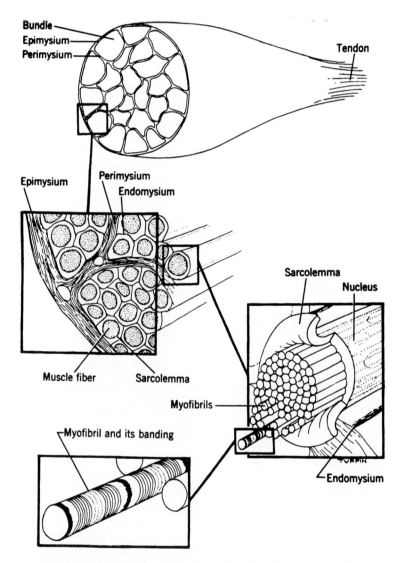

FIG. 12–2.—Architecture of a skeletal muscle and its fibers. (Reproduced by permission from Torrey, *Morphogenesis of the Vertebrates,* courtesy of John Wiley & Sons.) (Berger, *Elementary Human Anatomy,* courtesy of John Wiley & Sons, 1964.)

nothing, a condition called atrophy. This is seen in "sweeny" of draft horses, when the suprascapular nerve is crushed by a collar, resulting in shrinking of the supraspinatus and infraspinatus muscles of the shoulder.

Detailed structure of the striated muscle fiber was very much in doubt until the electron microscope became available. There is now rather general agreement that the light portions or *I* (*isotrophic*) *bands* of the fiber consist of small filaments of the protein *actin* (and possibly some *tropomyosin*). The *A* (*anisotrophic*) *band* consists largely of filaments of *myosin*

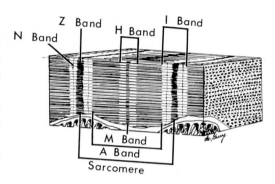

Fig. 12–3.—Three-dimensional representation of muscle bands. (Freeman and Geer, *Cellular Fine Structure*, courtesy of the Blakiston Co.)

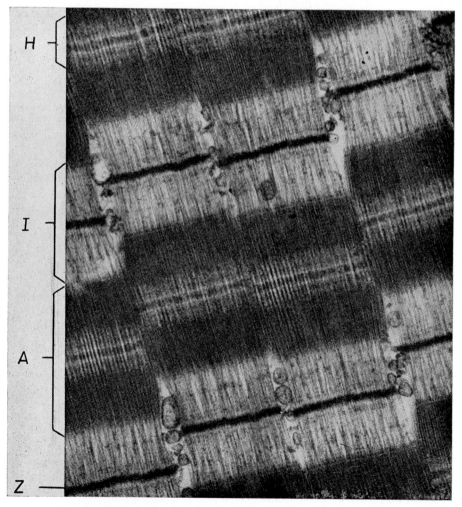

Fig. 12–4.—Electron micrograph showing H, I, and A bands and Z discs of rabbit striated voluntary muscle. (Copenhaver, *Bailey's Textbook of Histology*, 15th ed., courtesy of Williams & Wilkens Co.)

which interdigitate with the actin filaments. About six actin filaments surround each myosin filament. There is a dark Z disc passing through the center of the light I band. Evidence from electron microscope studies suggest the Z disc may be a disc extending inward from the sarcolemma to the interior of the fiber. The Z disc may function in transmission of the impulse for contraction to all myofibrils. The *H band* (or zone) is a lighter area in the middle of the A band. Presumably it consists only of myosin filaments, while the remainder of the A band consists of both myosin and actin filaments.

It is estimated that each striated muscle fiber may contain from several hundred to several thousand *myofibrils*, and each myofibril contains about 2500 myosin and 2500 actin filaments.

Huxley and Hanson report that each myosin filament is made up of 424 molecules of myosin with a molecular weight of 424,000 each. (As a comparison, hydrogen (H_2) has a molecular weight of 2.) An actin filament is composed of 600 molecules of actin with a molecular weight of 70,000 each.

MECHANICS OF CONTRACTION

The exact mechanism of contraction is not completely understood. However, the actin filaments appear to slide longitudinally in relation to the myosin filaments without any actual change in length of either filament. This type of movement might be compared with the piston and cylinder of a hydraulic jack which lengthens and shortens by means of the piston sliding within the cylinder, but both piston and cylinder remain the same length.

Tiny cross bridges have been described extending from the myosin filament toward the actin filaments. These bridges are believed to produce the sliding action of myosin and actin filaments.

When the myofibril has shortened to 65 per cent of its resting length, the I bands completely disappear, and the Z disc touches the ends of adjacent A bands.

An alternative theory holds that contraction of muscle fibers is due to some type of folding of the protein molecules involved in the contraction process. This theory is based in part on the fact that actomysin precipitated from solution will contract when treated with ATP (adenosine triphosphate).

CHEMISTRY OF MUSCLE CONTRACTION

ATP (*adenosine triphosphate*) apparently is the immediate source of energy for muscle contraction. Myosin (in the presence of Ca^{++} ions) acts as an enzyme, *ATPase* (*adenosine tri phosphatase*). ATPase hydrolyzes (splits) ATP into *ADP* (*adenosine diphosphate*) and H_3PO_4 (phosphoric acid). This hydrolysis, also called "*dephosphorylation*," releases a large amount of energy which in some manner is utilized by the contracting fibers.

As long as ATP is being split, the muscle remains active. If ATP is absent, a condition known as *rigor* occurs which resembles contraction in that the muscle becomes stiff and rigid, possibly due to a locking together of the actin and myosin filaments. *Rigor mortis* is a hardening of the muscles that occurs several hours after death and may be used to estimate the time of death. If adequate ATP is present but is not being split (dephosphorylated), the muscle relaxes.

Small granules called *sarcosomes*, which lie close to the myofibrils in striated muscle, are assumed to supply ATP to the myofibrils.

Relaxation of muscle may be caused by a substance such as alphaglycerophosphate, which in the presence of Mg^{++} ions inhibits an enzyme activity of myosin, thereby preventing the splitting of ATP.

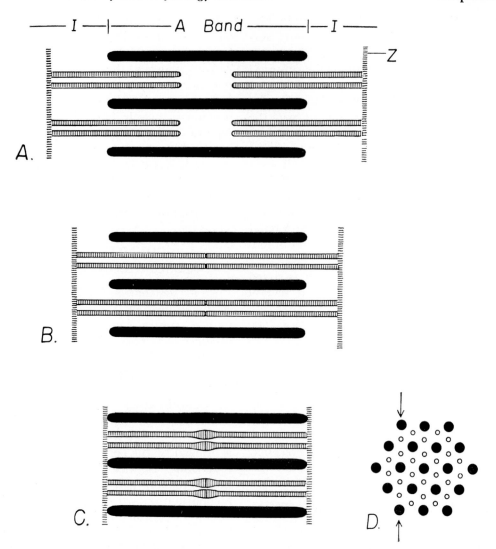

Fig. 12–5.—Diagram based on electron micrographs showing changes in fine structur e of skeltial muscle during contraction. *A*, resting muscle; *B*, partially contracted; *C*, contracted; and *D*, arrangement of myofilaments in cross-section through an *A Band*. Thick black filaments represent myosne. Thin cross-hatched filaments represent actin. (Copenhaver, *Bailey's Textbook of Histology*, courtesy of Williams & Wilkens Co.)

CA^{++} ions start the enzyme activity of myosin and are thought by some to be the immediate activating factors in contraction of muscle fibers.

Although ATP is generally believed to be necessary for muscle contraction, there are two views as to its exact function. The usual interpretation is that ATP transfers energy directly to the muscle upon being split by ATPase.

At one time it was believed that the breakdown of glycogen to lactic acid was the immediate source of energy for muscle contraction, since lactic acid and carbon dioxide increase while glycogen and oxygen decrease during muscular contraction. This concept was disproved when experiments showed that muscle can contract for a considerable period in the absence of oxygen, for example, in an atmosphere of nitrogen. In addition, a muscle treated with the drug sodium iodoacetate can also contract for an appreciable time, but it does not form any lactic acid.

Breakdown of *glycogen* into lactic acid and the oxidation of *lactic acid* provide energy for the recovery phase after muscle has contracted and relaxed. The actual contraction is dependent on energy stored in organic phosphates including adenosine triphosphate (ATP), adenosine diphosphate (ADP), and *creatine phosphate (CP)*.

The chain of reactions involved in supplying energy for muscle contraction and recovery may be summarized as follows:

Although muscle can contract for a short period in the absence of oxygen, the energy thus utilized can be replaced only by oxidation. The oxygen needed to replace the energy expended anaerobically is called the "oxygen debt." This oxygen debt must be repaid before normal muscle activity can resume.

HEAT PRODUCTION BY MUSCLE

Contraction is the primary function of muscle fibers, but only about one-fourth of the energy used is available for actual work in the physical sense of weight times distance, usually measured in foot pounds. The rest of the energy is dissipated as

Adenosine triphosphate (ATP)	$\rightarrow$ Adenosine diphosphate (ADP) + Phosphoric acid (H_3PO_4) + Energy (for immediate use in contraction)
Creatine phosphate (CP)	$\rightarrow$ Creatine + Phosphoric acid (H_3PO_4) + Energy (for resynthesis of ATP from ADP)
Glycogen	$\rightarrow$ Lactic acid + Energy (for resynthesis of Creatine phosphate from Creatine and Phosphoric acid)
$\frac{1}{5}$ of Lactic acid (formed above) + Oxygen (O_2)	$\rightarrow$ Water (H_2O) + Carbon dioxide (CO_2) + Energy (for resynthesis of remaining $\frac{4}{5}$ of above lactic acid back to glycogen)

This summary is greatly oversimplified. For example, the breakdown of glycogen to lactic acid, called *glycolysis*, is a complex process involving a number of reactions, several enzymes, and many compounds.

Essentially the adenosine and creatine serve as carriers for the phosphate radical, which acts as a convenient means of transferring energy needed for muscle contraction. This energy, which is passed from one organic compound to another by means of the phosphate radical, originally is derived from oxidation of lactic acid. The lactic acid in turn is derived from glycogen, so ultimately the glycogen must be replaced to provide energy for muscle contraction.

Oxygen must also be added because it is used up in oxidation of lactic acid.

heat. Although the efficiency of muscle as an engine is not high, it compares favorably with other types of engines. The mechanical efficiency of a gasoline engine also is rated at approximately 25 per cent.

Whenever environmental temperature is very much below the normal body temperature, heat production by muscles is a definite advantage. In fact when air temperature is extremely low, muscles may undergo spasmodic contractions called *shivering* to produce heat enough to maintain normal body temperature.

Heat production occurs in two distinct phases, the *initial heat* (heat of actual contraction), and the *heat of recovery*. The initial heat includes *heat of activation and maintenance*, *heat of shortening*, and *heat of relaxation*. The initial heat of contraction is the same whether the muscle contracts in oxygen or in nitrogen, because oxygen consumption does not occur until contraction and relaxation are over.

About nine-tenths of heat of recovery is derived from oxidation of food and one-tenth from anaerobic (without oxygen) metabolic processes. In the presence of oxygen, recovery is rapid, with heat production almost equal to initial heat. However, under anaerobic conditions, recovery extends over a period of twenty minutes, and the heat produced is equivalent to only about one-fifth of the initial heat.

STIMULUS FOR CONTRACTION OF MUSCLE

The description of the nerve impulse (Chapter 6, p. 93) indicates that it is simply a membrane phenomenon in which an electrical action potential is produced by a change in the balance of ions on the inside and outside of the nerve fiber due to an increased permeability of the membrane. However, the action potential, which is simply electrical activity of the nerve, does not travel beyond the nerve ending. Instead, a chemical is liberated at the *motor end plate*, which depolarizes the muscle-fiber membrane, thus initiating the contraction.

There is some difference of opinion as to whether the sarcolemma is the effective muscle-fiber membrane or whether the actual plasma membrane is a thin membrane (about 25 A across) just deep to the sarcolemma, which is about 75 to 100 A thick.

The presence of a chemical mediator of nerve impulses was first suspected when the similarity of action of *epinephrine* (*adrenaline*) and stimulation of the sympathetic nervous system was observed. Later *acetylcholine* was found to stimulate organs supplied by parasympathetic nerves and was also found in fluid sur-

rounding the motor end plates of striated muscle fibers following stimulation of their motor nerves.

It is suggested that acetylcholine is released only at a nerve ending or at the cut surface of a nerve, because it cannot penetrate the *myelin* sheath. The depolarization wave initiated by acetylcholine may be due to increased permeability of the muscle-fiber membrane. The wave spreads in all directions from the motor end plate, along the fiber membrane, and possibly reaches the individual myofibrils by way of the Z disc, which touches the sarcolemma.

The *endoplasmic reticulum*, a network within the fiber, described by some workers, has also been suggested as a means by which the impulse for contraction may spread throughout the muscle fiber. Recent work supports the latter theory.

From the time the impulse reaches the muscle fiber until contraction occurs, there is a latent period of about 0.003 seconds.

Almost as soon as acetylcholine initiates the impulse for muscle contraction, the acetylcholine is inactivated by an enzyme called *acetylcholinesterase*. This enzyme, which splits acetylcholine, is found in conductive tissues and appears to be localized in the nerve sheath rather than in the *axoplasm* of the nerve.

Acetylcholinesterase in turn is irreversibly inhibited by certain alklylphosphates, which are the basis of some very effective insecticides and the so-called "nerve gases" which have been studied extensively by the armed forces since World War II.

These insecticides, known both as *organic phosphates* and as *phosphate esters*, include such products as Co-ral, Delnav, Malathion, Ronnel, DDVPm Dipterex, Reulene, Neguvon, and Coumaphos. Products for both external application and oral administration are included in the organic phosphate insecticides. If improperly used, any of the organic phosphates is extremely dangerous, not only to domestic animals, but also to the person using it. Therefore, it is imperative that this class of insecticides be used under proper supervision, and that instructions for use be followed exactly. Poisoning will give a picture of parasympathetic stimulation as described in Chapter 6, p. 99. Some of the symptoms include constriction of the pupil of the eye, cramps, vomiting, diarrhea, and weakness.

The *"all or none" law* states that when a muscle fiber is stimulated to contract, muscle fiber will contract to its maximum. The size of the stimulus as long as it is above the threshold has no relationship to the speed or strength of contraction of a muscle fiber. The size of stimulus to an entire muscle, however, has a direct relationship to the strength of contraction, because the larger the stimulus the more motor units are caused to contract; hence the greater strength of contraction of the muscle.

A *muscle twitch* is a single strong contraction of a muscle fiber or a muscle belly. Frog gastrocnemius muscle at

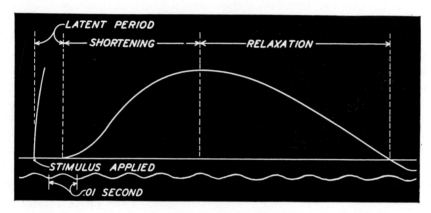

FIG. 12–6.—A single twitch of a frog muscle recorded on a rapidly moving smoked plate employing a lever. (Carlson, Johnson and Cavert, *The Machinery of the Body*, courtesy of the University of Chicago Press.)

it will contract to the maximum of its ability under the particular conditions, or it will not contract at all. Another way of stating this law is that a stimulus to a muscle fiber causes an action potential to travel over the entire fiber causing contraction, or it fails to stimulate the muscle fiber at all.

The "all or none" law applies to a single motor fiber or a single motor unit (a motor nerve and all the muscle fibers it supplies); it does not apply to an entire muscle. The "all or none" law also does not state that a muscle fiber will always contract with the same speed or the same force but only that for the conditions at the time of stimulation the

21° C. shows a muscle twitch which lasts about 0.1 seconds. Three phases of the twitch are described: (1) a *latent perioa* between the application of the stimulus and the beginning of the response (about 0.01 seconds); (2) a *period of contraction,* during which the muscle shortens (about 0.04 seconds); and (3) a *period of relaxation* (about 0.05 seconds).

Much of the physiological information about voluntary muscle activity has been obtained from experiments using a muscle-nerve preparation connected to a kymograph and a source of electrical stimulation. A *muscle-nerve preparation* consists of an isolated muscle, usually the gastrocnemius muscle of the frog, with one end attached to a clamp and the other end attached to a lever which writes on a rotating *kymograph* drum. The nerve supplying the muscle (tibial branch of the sciatic nerve for the gastrocnemius muscle) is exposed and connected to an electrical stimulator. The response of the muscle to stimulation under various conditions such as changes in load, changes in frequency of stimulation, and changes in strength of stimulation can be analyzed by study of the record written on the kymograph drum by the lever. The physiograph is a more advanced electronic device that can be used for the same purpose.

Electricity from an induction coil (inductorium) is the most commonly used stimulus for experiments in muscle physiology. This type of stimulus is more easily controlled and similar results can be obtained more readily than with other types of stimuli. Striated muscle can also be caused to contract by mechanical stimuli such as tapping, stretching, or pinching; chemical stimuli such as acids or salts; and application of heat.

Three types of contraction are described; concentric (shortening), static (isometric), and eccentric (lengthening).

Concentric contraction is the usual form of contraction, in which the muscle moves a bone or segment by shortening. An example would be flexion of the elbow by contraction of the biceps brachii.

Isometric contraction occurs naturally whenever a limb or portion of the body is held stationary against resistance such as gravity. In order to hold the head up in a fixed position, the dorsal neck muscles must contract isometrically.

Eccentric contraction occurs in the extensor muscles of the neck when an animal lowers its head gradually. Antagonistic muscles may also undergo eccentric contraction when unsuccessfully opposing the actions as a prime mover.

Isotonic contraction refers to a contraction in which the length of the muscle changes but the tension remains the same. This is primarily an experimental situation found in a muscle-nerve preparation where an isolated muscle lifts a given weight upon proper stimulation.

FACTORS INFLUENCING CONTRACTION

Treppe (*staircase effect*) is the repeated increase in strength of contraction of a

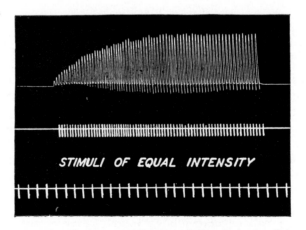

STIMULI OF EQUAL INTENSITY

FIG. 12–7.—The staircase phenomenon. Application of electrical stimuli in rapid succession to a frog heart whose spontaneous beat is arrested induces contractions of gradually increasing strength. Changes occur in the heart muscle as a result of one stimulus, making it more contractile when stimulated a second time, unless too long an interval elapses between stimuli. Skeletal muscle also displays this phenomenon. Time is shown in 5-second intervals. (Carlson, Johnson and Cavert, *The Machinery of the Body*, courtesy of the University of Chicago Press.)

muscle fiber due to successive stimulations a few seconds apart. The strength of contraction continues to increase for about thirty contractions. This effect may be due to an increasing concentration of Ca^{++} ions within the muscle fiber, which increases activation of the myofibrils.

While this phenomenon, treppe, may appear to violate the "all or none" law, it should be remembered that each contraction is a separate entity and for the given conditions each contraction will be maximal or will not occur. Thus the conditions change for each contraction, but the law still holds.

When a muscle fiber is stimulated so rapidly that it does not have time to relax between contractions, a condition called *tetanus* occurs. Tetanus also occurs in an entire muscle if a series of maximal stimuli are applied to the motor nerve or to the muscle directly. Strength of contraction increases with each stimulus, a condition known as *summation*, until the muscle appears to remain contracted (in a state of tetanus). This condition is seen in lockjaw which is also called tetanus (a disease caused by a bacterial toxin). Although the muscle is contracted and shows no physical change, an action potential in the muscle occurs following each stimulus. The elasticity of the sarcoplasm, sarcolemma, and connective-tissue elements may dampen any intermittent contractions and make the muscle appear rigid.

Elasticity of a muscle fiber is due largely to the sarcolemma and connective tissue surrounding the fiber. If the tendons are cut, a muscle will shorten about 20 per cent of its normal resting length, due to elasticity. This new length with zero tension is called the *equilibrium length*. The fiber can be stretched about one and one-half times the equilibrium length without permanent damage. When stretched excessively, rupture of a muscle fiber will usually occur at less than three times equilibrium length.

Optimum length of any muscle fiber in the body is about the maximum length that particular fiber attains under normal conditions. This length is about one and one-fourth times equilibrium length.

The rate of contraction and amount of shortening of a muscle depend on the load it must lift. With no load at all, the speed of contraction and amount of shortening are greatest. As the load increases, both speed and amount of short,

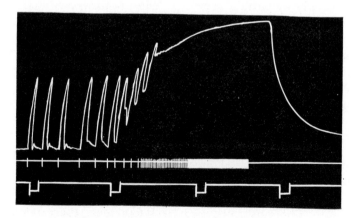

Fig. 12–8.—Tetanus in skeletal muscle. When stimuli are applied to a muscle at a gradually increasing rate of frequency (*indicated by signal*), the individual muscle twitches blend together so that when the stimuli are applied in very rapid succession, a smooth, sustained contraction results. Ordinary muscle movements are of this tetanic nature. Note that the height of contraction is greater in tetanus than in a single twitch. Time is shown (*bottom line*) in 5-second intervals. (Carlson, Johnson and Cavert, *The Machinery of the Body*, courtesy of the University of Chicago Press.)

ening decrease. With a load too heavy to lift, the speed becomes zero but the tension is maximum, producing an isometric contraction.

The maximum amount a muscle fiber can contract is to about one-half of its resting length. This would also be true of a complete muscle only if the fibers are parallel, as in the abdominal muscles.

Reciprocal innervation of muscles is an arrangement whereby the antagonists relax when the agonists are stimulated to contract in a given muscular action. This arrangement produces efficient use of muscles by insuring that the muscles producing a specific action (the agonists) do not have to overcome any resistance from muscles with opposite actions (the antagonists).

If the muscle fibers are arranged in a pennate manner, distance of contraction will be about one-half the length of the individual fibers. This distance, which may be called the *physiological length* of the muscle, is the distance from the origin of the muscle fiber to the place on the tendon of insertion where the particular fiber attaches.

Likewise, measurement of the strength of contraction of a muscle must be based on the *physiological cross-sectional area* of the muscle and not simply by cutting across the muscle at right angles to the tendon (unless the muscle fibers are parallel). The physiological cross-sectional area is difficult to measure or calculate for pennate muscles, as all muscle fibers must be cut at right angles. Estimates of strength of contraction of human muscle fibers range from 35 to 150 pounds per square inch.

The physiological cross-sectional area of parallel muscles is small compared with the physiological cross-sectional areas of pennate muscles. The physiological length of parallel muscles is relatively greater than the physiological length of pennate muscles.

For the same volume of muscle fibers, long parallel muscles have a greater distance of contraction but are relatively weak, while pennate muscles have a shorter distance of contraction but are much stronger.

Since almost all bones act as levers and most joints act as fulcrums, the law of levers can be used to determine the mechanical advantage or disadvantage of a particular muscle. The *"law of levers"* which applies equally well to all three classes of levers states that resistance times the resistance arm equal force times the force arm ($R \times RA = F \times FA$). The pivot point, called the *fulcrum*, is the point on the lever about which the lever rotates. The fulcrum may be located at either end of the lever or any place between the ends. The *force arm* is measured from the fulcrum to the point of application of the force. In the body the force is usually applied where the tendon of insertion of a muscle attaches to the bone. The *resistance arm* is measured from the fulcrum to the point on the lever where the resistance is applied. In some cases in the animal body resistance may be represented simply by the weight of a limb, or a segment of a limb. In extreme cases the weight of the entire animal may represent the resistance.

Most of the levers used in everyday life exhibit a mechanical advantage because the force arm is longer than the resistance arm. For example, a relatively small person can lift one wheel of a heavy car off the ground by placing a pole over a block located near the axle of the car. The segment of the pole from the fulcrum (block) to the resistance (axle) is the resistance arm. The long segment from the fulcrum to the point where the force is applied is the force arm. If the force arm is 10 feet long and the resistance arm is 1 foot long, every pound of force applied to the force arm will lift 10 pounds on the resistance arm. However, for every foot the resistance arm is raised, the force arm must be depressed 10 feet,

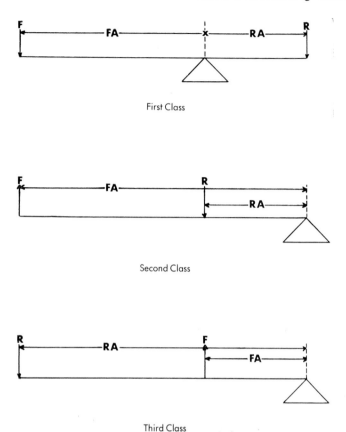

First Class

Second Class

Third Class

Fig. 12–9.—The three classes of levers.

so the gain in force is offset by the greater distance the force arm must move.

In most instances in the animal body the muscles are working at a mechanical disadvantage. The force arm is shorter than the resistance arm, so the muscles must exert a much greater force than the resistance they overcome. Thus we see the desirability of having pennate muscles attached to the short arm of a bony lever. The pennate arrangement gives increased strength at the expense of distance, while the lever with a mechanical disadvantage requires greater force but gives increased distance of movement. Examples of this combination of pennate muscles attaching to the short arm of a lever include the *triceps brachii*, which attaches to the olecranon process of the ulna; the *middle gluteus*, which attaches to the greater trochanter of the femur; and the gastrocnemius, which attaches to the *tuber calcis* of the hock. In each of these examples the limb distal to the joint where the muscle attaches is the resistance arm.

Angle of pull, the angle at which a tendon meets the segment (bone) to which it attaches, is also an important factor in the efficiency of action of a muscle. The force exerted by a muscle usually results in two components. The *rotary component* is that portion of the total force which tends to cause movement (rotation) in the joint. The other component, the *stabilizing component*, is that portion of the total force that tends to hold in apposition the segments making up the joint. If the muscle pulls at right angles (exactly 90°) to the segment to which it attaches, the entire force acts as a rotary component. However, if the pull is parallel to the segments (0°), the entire force acts as a stabilizing component. The larger the angle of pull up to 90°, the larger is the rotary component, and the smaller is the stabilizing component. The smaller the angle of pull, the greater is the stabilizing component, and the smaller is the rotary component.

If the angle of pull and the total force are known, both the rotary component and the stabilizing component can be calculated by trigonometry or by a scale drawing of a parallelogram of forces.

The graphic determination of rotary and stabilizing components is illustrated in Figure 12–10, using 30° as an example of a specific angle of pull. A right tri-

angle is constructed on a scale diagram. The base of the triangle extends along the segment to which the tendon of insertion attaches (usually the distal segment). The hypotenuse extends along the line of pull of the muscle meeting the segment at the predetermined angle (30° in this example). The pull of the muscle in pounds, converted to convenient units of linear distance, is then measured along the hypotenuse from the angle. If the total force (pull) of the muscle is assumed to be 150 pounds, 15 centimeters ($\frac{150}{10}$) is measured along the line of pull from its intersection with the distal segment. The altitude of the right triangle is constructed at right angles to the base so that it (the altitude) intersects the line of pull exactly 15 centimeters from the apex of the original angle. The altitude of this triangle represents the rotary com-

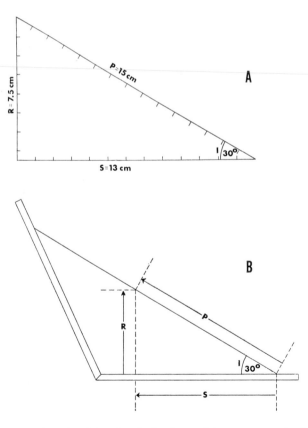

Fɪɢ. 12–10.—Construction of a right triangle for determining components of muscular force.

ponent, which can now be determined by measuring the line in centimeters and multiplying by 10 to convert the linear measure to pounds. Likewise the base of the triangle represents the stabilizing component, which can also be converted to pounds by multiplying by 10, since 1 centimeter represents 10 pounds. In this example the following may be found:

angle or pull and any force to calculate the rotary component and the stabilizing component. However, as the muscle moves the distal segment by contracting, the angle of pull constantly changes, so that the relationship of stabilizing component to rotary component changes at the same time.

Thus we see that the final effect of con-

hypotenuse—line of pull   —15.0 centimeters = 15.0 × 10 = 150 pounds

altitude   —rotary component   — 7.5 centimeters =   7.5 × 10 = 75 pounds

base   —stabilizing component—13.0 centimeters = 13.0 × 10 = 130 pounds

Anyone familiar with plane geometry will recognize this method as an application of the *Pythagorean theorem* which states the relationship of the sides of any right angle: "the square of the hypotenuse is equal to the sum of the squares of the other two sides."

By using a table of sines and cosines, the value of the total force, and the angle of pull, the rotary component and the stabilizing component can be calculated by trigonometric means. Since the sine of an angle in a right triangle is the ratio of the side opposite (rotary component) to the hypotenuse (side opposite divided by the hypotenuse), the value of the hypotenuse multiplied by the sine of the angle gives the value of the side opposite (rotary component). In our example, the hypotenuse (total force of 150 pounds) multiplied by the sine of 30° (the angle of pull) which is 0.5 equals 75 pounds, the rotary component.

The cosine of an angle is the ratio of the side adjacent to the angle (stabilizing component) divided by the hypotenuse. The cosine of 30° is 0.866. To find the stabilizing component in our example, the hypotenuse (total force of 150 pounds) is multiplied by 0.866 (cosine of 30°) which equals 129.9 or approximately 130 pounds.

Either the graphic method or the trigonometric method can be used for any

traction of a single muscle is influenced by a number of factors which include the physiologic cross section of the muscle, the mechanical advantage or disadvantage of the muscle (law of levers), and the angle of pull of the muscle.

PHYSIOLOGY OF MUSCULAR EXERCISE

Fatigue is a decrease in work capacity caused by work itself. Fatigue of striated muscle may result from depletion or lack of available energy in the form of food; lack of oxygen; accumulation of end products of metabolism, such as lactic acid and carbon dioxide; or other changes in the chemical state of the body, such as depletion of chlorides. A fatigued muscle may undergo physiological contracture, in which the muscle remains contracted because sufficient energy for relaxation is not available. As soon as more ATP is formed, the muscle relaxes, and the state of contracture is over.

Physical contracture refers to the tendency of a muscle to adapt its resting length to the position in which the part may be maintained over a fairly long period. This new length may be either shorter or longer than the original length, although the term usually is applied to a shortened muscle. For example, if a person's arm is carried in a sling for

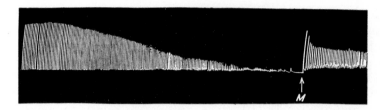

FIG. 12–11.—Fatigue. Contractions of a muscle (recorded by means of a muscle lever) induced by rapidly repeated stimuli to the nerve of the muscle. When the muscle no longer responded to nerve stimulation, stimuli applied directly to the muscle (beginning at *M*) caused definite contractions, indicating that the fatigue was not primarily in the muscle. (Carlson, Johnson and Cavert, *The Machinery of the Body*, courtesy of the University of Chicago Press.)

several weeks with the elbow bent, the elbow flexors undergo physical contracture and assume a shorter length. After the sling is removed, the person finds a flexed position of the elbow more comfortable because letting the arm hang straight at the side in an extended position stretches the shortened elbow flexors too much. Tail sets used on gaited horses may produce physical contracture of the dorsal muscles, which helps keep the tail elevated.

The term "*muscle tone*" usually refers to a residual degree of contraction in an otherwise relaxed muscle. It may be due to reflexes arising in the muscle itself.

However, completely relaxed muscles show no action potential, so the firmness of the muscle may be due only to the elasticity of the muscle fibers. The action potential produced by contracting muscle fibers can be recorded with appropriate instruments from the skin overlying the muscle. This record is called an electromyogram and in principle resembles an electrocardiogram of the heart.

Loss of nerve supply of a muscle causes *atrophy*, which, if it lasts more than about four months, may become irreversible because of death of muscle cells and infiltration with fat and fibrous connective tissue.

CHAPTER 13

BLOOD AND OTHER BODY FLUIDS

GENERAL

SINGLE-CELL organisms which live in sea water have an external environment that provides for all the needs of the organism such as food, excretion of wastes, and relatively constant conditions for maintenance of life. As the complexity of organisms has increased, the problem of supplying each cell with a proper environment has become more acute. Higher forms of animals have developed circulating blood and the fluids derived from it as a means of maintaining a relatively constant internal environment for all cells.

Like other tissues, blood consists of cells and intercellular material. Unlike most other tissues, however, the intercellular material is a fluid called plasma, and the cells are separate individuals which are free to move about within the vascular system. Some blood cells, the leukocytes, may even migrate through vessel walls to combat infections.

Most of the functions of blood are included in the following list:

1. Blood carries nutrients made available by the digestive tract to body tissues.
2. It carries oxygen from the lungs to the tissues.
3. It carries carbon dioxide from tissues to the lungs.
4. Waste products from various tissues are carried to the kidneys for excretion.
5. Hormones are carried from endocrine glands to other organs of the body.
6. Blood plays an important part in temperature control by transporting heat from deeper structures to the surface of the body.
7. Water balance is maintained by the blood.
8. Buffers such as sodium bicarbonate in the blood help maintain a constant pH of tissues and body fluids.
9. The clotting ability of blood prevents excess loss of blood from injuries.
10. Blood contains important factors for defense of the body against disease.

CELLULAR COMPONENTS

Cellular components of the blood, or more accurately the non-fluid components of the blood, include red blood cells, white blood cells, and blood platelets. Because the red blood cells and the platelets both lack nuclei, they are not typical cells but might better be considered as portions of cells (see Fig. 1–10).

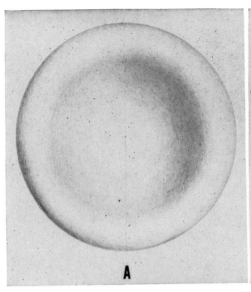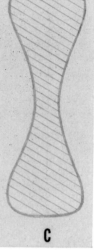

Fig. 13–1.—Red blood cell (erythrocyte). *A*, Viewed from above; *B*, viewed from an angle; and *C*, cross-section.

ERYTHROCYTES

Red blood cells or *erythrocytes* (Gr. erythro—red, cyte—cell) are cells ranging from 5.0 to 7.34 μ in diameter which specialize in the transporting of oxygen. They are biconcave discs having a thick circular margin, and a thin center. The biconcave disc presents a relatively large surface area for oxygen exchange across the cell membrane.

The presence of *hemoglobin* within the erythrocyte is responsible for the ability to transport oxygen and for the red color of the erythrocytes. Chemically, hemoglobin is a complex organic compound made up of a *porphyrin*, a *globin*, and *iron*. Hemoglobin absorbs oxygen from the air of the lungs to form *oxyhemoglobin*, which in turn readily gives up its oxygen to tissue cells within the body. Because of the presence of hemoglobin, blood can carry about 60 times as much oxygen as a similar quantity of water under the same conditions.

Oxygen from the lungs forms a loose combination with hemoglobin (Hb$_4$),

2 α-ketoglutaric acid + glycine $\longrightarrow$ (pyrrole)

4 pyrrole $\longrightarrow$ protoporphyrin III

protoporphyrin III + Fe $\longrightarrow$ heme

4 heme + globin $\longrightarrow$ hemoglobin

which results in a product called oxy-hemoglobin, according to the equation: $Hb_4 + 4O_2 = Hb_4O_8$. This process is oxygenation and not a true oxidation, but requires the presence of ferrous iron in the hemoglobin molecule. The combined oxygen is proportional to the amount of iron present, with two atoms of oxygen united with each atom of iron. Each gram of hemoglobin will absorb about 1.34 cubic centimeters of oxygen.

When the blood reaches tissues deficient in oxygen, the loosely held oxygen of the oxyhemoglobin is given up readily, again forming reduced hemoglobin.

Methemoglobin is a true oxidation product of hemoglobin which is unable to transport oxygen because the iron is in the ferric (Fe^{+++}) rather than the ferrous (Fe^{++}) state. Certain chemicals such as nitrites and chlorates produce a met-hemoglobinemia (presence of methemoglobin in the blood). Nitrate poisoning has been reported in cattle grazing on highly fertilized rank plant growth. In these cases nitrates in the plants are converted to nitrites in the rumen and cause the formation of methemoglobin when absorbed into the blood. Chlorates are sometimes used as weed killers and may be eaten by livestock.

Carboxyhemoglobin is a stable compound formed when carbon monoxide (present in exhaust fumes) unites with hemoglobin. The carboxyhemoglobin is unable to carry oxygen, and the animal essentially dies of suffocation, although the blood is typically cherry red in color.

Cyanide poisoning, also called *prussic acid poisoning*, produces asphyxia (suffocation) by interference with internal respiration, the utilization of oxygen by tissues. It has no effect on the oxygen-carrying ability of the blood. Cyanide poisoning may occur when cattle eat stunted or frosted grain sorghums. *Methylene blue* is used in the treatment of cyanide poisoning because it forms met-hemoglobin in the blood which reacts with the cyanide to form *cyanmethemoglobin*, a relatively inactive compound that is slowly broken down and detoxified by the body.

Formation of red cells in the adult occurs normally in the red bone marrow, which also produces granular leukocytes. However, in the fetus, red cells are also produced by the liver, the spleen, and the lymph nodes. Although mature red corpuscles of mammals have no nuclei, the immature cells from which they are derived, erythroblasts, are nucleated. In birds, nuclei persist in the red cells throughout the life of the cells.

Destruction of red cells occurs after three to four months in the circulation. Most red cells disintegrate and are removed from the circulation by the *reticulo-endothelial system*, which consists of special cells in the liver, spleen, bone marrow, and lymph nodes. These reticuloendothelial cells phagocytose (engulf) the blood cells. Some of the products formed from red-cell destruction include the bile pigments *bilirubin* and *biliverdin*, which normally are excreted by the liver in the bile. If an excess of these pigments gets into the blood stream, the visible mucous membranes such as the mouth and eye become yellow, a condition called *jaundice*, or *icterus*.

Icterus may be caused either by liver damage, by occlusion of the bile ducts, or by destructive blood diseases. In case of either liver damage or blockage of the bile ducts, the bile pigments are not excreted into the intestine but are resorbed into the circulatory system and show up in the visible mucous membranes. When blood damage is excessive, as in some parasitic blood diseases such as *anaplasmosis*, the bile pigments are liberated into the blood faster than the liver can excrete them, and icterus results.

Hemolysis consists of a breakdown of red cells so that the hemoglobin escapes into the plasma. It may be caused by bacterial toxins, snake venoms, blood parasites, hypotonic solutions, and many chemical substances. The resulting hemoglobin in the plasma gives it a reddish color, and the condition is called hemoglobinemia. If hemoglobin is then excreted in the urine, the condition is called *hemoglobinuria (red water)*.

Hemagglutination is a clumping of red cells of blood. Usually cells from one species will agglutinate when injected into the blood stream of an animal of another species. Clumping may occur within the same species, such as man, if blood of the wrong type is used. There appear to be a number of blood types in horses, so matching of the blood is desirable before attempting transfusion. Usually little trouble is encountered in transfusing cattle or dogs with blood from another animal of the same species.

Sedimentation rate is a measure of the distance the red cells settle in citrated blood in a given period, usually thirty minutes or one hour. Standard *hematocrit tubes* are filled with blood and placed in an absolutely vertical position. The amount of settling is measured in millimeters at specified intervals. Sedimentation rates are increased in cases of acute general infections, malignant tumors, and pregnancy. Normal sedimentation rates are shown in Table 13–1.

*TABLE 13–1.—NORMAL VALUES IN CIRCULATORY SYSTEM

	Horse	Cow	Sheep	Pig	Dog
Sedimentation rate mm./minutes	2 to 12/10 15 to 30/20	0/30 0/60	0/30 0/60	0 to 6/30 1 to 14/60	1 to 6/30 5 to 25/60
Red blood cell count million/cu.mm.	7	7	11	7	7
Diameter red cells—microns	5.6	5.6	5.0	6.2	7.3
Hemoglobin—grams/100 cc.	12.5	12	11	12	13.5
Hematocrit—volume per cent red cells	42	40	32	42	45
White blood cells— thousands/cu. mm.	9	9	8	15	12
Differential white count—per cent					
Neutrophils	55	30	40	40	60
Eosinophils	4	5	4	2	5
Basophils	1	1	1	1	1
Monocytes	10	5	6	8	8
Lymphocytes	30	60	50	50	25
Blood pH—average and range	7.4 (7.35 to 7.43)	7.3 (7.20 to 7.55)		7.4	7.5 (7.32 to 7.68)
Coagulation time—minutes	11.5	6.5	2.5	3.5	2.5
Specific gravity	1.060	1.043	1.042	1.060	1.059
Heart rate—per minute average and range	32 to 44	60 to 70	70 to 80	60 to 80	70 to 120
Blood pressure mm.—Hg. syst./diast.	80/50	134/88	114/68	169/108	148/100
Carotid pressure—average and range mm.—Hg.	169 (152 to 194)	125 to 166	114 (90 to 140)	169 (144 to 185)	155 (120 to 176)
Blood volume—per cent of body weight	9.7	7.7	8.0		7.2

* Data compiled from standard references including Benjamin, Dukes, Payne, and Spector.

Blood counting provides a useful laboratory procedure for estimating the numbers and types of cells in the circulating blood of a given animal at a given time. Total cell counts are expressed as number of cells per cubic millimeter of whole blood. This is true of both red-cell counts and white-cell counts, although the equipment and technique are slightly different for each.

Total red-cell count is determined by diluting a definite small amount of whole blood with a specific amount of diluting fluid in a red-cell pipette to produce a

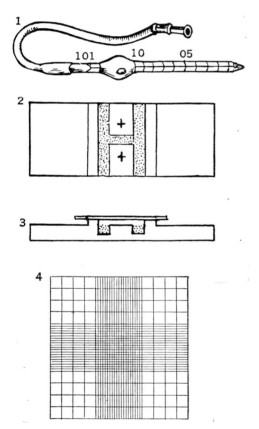

dilution of one part of blood to 200 parts of diluting fluid. The blood and fluid are thoroughly mixed in the special pipette and the counting chamber of a special slide is then filled with the mixture to a depth of 0.1 millimeter. One square millimeter of the counting chamber is ruled into 400 smaller squares. The red cells are counted in the 400 squares or a specified fraction of them. The number of red cells thus counted is multiplied by the proper number to give the total number of red cells in 1 cubic millimeter of diluted blood, and this number in turn is multiplied by the dilution to give the number of red cells in 1 cubic millimeter of whole blood. Most domestic animals have a red-blood-cell count of about seven million cells per cubic millimeter of blood.

Anemia (Gr. an–without; emia–blood) results if either the number of red cells or the quantity of hemoglobin is decreased very much below normal. Anemia may be due to deficient blood formation because of poor nutrition, including dietary deficiency of iron, copper, vitamins, or amino acids. Anemia may also be caused by loss of blood due to hemorrhage from wounds or because of parasites such as stomach worms or lice.

Hemoglobin concentration is measured in grams per 100 cubic centimeters of blood. Normal hemoglobin concentration ranges from 11 in sheep to 13.5 in the dog with a value of 12 for the cow and pig and 12.5 for the horse.

Hematocrit value, or packed cell volume, is a term that means the percentage (by volume) of whole blood that is constituted by red blood cells. It is determined by filling a graduated hematocrit tube with blood treated so that it will not clot and then centrifuging the tube until the cells are packed in the lower end. The hematocrit value then is read directly from the tube. Normal hematocrit values range from 32 in the sheep to 45 in the dog with 40 for the cow and 42 for the horse and pig. The hematocrit is generally considered to be as useful as total red cell count and is much easier to perform.

Hemoconcentration is the opposite of anemia, which means that the ratio of red cells to fluid is above normal. This is indicated by an excessively high red cell count or high hematocrit value. Actually

BLOOD PLATELETS

Blood platelets, also called *thrombocytes*, are fragments of protoplasm found in the blood. Platelets are believed to be formed by *megakaryocytes*, large cells in bone marrow. The appearance of blood platelets in a stained smear may be considerably different from their actual ap-

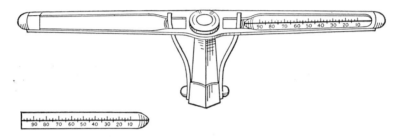

Fig. 13–3.—Hematocrit. Blood to which sodium oxalate or other anticoagulant agent has been added is drawn into the graduated tubes which are then placed in the holder and rotated in a centrifuge at a rate of 3000 revolutions per minute. The blood is thus separated into a red (cells) and a straw-colored portion (plasma), the proportions of each being easily determined by means of the graduations on the tubes. (Best and Taylor, *The Living Body*, courtesy of Henry Holt and Co.)

the total number of red cells in the body may not be increased (a condition called polycythemia), but more likely there has been a loss of fluid. Either a lowered intake of water or excess loss of water will cause hemoconcentration which then is a form of dehydration. Vomiting and diarrhea as well as diseases with high temperatures, if continued over a long period, will result in dehydration.

To correct *dehydration* it may be necessary to supply water to the animal in the form of physiological saline or glucose solution *parenterally*. This means that it is given by some route other than by mouth, since an animal that is vomiting may be stimulated to vomit even more upon drinking water. Fluid may be injected *hypodermically* (under the skin), *intravenously* (into a vein), or *intraperitoneally* (into the peritoneal cavity in the abdomen).

pearance in circulating blood, where they are oval discs. In smears they may appear as circular discs, star-shaped fragments, or clumps of irregular shape. Electron microscope studies have shown platelets to contain mitochondria, vesicles, and granules, but relatively little *RNA* (ribonucleic acid).

Platelets function chiefly to reduce loss of blood from injured vessels. By adhering to vessel walls and to each other in the area of the injury, platelets may form a white thrombus (clot) that can occlude the vessel and prevent further loss of blood. Materials released by injured platelets may stimulate formation of an ordinary clot (as described later in this chapter), may cause contraction of a clot making it more solid, and may cause local constriction of the injured blood vessel. This last action is believed to be due to a substance called *serotonin* that is carried by the platelets and may reduce blood pressure as well as causing local vasoconstriction.

LEUKOCYTES

White blood cells, or *leukocytes* (Gr. leuco–white), differ considerably from erythrocytes in that they are nucleated and possess independent movement. Leukocytes are classified according to the following table:

Granulocytes
  Neutrophils
  Eosinophils
  Basophils
Agranulocytes
  Monocytes
  Lymphocytes

Granulocytes, as the name implies, contain granules within the cytoplasm which stain with common blood stains, such as Wright's stain. These stains contain an acid dye, eosin, which is red, and a basic dye, methylene blue, which is bluish. Granulocytes are named according to the color of the stained granules. The nuclei of granulocytes appear in many shapes and forms leading to the name polymorphonuclear leukocytes (Gr. poly–many; morpho–form). Common usage restricts the term polymorphonuclear leukocyte to neutrophils. In the normal adult the granulocytes are formed in the red bone marrow.

Neutrophils contain granules which stain indifferently and are not markedly red or blue. They constitute the first line of defense against infection by migrating to any area invaded by bacteria, passing through the vessel walls, and engulfing the bacteria to destroy them. In the process, many of the neutrophils also dissolve dead tissue in the area, and the resulting semiliquid material is known as pus. Neutrophils, therefore, are sometimes known as pus cells. A localized accumulation of pus is called an *abscess*. *Actinomycosis* (lump jaw) in cattle and distemper in horses frequently result in abscess formation in the mandibular lymph nodes.

The number of neutrophils in the blood increases very rapidly whenever acute infection is present. A blood count showing this increase is useful in diagnosis of infections.

Eosinophils, also known as *acidophils*, show red-staining granules in the cytoplasm. These cells, which normally are quite scarce, have been observed to increase in numbers in certain chronic diseases such as infection with parasites. Some people believe that the eosinophils contain much of the *histamine* that is present in the blood. Histamine causes the symptoms of allergic reactions.

Basophils, which contain blue-staining granules, are also quite rare in normal blood. The function of basophils is unknown.

Agranulocytes (Gr. a–without) usually show very few granules in the cytoplasm. These cells include monocytes, which are formed in lymph nodes and the spleen; and lymphocytes, which are formed in all types of lymphoid tissue, including lymph nodes, spleen, tonsils, and possibly the thymus.

Monocytes, like neutrophils, are phagocytic; that is, they have the ability to engulf foreign matter such as bacteria. However, while the neutrophils act mainly on pus-producing organisms, the monocytes are called into action by less acute infections such as *tuberculosis*. When monocytes from the blood stream enter tissues, they develop into larger phagocytes called *macrophages*.

Lymphocytes apparently are important in forming barriers against local disease conditions and may be involved in antibody formation in the development of immunity to disease.

Total white cell counts are made in a manner similar to red cell counts. However, since white cells are much less numerous than red cells, the blood is not diluted as much, and the counting squares on the slide are larger. White cell counts are given in thousands per cubic millimeter of whole blood. The normal white cell count per cubic millimeter ranges from 8 thousand in the sheep to 15 thousand in the pig, with 9 thousand for the horse and cow and 12 thousand for the dog.

Differential counts indicate the percentage of each type of white cell in the blood sample. This is important to know if the total leukocyte count is very much above normal for the particular species.

A differential count is made by spreading a drop of whole blood very thinly on a glass slide to form a blood smear. The smear is dried and stained with a blood stain such as Wright's stain. After staining is complete, the slide is examined with a microscope and the number of white cells of each kind is tabulated until a predetermined total number of white cells has been counted. The number counted is usually a multiple of 100 and the percentage of each leukocyte type observed in a given sample of blood is called the differential leukocyte count. The normal percentage of each type of leukocyte for each species is shown in Table 13–1.

A definite increase in the number of leukocytes usually indicates that infection is present. However, a cancer of the leukocyte-producing tissues also results in an abnormally high white cell count. This type of cancer is called *leukemia*.

PLASMA

When a sample of blood is treated to prevent clotting and permitted to stand undisturbed, the cells gradually settle to the bottom of the container, leaving a straw-colored fluid above. This fluid portion of the blood, called *plasma*, was referred to by Claude Bernard as the "internal environment" which directly or indirectly bathes all cells of the body and protects them from external influences. Thus the plasma of the blood of higher vertebrates replaces the sea water in which primitive life probably developed.

Plasma is made up of about 90 per cent water and 10 per cent solids. The kid-

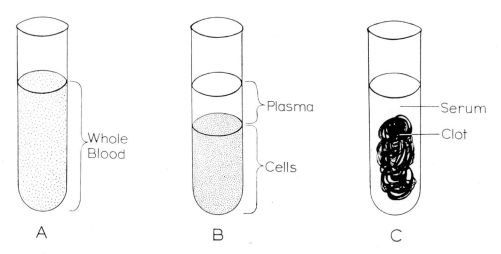

A   B   C

Fig. 13–4.—Blood.—Diagram illustrating different physical states of blood. *A*, Unclotted blood, cells dispersed uniformly throughout; *B*, blood treated with anticoagulant. Cells permitted to settle leaving clear plasma. *C*, Clotted blood. Serum separated from clot.

neys are responsible for maintaining constant proportions of water and other constituents of the plasma by selective filtration and resorption of water and other chemicals from the blood plasma.

The solids include about 7 per cent proteins, and 0.9 per cent inorganic matter; the remainder is non-protein organic matter.

Serum albumin and *fibrinogen* probably are produced by the liver, and the globulin is formed by the lymphocytes. The plasma proteins are large molecules which do not readily pass through vessel walls, so they aid in keeping fluid in the blood vessels by increasing the osmotic pressure of the blood.

Globulin is the fraction of the blood associated with immunity and resistance to disease. Following vaccination and during recovery from disease the globulin content of the blood increases.

Fibrinogen is an essential part of the blood-clotting mechanism described later in this chapter.

The other organic compounds in plasma include lipids, cholesterol, hormones, enzymes, and non-protein nitrogenous material.

The *non-protein nitrogen* fraction contains both amino acids, which are used by body cells to build protein, and waste products of metabolism, such as urea, uric acid, creatine, creatinine, and ammonium salts.

Glucose and fats, as well as the amino acids, are nutrititive substances absorbed into the blood stream following digestion.

The inorganic chemicals consist chiefly of chlorides, carbonates, sulfates and phosphates of sodium, potassium, calcium, and magnesium. Some of these compounds are essential for cell metabolism, and some function as buffers to maintain the pH (degree of acidity or alkalinity) of the blood within a normal range. Most of the carbon dioxide from the cells is carried by the blood dissolved in the plasma, but the oxygen carried to the cells is almost entirely combined with hemoglobin in the red cells. Other gases such as nitrogen may be found in minute quantities in the plasma.

SERUM

Serum is the fluid that remains after a sample of blood is permitted to clot. Essentially, serum is defibrinated plasma, or blood with the *fibrin* and cellular components removed. The fact that serum contains antibodies the animal may have formed, makes it useful in prevention and treatment of disease. Immune serum or hyperimmune serum is produced by inoculating an animal with disease-producing agents such as bacteria or viruses (usually killed organisms). When the animal is repeatedly injected with a specific antigen (disease agent), it produces a large excess of antibodies against that particular antigen. Serum from that animal can then be injected into an animal susceptible to the same disease to provide a passive protection for as long as the antibodies remain in the susceptible animal. This provides merely a temporary immunity which leaves the animal as susceptible to the disease after the serum wears off as before it was administered. For example, hogs injected only with hog-cholera serum will be protected from hog cholera for a period of one or two weeks and then will be as susceptible as before. However, if some live or modified hog-cholera virus is given at the same time the immune serum is given, the hogs not only will receive passive protection from the serum, but also will develop active immunity by producing their own antibodies in response to the injected virus.

Reaction (pH) of the blood refers to the hydrogen-ion concentration, which determines the relative acidity or alkalinity of the solution. In distilled water the hydrogen ions (H^+) (which are acid) equal the hydroxyl ions (OH^-) (which are basic or alkaline). The pH of water is 7 indicating the reaction is neutral, neither acid nor alkali. Solutions with pH between 1 and 7 are acid; the smaller the number, the more acid the solution. The pH of alkaline solutions ranges from 7 to 14; the larger the number, the more alkaline the solution.

Normally the pH of blood lies between 7.35 and 7.45, just slightly on the alkaline side of neutral.

The reaction of blood is kept within rather narrow limits by the presence of chemical buffers, chiefly sodium bicarbonate. Buffers react with strong acids or strong alkalies to produce a neutral salt and a weak acid or weak base. An example is the sodium-bicarbonate, carbonic-acid system shown below.

$$HCl + NaHCO_3 \rightarrow NaCl + H_2CO_3$$
$$NaOH + H_2CO_3 \rightarrow NaHCO_3 + H_2O$$

This ability to neutralize acids resulting from metabolism leads to the term "*alkali reserve*" as a synonym for sodium bicarbonate in the blood. The resulting carbon dioxide is removed from the blood when it passes through the lungs. Thus overventilation by removing too much carbon dioxide can result in a temporary *alkalosis* of the blood.

In some diseases the alkali reserve becomes depleted, resulting in an acid condition of the blood called *acidosis*.

BLOOD CLOTTING

Blood clotting, or coagulation, occurs in blood which is drawn into a container and allowed to stand. A jelly-like mass results, which then shrinks to produce a firm clot and some clear fluid, the blood serum. The actual clot consists of filaments of fibrin which enmesh red blood cells, white blood cells, and platelets. The precipitation of fibrinogen in blood is believed to be initiated by *thromboplastin*, a phospholipid released from injured tissue, and by the breakdown of

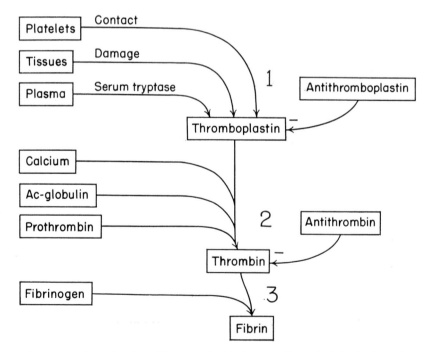

Fig. 13–5.—The formation of a clot. (Dukes, *The Physiology of Domestic Animals*, 7th ed., courtesy of Comstock Publishing Co.)

blood platelets. Fibrinogen, calcium and *prothrombin* circulate in the blood until sufficient thromboplastin is released to react with the inactive prothrombin and calcium to form active thrombin. The thrombin thus formed reacts with soluble fibrinogen to produce fibrin, which precipitates a thread-like mass.

Serum tryptase has been postulated as an enzyme that catalyzes the reaction between thromboplastin, prothrombin, and calcium to form *thrombin*. It may also function in retraction (shrinkage) of the clot and possibly in finally dissolving the clot. When blood is withdrawn from a vessel the serum tryptase may become activated and initiate clotting. A globulin in the plasma called *Ac-globulin* is believed to accelerate the conversion of prothrombin to thrombin. Clotting within blood vessels is presumably prevented by two substances in normal blood called *antithromboplastin* and *antithrombin*. Figure 13–5 shows the relationships of these substances in clot formation.

Lack of prothrombin is associated with insufficient *vitamin K*. *Dicoumarin*, found in sweet clover inhibits the clotting of blood because it is antagonistic to vitamin K, thus reducing the amount of prothrombin in the blood. *Sweet clover disease* is the hemorrhagic condition resulting from excess Dicoumarin. In this condition small cuts or bruises result in bleeding that is difficult to stop. Therefore, routine surgery such as dehorning or castration should be avoided while animals are being fed sweet clover hay or are grazing on sweet clover pasture. Dicoumarin is used commercially in rodent poisons, and rats and mice that eat these poisons usually die from internal bleeding or bruising.

In the absence of vitamin K in the diet, poultry develop fatal hemorrhages, but bacteria in the intestines of mammals synthesize vitamin K, so its presence in their feed is less important.

Heparin, which is produced in the liver, and dicoumarin are both used to prevent clotting in the circulating blood, as in the treatment of *coronary thrombosis* (occlusion of heart vessels.)

Other *anticoagulants* include oxalates, citrates, and fluorides. These compounds inhibit clotting by precipitating the calcium ions of the blood to form insoluble compounds and frequently are used to prevent clotting in blood that has been withdrawn from animals for use in laboratory tests such as blood-cell counts.

Coagulation time is the length of time from drawing a fresh blood sample until coagulation occurs. It may be determined by placing 1 cc. of blood in each of three test tubes. One tube is tilted at thirty-second intervals to test for coagulation. As soon as coagulation in the first tube occurs, the second tube is tilted, and then the third. *Coagulation time* is measured from the time blood enters the syringe till the blood in the third tube coagulates. Coagulation time for the dog and sheep is two and one-half minutes, pig three and one-half minutes, man five minutes, cow six and one-half minutes, and horse eleven and one-half minutes. Variations in technique may cause appreciable differences in coagulation time.

SPECIFIC GRAVITY OF BLOOD

Specific gravity is an index, or ratio, of the weight of a substance compared to the weight of an equal volume of water. A substance that weighs less than an equal volume of water will have a specific gravity of less than 1.000; if it weighs more than the same volume of water its specific gravity will be more than 1.000. Specific gravity is commonly measured with an instrument called a *hydrometer*. The amount of antifreeze in a radiator and the charge of a storage battery are both determined by the use of a hydrometer to measure specific gravity of the fluid involved.

Whole blood has a slightly higher specific gravity than water primarily because of the blood cells: the red cells are heavier than the white cells, and both of them are heavier than the plasma. Specific gravity of blood varies slightly between species, with that of the sheep being 1.042; cow, 1.043; dog and man, 1.059; and horse and pig, 1.060.

BLOOD VOLUME

Blood volume refers to the total amount of blood in an animal's body. It can be determined directly by bleeding an animal as completely as possible and then washing out the remaining blood which cannot be removed by ordinary bleeding. A known volume of dye can also be injected into the blood stream and the volume calculated from the dilution of the dye after it is thoroughly mixed with the blood. This is an indirect method which does not interfere with the life of the animal.

Blood volume can be readily calculated if the percentage of body weight normally comprised of blood is known. Average figures, in percentage of body weight due to blood, are: Dog 7.2, cow 7.7, sheep 8.0, and horse 9.7.

LYMPH

Much of the fluid that passes through the capillary walls into the tissue spaces is reabsorbed into the venous capillaries, but some remains as tissue fluid in the tissue spaces. Excess tissue fluid which is not absorbed by the blood capillaries is picked up by a system of blind capillaries called lymphatics. As soon as the tissue fluid enters the lymph capillaries it is called *lymph*. (The lymphatic system is described in the next chapter, p. 215.)

Lymph is a clear, colorless liquid somewhat similar to blood plasma from which it is derived. There may be a few red cells and numerous *lymphocytes* as well as inorganic salts, glucose, non-protein nitrogenous substances and some proteins. Neutrophilic leukocytes normally are not present in great numbers except during acute infections.

The quantity of protein in lymph is considerably less than in plasma, but the content of simple chemical substances, crystaloids, is about the same.

Lymph which drains from the intestine during digestion may contain large quantities of fat, giving it a milky appearance. This milky lymph, called *chyle*, results from the absorption of fat into the *lacteals*, the small lymphatics of the intestine. Eventually all lymph is returned to the blood stream by way of large veins cranial to the heart.

CEREBROSPINAL FLUID

Cerebrospinal fluid is formed by *choroid plexuses* (tufts of capillaries) in the ventricles of the brain. It circulates throughout the subarachnoid space, between the *pia mater* and *arachnoid membrane*, over the entire surface of the brain and spinal cord. (See Chapter 5, p. 77 for a description of the ventricles and meninges.)

Cerebrospinal fluid also resembles blood plasma from which it is derived, but has less protein and few if any cells except some lymphocytes. It probably serves as a nutritive medium for the brain and spinal cord as well as cushioning these structures against shock.

SYNOVIAL FLUID

Synovial fluid is a thick, tenacious liquid found in joint cavities and bursae. It owes its physical properties and lubricating ability to the presence of mucopolysaccharides and possibly hyaluronic acid. Besides reducing friction in joints, synovial fluid probably helps nourish the articular cartilages.

SEROUS FLUIDS

Serous fluids found in the respective body cavities include peritoneal fluid, pleural fluid, and pericardial fluid. Normally these fluids are present as a thin film which reduces friction between apposed surfaces. Inflammation or infection of the serous membranes causes increased production of serous fluids. Examples are traumatic pericarditis (hardware disease) of cattle, pleuritis (pleurisy), and peritonitis.

OTHER BODY FLUIDS

Other body fluids include the *aqueous humor* of the eye and the *perilymph* and *endolymph* of the inner ear. They are discussed in Chapter 7, pages 113 and 107.

CHAPTER 14

THE CIRCULATORY SYSTEM

GENERAL

THE circulatory system consists of a four-chambered pump, the heart, and a system of vessels for circulating the blood.

Vessels which carry blood away from the heart are called *arteries*. Vessels which carry blood toward the heart are called *veins*. In addition, a system of vessels which carry tissue fluid or lymph to large veins are called lymph vessels, or lymphatics.

HEART

The heart is a cone-shaped, hollow, muscular structure. The base is directed dorsally or cranio-dorsally and is attached to other thoracic structures by large arteries, veins, and the pericardial sac. The apex of the heart is directed ventrally and is entirely free within the pericardium.

THE PERICARDIUM

The heart is partially surrounded by a serous sac called the *pericardium*, or pericardial sac. The pericardium, like other serous sacs (the pleura and peritoneum)- is a completely closed sac which contains only a small amount of fluid for lubrication. The heart is invaginated into the pericardium much as would occur if one thrust his fist into the side of an inflated balloon. This arrangement results in two distinct layers of pericardium. The inner layer which is intimately adherent to the outer surface of the heart is called *visceral pericardium*, or *epicardium*. The outer layer, called *parietal pericardium*, is continuous with the visceral layer at the base of the heart and is reinforced by a superficial fibrous layer, which, in turn is covered by a layer of pleura.

STRUCTURE OF HEART

The heart wall consists of three layers: an outer serous covering called epicardium, an inner endothelial lining called endocardium, and a thick muscular layer called myocardium.

The *epicardium* is actually the visceral layer of pericardium.

The *endocardium* is a layer of simple squamous endothelial cells which lines

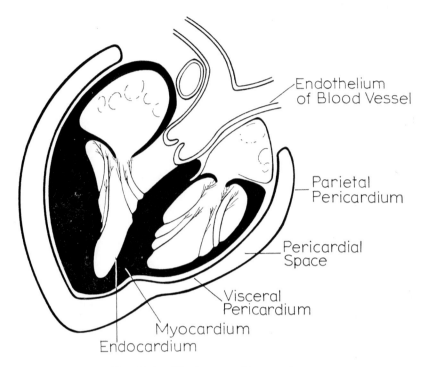

Endothelium
of Blood Vessel

Parietal
Pericardium

Pericardial
Space

Visceral
Pericardium

Myocardium

Endocardium

Fig. 14–1.—The heart and its coverings.

the chambers of the heart, covers the heart valves, and is continuous with the lining of the blood vessels.

The *myocardium* consists of cardiac muscle which is also called involuntary striated muscle. Cardiac muscle has been described in Chapter 12, p. 171 where muscle was considered as a tissue. Cardiac muscle cells do have cross-striations, but the nuclei are more centrally located than in voluntary striated muscle cells. The muscle fibers making up the heart are arranged in whorls or spirals because the heart develops from a single tube which becomes divided and twists upon itself. Details of this developmental process may be found in standard embryology texts.

The heart is divided into a right and a left side. Each side consists of an *atrium*, which receives blood by way of large veins, and a *ventricle* which pumps blood from the heart by way of a large artery. Between the atrium and the ventricle of each side is a large valve called the *atrioventricular valve*, or A-V valve. The left A-V valve is also called the *bicuspid valve* because in man it has two distinct flaps or cusps. Another synonym is *mitral valve* because of the imagined resemblance of the left A-V valve to a bishop's miter, or two-sided hat. The right A-V valve is also called the *tricuspid valve* because it has three flaps or cusps. Each cusp is somewhat triangular in shape. The upper border is attached to the inner wall of the ventricle at the junction of atrium and ventricle. The free margin or margins of the cusp are indirectly attached to the ventricular wall by means of fibrous cords called *chorda tendineae*. These chorda tendineae, which resemble strings on a parachute, prevent the valve from everting into the atrium when the ventricle contracts and closes the A-V valve by forcing blood against the ventral side of the valve.

The *aortic semilunar valve* is a three-

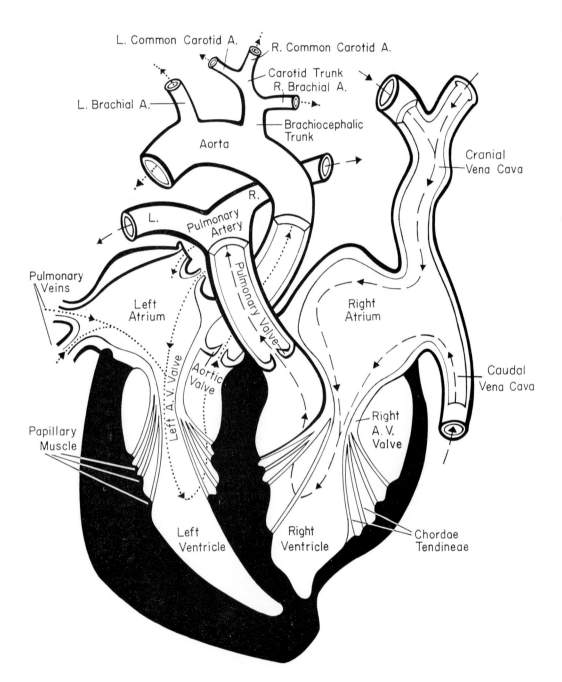

FIG. 14–2.—Structure of the heart. Arrows indicate direction of blood flow. Dotted lines represent oxygenated (arterial) blood. Broken lines represent unoxygenated (venous) blood.

cusped valve located at the junction of the left ventricle and aorta. The *pulmonary semilunar valve* is a similar valve located at the junction of the pulmonary artery and right ventricle. Each semilunar valve prevents blood from returning into the respective ventricle when the ventricles relax.

The simplest way to get an idea of the internal arrangement of the heart is to follow the course of the blood through the heart and lungs. Blood returning to the heart from the systemic circulation, commonly called venous blood, is relatively low in oxygen content. Since this same blood is also carried to the lungs by the pulmonary artery, the term venous seems somewhat inappropriate to the author, so in this text it will be called unoxygenated blood rather than venous blood. The blood returned to the heart by pulmonary veins and subsequently distributed to the body by way of systemic arteries, commonly called arterial blood, is relatively high in oxygen content. In this text it will be called oxygenated blood rather than arterial blood.

Unoxygenated blood returns to the heart by the *cranial* and *caudal venae cavae*. These large veins enter the right atrium of the heart, which is a thin walled area for collection of returning blood.

Next, the blood passes through the right A-V valve into the right ventricle. The right ventricle does not quite reach the apex of the heart as the apex is formed entirely by the more muscular left ventricle. From the right side, the right ventricle spirals around the cranial side of the heart and terminates as the *conus arteriosus* of the left side of the base. The conus arteriosus is the *funnel-shaped* origin of the pulmonary artery.

The *pulmonary artery* almost immediately divides, each branch carrying unoxygenated blood to the capillaries of the respective lung.

The *pulmonary veins* return (oxygenated) blood from the lungs to the left atrium,

another large thin-walled chamber of the heart. From the left atrium blood passes through the left A-V valve into the very thick-walled left ventricle.

The left ventricle then pumps the oxygenated blood past the aortic semilunar valve into the *aorta*. The aorta and its subdivisions carry (oxygenated) blood to all parts of the body, including the heart and lungs themselves.

VESSELS

Blood vessels resemble the branching of a tree, in that the arteries start as large vessels and divide into smaller and smaller branches. The smallest arteries are called arterioles. The arterioles in turn are continuous with the smallest blood vessels, capillaries. Capillaries again unite to form venules, which in turn unite to form larger and larger veins. The largest veins finally empty into the atria of the heart.

ARTERIES

Arteries are tubular structures which carry blood away from the heart. The largest arteries are known as elastic arteries because a large portion of the arterial wall consists of elastic tissue. This elasticity is important in maintaining blood pressure during diastole, the period during which the ventricles are relaxed.

Smaller arteries contain a large amount of smooth muscle in the arterial wall in place of the elastic tissue. This smooth muscle controls the size of the vessel and consequently the amount of blood that can flow through it during a given period of time.

Arterioles, the smallest arteries, are very muscular immediately before giving rise to capillaries. The heavy, circular, smooth muscle surrounding the terminations of the arterioles is important because it controls the amount of blood each capillary receives. Tension of the muscle around the arterioles also aids in maintaining blood pressure throughout the arterial system. In case of shock, the arterioles dilate or relax, and a large part of the blood volume is lost within the capillary beds, particularly those of the viscera.

CAPILLARIES

Capillaries are tiny tubes almost entirely composed of endothelium, a continuation of the simple squamous epithelium which lines the heart and blood vessels. These thin-walled vessels are only large enough in diameter to accommodate a single file of erythrocytes. The wall acts as a semi-permeable membrane which permits water, oxygen, and nutrients to leave the blood stream for tissue cells and permits waste products from tissue cells to enter the blood. Much of the fluid that passes out of the capillaries into tissue spaces again returns to the blood stream by passing back through the capillary walls. Some fluid remains in the tissues as tissue fluid, and the excess fluid normally is removed by lymph vessels (see p. 205). In addition to the capillary networks or capillary beds, which are interposed between arterioles and venules, there are larger connections called *arteriovenous anastomoses*. These direct anastomoses permit more blood to flow through a given part than could get through the capillaries alone. This increased blood flow may serve to warm the area and also increases the blood pressure in the venous side, thus aiding return of blood to the heart.

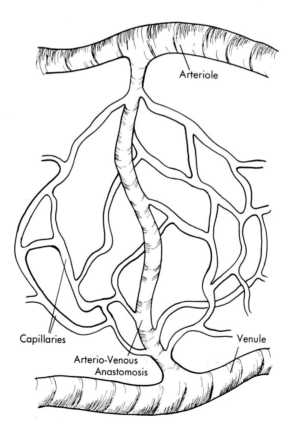

Fig. 14–3.—Capillary bed interposed between an arteriole and a venule, showing an arterio-venous anastomosis.

VEINS

As previously mentioned, capillaries unite to form venules, which in turn form larger and larger veins. *Veins* are larger than the arteries they accompany and have much thinner walls, with only a slight amount of muscle tissue present. Valves, usually consisting of two cusps each, are scattered at irregular intervals throughout the venous and lymphatic systems. A valve frequently is present where two or more veins unite to form a larger vein. The valves are always directed so blood will flow only toward the heart. These valves prevent blood being forced back into capillary beds and also permit muscle contractions and movement of body parts to aid the flow of blood toward the heart. Blood pressure in veins is quite low, since very little arterial pressure is transmitted through the capillaries to the veins. This situation may be compared to water from a river entering a lake with considerable force, while the water leaving the other side of the lake has little of the force found at the inlet.

All veins are tributaries to larger veins which eventually enter the right or left atrium of the heart.

LYMPHATICS

The walls of capillaries are thin enough to permit fluid as well as nutrients and gases to escape into spaces between tissue cells. Much of this intercellular fluid (tissue fluid) does not re-enter capillaries or veins directly but is picked up by extremely thin-walled lymph vessels which resemble veins, in that they contain numerous valves permitting the contents to flow only toward the heart. The smallest lymph vessels are capillary-size structures that begin blindly in intercellular spaces where they accumulate tissue fluid which is then transported to larger and larger lymph vessels and finally is emptied into

the cranial vena cava or one of its tributaries.

This movement of lymph, as tissue fluid within lymph vessels is called, is produced entirely by gravity or changing pressures of adjacent structures. For example, contraction of a muscle applies pressure to the adjacent lymphatic vessels and forces the lymph out of the muscle toward the heart, since the valves effectively prevent backflow. The lymph is filtered by nodular structures called lymph nodes (or lymph glands) scattered along the course of most lymph vessels.

CIRCULATORY SYSTEMS

Pulmonary Circulation

The pulmonary circulation is that part of the blood vascular system which circulates all the blood through the lungs. The right atrium receives unoxygenated blood via the caudal and cranial venae cavae. The blood then passes through the right A-V valve into the right ventricle, and then into the pulmonary artery. The pulmonary semilunar valve prevents backflow of blood from the pulmonary artery into the right ventricle, and elasticity of the artery insures a continuous flow of blood through the capillary bed of the lungs.

After a short distance the pulmonary artery divides into a right branch going to the right lung and a left branch going to the left lung. Each branch again subdivides into lobar arteries going to each of the lobes of the lungs. The lobar arteries again subdivide many times, finally forming arterioles which supply the extensive capillary beds of the lungs.

Lung capillaries are intimately associated with alveoli (the smallest terminations of air passages) of the lungs. Here a minimal amount of tissue separates the blood of the pulmonary circulation from air within the alveoli, thus affording an opportunity for oxygen of the air to be exchanged for carbon dioxide in the blood. As this gaseous exchange occurs, the color of the blood changes from the bluish color of unoxygenated blood, called venous blood, to the bright red of oxygenated blood, called arterial blood. It is worth noting that in the adult the pulmonary circulation is the only place where unoxygenated blood is found in arteries and oxygenated blood is found in veins.

After the blood is forced through the capillary bed of the lungs, it enters the venules which combine to form pulmonary veins. These pulmonary veins, after leaving the lungs, immediately empty oxygenated blood into the left atrium, thus completing the pulmonary circulation.

Systemic Circulation

Systemic circulation, also called *somatic circulation*, refers to the movement of oxygenated blood to all areas of the body and the subsequent return of unoxygenated blood to the heart. The systemic circulation can be divided into a number of circulations, each of which supplies a specific region or part of the body. These circulations include such subdivisions as circulation of the head, circulation of the front limb, circulation of the hind limb, etc. Each regional circulation in turn can be broken down still further to the circulation of any given part of the region. For example, we can study the circulation of the biceps brachii muscle, or the circulation of the eye. No matter how small or how large a segment of systemic circulation we consider, the basic pattern is the same. Arteries divide into arterioles, which supply blood to capillaries; then the capillaries in turn recombine to form venules, which again form veins that drain blood from the area.

The systemic circulation will be discussed in the following order:

The aorta, origin and course

The thoracic aorta and its branches
The abdominal aorta and its
    branches
The anterior vena cava and its
    tributaries
The posterior vena cava and its
    tributaries
The hepatic portal system

The Aorta—Origin and Course.— The left ventricle receives oxygenated blood from the left atrium and then pumps the blood throughout the systemic circulation by way of the largest artery in the body, the *aorta*. The aortic valve located at the junction of the left ventricle and aorta prevents backflow of blood from the aorta into the left ventricle when the ventricle relaxes.

After leaving the heart, the aorta first passes dorsally and then caudally just ventral to the bodies of the thoracic vertebrae. The thoracic aorta continues caudally through the aortic hiatus between the two roots of the diaphragm to become the abdominal aorta. Ventral to the last few lumbar vertebrae, the aorta terminates by dividing into two *external iliac arteries* and two *internal iliac arteries*. This division can be compared to the four fingers of your hand, with the index finger and little finger representing the right and left external iliac arteries and the middle and ring fingers representing the internal iliac arteries. In some species a *middle sacral artery* emerges between the two internal iliac arteries.

The Thoracic Aorta and Its Branches. —The first branches of the aorta are given off before the aorta leaves the heart. These are the *right* and *left coronary arteries*, which form a crown-shaped ring around the base of the heart and supply the heart muscle (myocardium) itself with blood. The term *coronary thrombosis*, or *heart attack*, refers to a clot in a coronary artery or one of its branches and may cause severe damage to the heart from lack of oxygen.

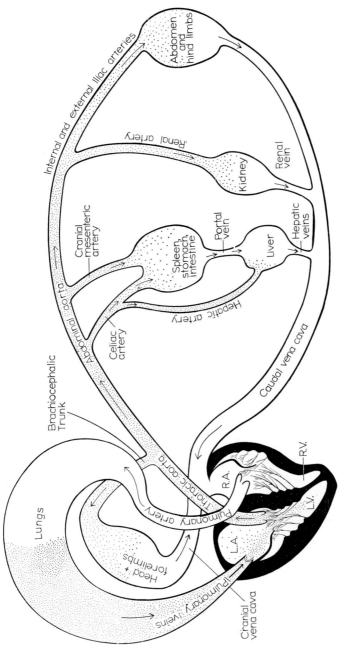

Fig. 14–4.—General scheme of the adult circulation. Relatively higher oxygen content of blood is indicated by stippling.

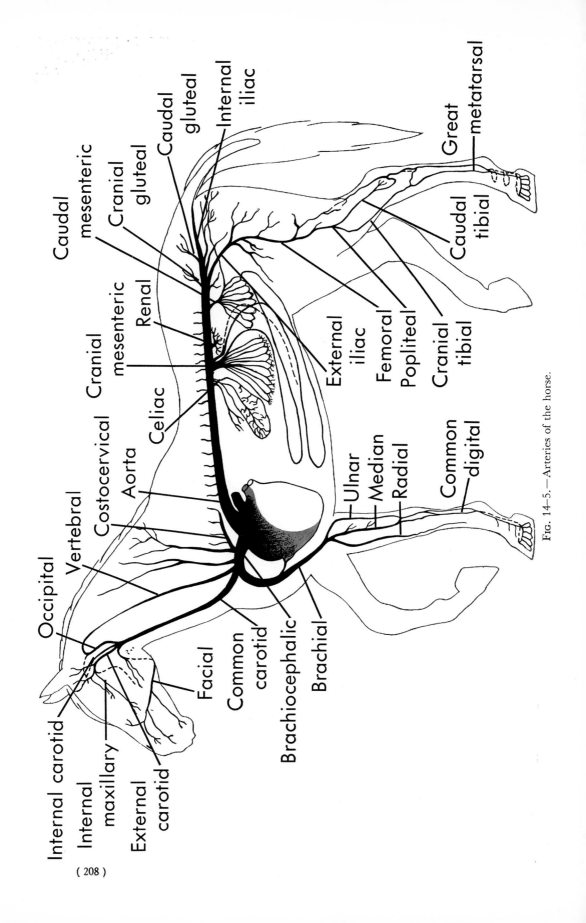

Caudal mesenteric

Cranial gluteal

Caudal gluteal

Internal iliac

Great metatarsal

Caudal tibial

Renal

External iliac

Femoral

Popliteal

Cranial tibial

Cranial mesenteric

Celiac

Costocervical

Aorta

Vertebral

Ulnar

Median

Radial

Common digital

Occipital

Facial

Common carotid

Brachiocephalic

Brachial

Internal carotid

Internal maxillary

External carotid

Fig. 14–5.—Arteries of the horse.

(208)

Most of the blood from the capillary bed of the heart is returned to the right atrium by way of the *coronary veins*, which empty into the *coronary sinus* of the right atrium. However, some of the venous blood from the coronary circulation passes directly through the heart wall into the chambers of the heart.

The Brachiocephalic Trunk.—In the cow, the first branch of the aorta after the coronary arteries are given off is the *common brachiocephalic trunk*, which gives rise to the left brachial artery and then continues as the *brachiocephalic artery*. The brachiocephalic artery divides into a right brachial artery and *bicarotid trunk*. The bicarotid trunk in turn divides into *right* and *left common carotid arteries*, which pass up the respective sides of the neck to supply a great part of the blood to the head and face region. Much of this blood is then returned to the cranial vena cava by way of the jugular veins. The *external jugular veins* are present in all animals as the superficial veins along the neck. In all farm animals except the horse an additional vein, the *internal* jugular, passes caudally with each common carotid artery.

The *right* and *left brachial arteries* follow essentially the same course on each side of the body, and each gives off similar branches. Each brachial artery passes in front of the first rib on the respective side and supplies the shoulder, neck, and front limb of that side. Within the thorax the brachial artery gives off a number of branches, including the *vertebral*, the *costo-cervical*, the *inferior cervical*, and the *internal thoracic arteries*. These branches of the brachial artery supply blood to the caudal part of the neck, the first few ribs, and the dorsal part of the shoulder. After the brachial artery passes around the first rib, it continues distally along the medial side of the fore-limb.

In most animals, the brachial artery terminates near the distal end of the forearm by dividing into *radial* and *ulnar*

arteries. The ulnar artery is usually the larger of the two terminal branches and therefore is the chief blood supply to the metacarpal and digital regions of the foot. Some authorities call the portion of the brachial artery which lies within the thorax, the *subclavian artery*, and that portion from the first rib to the insertion of the *teres major muscle* they call the *axillary artery*, since it is located in the axilla, or arm pit.

In the horse, the brachial artery is continued at the elbow by the *median artery*. Branches of the median artery then supply the forearm and carpus, and the continuation of the median artery into the metacarpal region is known as the *common digital artery*.

As the aorta passes backward in the thorax ventral to the bodies of the vertebrae, it gives off a number of small branches to thoracic structures. Branches are given to the esophagus, the diaphragm, and the lungs. The *bronchial arteries* pass along the bronchi and supply oxygenated blood to the lung tissues. This is in addition to unoxygenated blood carried to the lungs by the pulmonary artery. *Inter-costal arteries* (most arising from the aorta) pass laterally and ventrally immediately behind each pair of ribs. In other words, there is a pair of intercostal arteries for each pair of ribs. The muscular portion of the diaphragm is supplied with blood by the phrenic branches of the *thoracic aorta*.

The Abdominal Aorta and Its Branches.—Shortly after the aorta passes through the diaphragm, the *celiac artery* is given off. This celiac artery is a large unpaired artery, which supplies, in general, the stomach, the spleen and the liver by gastric, splenic, and hepatic branches respectively. Of course, the exact branching of this artery depends to a great extent upon the type of stomach. The ruminant has a much more complex subdivision of the celiac artery than does the non-ruminant, or animal with a simple stomach.

Immediately posterior to the celiac artery, is the *cranial mesenteric artery*. This is a large unpaired artery which soon divides into a number of smaller arteries that supply blood to most of the small intestine and much of the large intestine. The caudal part of the large intestine receives blood from a relatively small unpaired artery called the *caudal mesenteric artery*.

The *renal arteries* supply blood to the kidneys. They are paired arteries which arise immediately behind the anterior mesenteric artery. Each renal artery appears quite large in relation to the size of the kidney. The function of the renal artery is not merely to supply arterial blood to the kidney, but to carry a large amount of the total blood to the kidney for filtration and purification. The *adrenal arteries* originate directly from the aorta, from the renal arteries, or from intercostal or lumbar arteries. In the male, the testicles originate just behind the kidneys, so the blood supplies for the testicles, the *internal spermatic arteries*, likewise arise behind the respective renal arteries. The internal spermatic arteries are paired arteries, each supplying the respective testicle. In the female, the comparable artery supplying the ovary is known as the *utero-ovarian artery*, since it also supplies a part of the uterus as well as the ovary. These arteries also are paired arteries.

The *abdominal aorta*, like the thoracic aorta, gives rise to a number of paired intercostal arteries which arise behind the diaphragm. Immediately caudal to the intercostal arteries, the paired *lumbar arteries* are found. One pair of lumbar arteries passes laterally and ventrally behind each respective lumbar vertebra to supply the body wall in that area.

The *internal iliac arteries* are the most medial terminations of the aorta. Again, they are paired right and left arteries.

The internal iliac and its many branches supply the region of the pelvis, the hip, and much of both the male and female genitalia. Branches include the *cranial gluteal*, the *obturator*, the *caudal gluteal*, and the *internal pudic arteries*.

The *external iliac arteries* give some blood to the flanks and to the ventral abdominal wall and continue into the hind legs as the *femoral arteries*. The femoral artery descends on the medial side of the thigh, giving branches to the large muscles surrounding the *femur*. The femoral artery is continued in the region of the posterior part of the stifle joint as the *popliteal artery*. After a very short course the popliteal artery divides into a *cranial tibial artery* and *caudal tibial artery*. The caudal tibial artery supplies the muscles of the gaskin, or true leg. The cranial tibial artery is larger and passes forward between the *tibia* and *fibula* and descends on the front of the leg to the hock. The anterior tibial artery supplies branches to the hock joint and descends in the metatarsal region as the *great metatarsal artery*.

Veins.—With some notable exceptions, the veins may be said to accompany arteries of the same name. The veins are always larger than their respective arteries and frequently more numerous. For example, the brachial artery carrying blood to the forearm and digit may be accompanied by two or more brachial veins returning the same blood to the heart. Often veins are more superficial or closer to the skin than their respective arteries. As indicated earlier, nearly all veins eventually drain into the caudal or cranial cava, and thus unoxygenated blood returns to the right atrium of the heart.

The Cranial Vena Cava and Its Tributaries.—The cranial vena cava drains the head, neck, front limbs, and part of the thorax. Tributaries to the cranial vena cava include the jugular veins (internal and external), *brachial veins, internal thoracic veins, vertebral veins,*

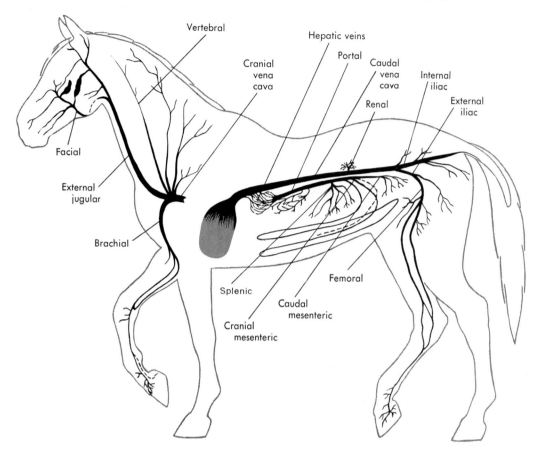

Fig. 14–6.—Veins of the horse.

and the unpaired *vena azygos vein*. The external jugular veins drain much of the head region while the internal jugular veins if present, along with the vertebral veins drain most of the blood from the brain. The brachial veins drain the same area that is supplied with blood by the brachial artery and its branches which go to the shoulder, neck, and forelimbs.

The Caudal Vena Cava and Its Tributaries.—The caudal vena cava is formed by the junction of the paired *internal iliac veins* and *external iliac veins*. It receives in addition *lumbar veins, internal spermatic* or *utero-ovarian veins, renal veins, adrenal veins* and *intercostal veins*; also as the caudal vena cava passes by the liver, a number of short *hepatic veins* enter

the caudal vena cava directly from the liver.

The Hepatic Portal System.—The hepatic portal circulation is an important exception to the usual arrangement of the systemic circulation, in which an artery breaks up into capillary beds which recombine to form veins that are direct tributaries to the cranial or caudal vena cava. In the hepatic portal circulation most of the branches of the celiac artery and the cranial mesenteric artery supply capillary beds of the *spleen* and digestive tract.

Blood drained from the stomach, spleen, intestines, and pancreas is filtered through the liver by the hepatic portal circulation before it enters the general circulation. Blood from these areas

14

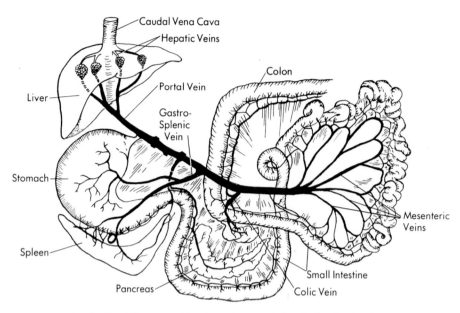

FIG. 14–7.—Diagram of the hepatic portal circulation in the dog.
See text for description.

drains into the *portal vein* which is the beginning of the hepatic portal system. Tributaries to the portal vein include the *gastric vein* from the stomach, the *splenic vein* from the spleen, the *mesenteric veins* from the intestines, and the *pancreatic veins* from the pancreas. The portal vein enters the liver and immediately breaks up into smaller and smaller branches in the liver, finally ending in the sinusoids (capillary network) of the liver. From these liver capillaries the *hepatic veins* are formed and empty directly into the caudal vena cava.

The *hepatic artery*, a branch of the celiac artery, carries oxygenated blood to the liver. It enters the hilus of the liver at about the same place the bile duct leaves the liver. Here the blood comes into direct contact with cells of the liver cords. After being acted upon by the liver cells, the blood passes from the sinusoids of the liver into the central vein of each liver lobule. These central veins then combine and eventually form hepatic veins which empty their blood directly into the caudal vena cava.

It is desirable that blood drained from the digestive tract be exposed to the liver cells before entering the general circulation. This contact permits nutrients to be modified and/or stored in the liver for future use and gives the liver a chance to detoxify any harmful substances that may have been absorbed from the digestive tract.

Other Portal Systems

The arrangement in which a vein breaks up into capillaries and then recombines again to form another vein is spoken of as a portal system or portal circulation. A portal circulation is described in relation to the pituitary gland, the *hypophyseal portal circulation*. In birds, reptiles, and amphibians some blood returning from the hind limbs enters the kidneys to form the *renal portal circulation*.

Fetal Circulation

Throughout the entire gestation period, the fetus is dependent on the dam for nutrients, water, and oxygen needed for

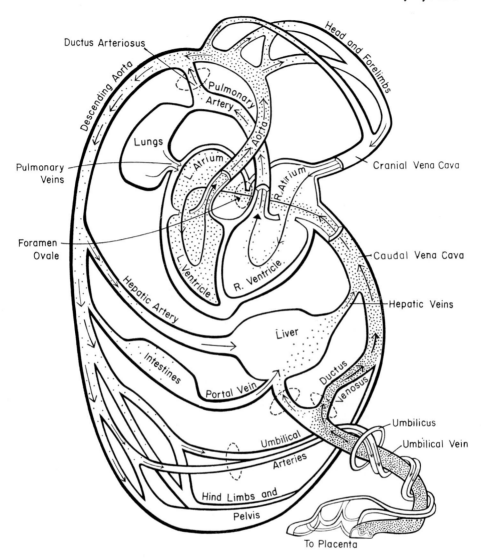

Fig. 14–8.—Fetal circulation. Structures circled with dotted lines become nonfunctional at birth or shortly after and remain nonfunctional throughout the rest of the animal's life. These structures include the ductus arteriosus, the foramen ovale, the ductus venosus, the umbilical vein, and the umbilical arteries.

growth and for elimination of carbon dioxide and other waste products of fetal metabolism. This exchange for the most part occurs between fetal blood in the fetal placenta and maternal blood in the uterus of the dam without any actual interchange of blood from one to the other. The amount and types of material that can cross the placental barrier depends on the type of placenta and varies in different species (see Chap. 25, p. 351). In effect, the fetal circulation performs functions that are carried on in the adult, by the lungs, the digestive system and the urinary system.

The fetal circulation differs from the adult circulation in several respects. Much of the blood from the caudal end of the aorta (internal or external iliac arteries) is transported to the placenta by means of two *umbilical arteries*. After passing through the placental capillaries, the blood is returned to the fetal heart by the *umbilical vein*.

In the adult, the same amount of blood passes through the pulmonary circulation as passes through the systemic circulation in a given period of time. However, since the lungs are non-functional in the fetus, a relatively small amount of the total blood volume is found in the pulmonary circulation at any specific time. There are two by-passes or shortcuts from the right side of the heart (and pulmonary artery) to the left side of the heart (and aorta). These by-passes are the *foramen ovale* that connects the right and left atria and the *ductus arteriosus* that connects the pulmonary artery and aorta.

The fetal blood that passes through the placental capillaries comes into relatively close contact with maternal blood circulating through the uterus of the dam. The amount of tissue between fetal blood and maternal blood varies with the species, but normally there is no direct exchange of fetal and maternal blood in mammals. Circulation of fetal blood through the placenta exchanges carbon dioxide and waste products in the fetal blood for oxygen and nutrients from the blood of the dam.

Since the fetal lungs are collapsed or, more properly, do not expand until the new-born animal takes its first breath, there is greater resistance to pulmonary blood flow than to systemic blood flow. The by-passes permit more blood flow through the systemic circulation than through the pulmonary circulation.

The course of blood through the fetal heart and related vessels has been studied extensively in the living lamb fetus by means of cineradiography (x-ray movies). Barcroft and Barclay, Franklin, and Pritchard have reported their work in considerable detail, in which radioopaque material was injected into various fetal vessels and its course followed with x-ray movies. These records, coupled with careful dissections and other experimental techniques, produced an accurate picture of the anatomy and physiology of fetal circulation in the lamb that presumably is similar to, if not identical to, the fetal circulation of other mammals.

The umbilical vein passes forward from the *umbilicus* in a peritoneal fold, the *falciform ligament* and enters the liver close to the ventral border. Blood returning to the fetal heart from the placenta by way of the umbilical vein has the highest oxygen content of any fetal blood.

Several branches of the umbilical vein enter the substance of the liver before it communicates with the portal vein at the portal sinus. From the portal sinus, the *ductus venosus* forms a direct channel to the caudal vena cava. The ductus venosus appears to remain throughout fetal life in the ruminants and carnivora but is present for only a short time if at all in the fetal pig and fetal horse. Blood enters the fetal liver by way of the *portal vein* and the *hepatic artery* and leaves the liver by the ductus venosus and *hepatic veins* that go directly from the liver to the caudal vena cava.

The caudal vena cava also drains the abdominal wall, kidneys, pelvis, and hind legs as it does in the adult.

The caudal vena cava enters the right atrium, where a large part of its blood (still relatively high in oxygen content) is directed by a ridge, the *crista intervenosa*, (or *crista interveneus*) through the foramen ovale into the left atrium. Here this blood is joined by the small quantity of blood from the lungs, which enters the left atrium by way of the pulmonary veins. From the left atrium, the blood from the caudal vena cava that passed through the foramen ovale and the blood from the pulmonary veins passes through the left A-V valve into the left ventricle and then is forced through the aortic semilunar valve to the aortic arch. This blood still has the highest oxygen content of any blood leaving the heart, even though it is a composite of blood from the umbilical vein, portal vein, hepatic artery, caudal vena cava, and pulmonary veins. The heart itself, the head, the neck, and the forelimbs all receive this relatively rich blood before it is mixed with blood from the cranial vena cava in a manner to be described shortly. Blood returning to the heart from the cranial part of the fetus enters the right atrium by way of the cranial vena cava. This blood together with the undiverted portion of blood from the caudal vena cava passes through the right A-V valve into the right ventricle. From the right ventricle, it is forced through the pulmonary semilunar valve into the pulmonary artery. A large part of the blood in the pulmonary artery is shunted directly into the aorta by way of the ductus arteriosus which enters the aorta caudal to the branching of the brachiocephalic and/or brachial arteries from the first part of the aorta. The smaller part of the blood in the pulmonary artery enters the lungs and is returned to the left atrium by the pulmonary veins as already mentioned. Beyond the entrance of the ductus arteriosus, the aorta contains a mixture of all the blood that enters and leaves the heart. The aorta of the fetus has the same branches as the aorta of the adult and in addition gives off directly or indirectly from the external iliac arteries or internal iliac arteries two large umbilical arteries that carry blood to the placenta where it circulates through placental capillaries close enough to the maternal blood for exchange of fetal waste products for nutrients and oxygen from the dam's blood

In summary, the umbilical vein contains the purest blood with the highest oxygen content, most nutrients, and fewest waste products of any blood vessel in the fetus. As the blood is carried toward the heart, it is diluted with less pure blood from the liver (the portal vein, hepatic artery, and hepatic veins) and from the caudal vena cava. This mixed blood enters the right atrium, and most of it passes through the foramen ovale to the left atrium, where it is further diluted by blood returning to the heart by way of the pulmonary veins. This blood then supplies the heart, head, and forelimbs before further dilution occurs in the aorta by blood from the right ventricle that passes through the pulmonary artery and ductus arteriosus.

Barcroft describes closure of the foramen ovale followed by closure of the ductus arteriosus within a few minutes after ligation of the umbilical cord. Closure of the ductus arteriosus appears to be caused by smooth muscle within the wall, which is stimulated to contract by an increase in oxygen content of the blood reaching the ductus arteriosus. Attempts to correlate nervous stimuli with closure of the ductus arteriosus have been largely unsuccessful.

Respiratory movements in the fetus appear to be inhibited by a center located in the brain. This inhibition may be overcome and respiratory movements initiated by any one or any combination of external stimuli such as ligation or severing of the umbilical cord, handling the fetus, or simply exposing the fetus to a draft of air. The dam licking a newborn animal and the owner rubbing it with a rough cloth both may serve as a means of artificial respiration.

The Lymphatic System

The lymphatic system includes both the lymphoid tissue of the body and the lymph vessels associated with the lymphoid tissue. It serves as a system for draining tissue fluid that parallels and augments the venous circulation and acts as a defense mechanism against noxious materials by filtering them out of tissue fluid and by producing antibodies against them.

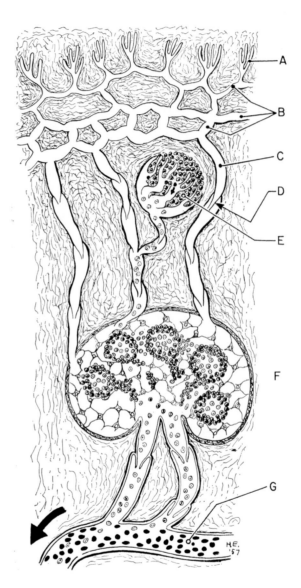

Fig. 14–9.—A generalized diagram of lymphatic drainage. Lymph is, in essence, tissue fluid taken up by lymph capillaries (*A*). It streams slowly through vessels of increasing caliber (*B, C*), many of which are provided with valves (*D*). Lymphocytes, many produced in solitary lymph nodules (*E*), are added. Lymph is filtered through lymph nodes (*F*). There more lymphocytes and antibodies are added. Finally, it joins the venous blood stream (*G*). (Elias and Pauly, *Human Microanatomy*, courtesy of Da Vinci Publishing Co.)

Lymphoid tissue consists of accumulations of *lymphocytes* trapped in the spaces between fibers of reticular connective tissue. The lymphoid tissue may be scattered diffusely in some organs, as in the intestinal submucosa, or aggregations of lymphoid tissue may be encapsulated to form specific organs, including lymph nodes, the tonsils, the thymus, and the spleen.

to form lymph vessels, which in turn unite to form larger and larger lymphatic vessels. All of the lymph collected from the body eventually returns to the venous system by way of the *thoracic duct*, and *right lymphatic duct* or *tracheal ducts*. These ducts enter the cranial vena cava or the jugular veins as they unite to form the cranial vena cava.

In many ways lymph vessels resemble

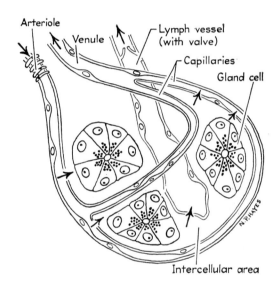

Fig. 14–10.—Diagram illustrating the relations of the body cell to blood circulation and lymph drainage. (Leach, *Functional Anatomy: Mammalian and Comparative*, courtesy of McGraw Hill Book Co.)

Lymph Vessels.—The lymphatic vessels constitute a one-way channel which parallels the venous system and eventually empties into the cranial vena cava or some of its tributaries. The smallest lymphatics begin blindly between tissue cells as lymph capillaries, which collect the tissue fluid that is not absorbed by the venous system. When the tissue fluid enters the lymphatic vessels, it is known as lymph, which consists of fluid originally derived from the blood and is on its way back to the blood.

The lymph capillaries form more or less complex networks throughout most tissues. These networks finally combine

veins. The lymph vessels have numerous valves scattered throughout their course. They are much thinner-walled than arteries and usually are thinner than veins. The valves, of course, permit the flow of lymph only in the direction toward the heart or great veins just cranial to the heart.

Lacteals (L. lact–milk) are a special group of the lymph vessels which drain the intestinal wall. These vessels absorb fat from the small intestine which then appears as a milky fluid called *chyle*.

Lymph Nodes. — *Lymph nodes*, also called *lymph glands*, are discrete nodular structures scattered along the course of

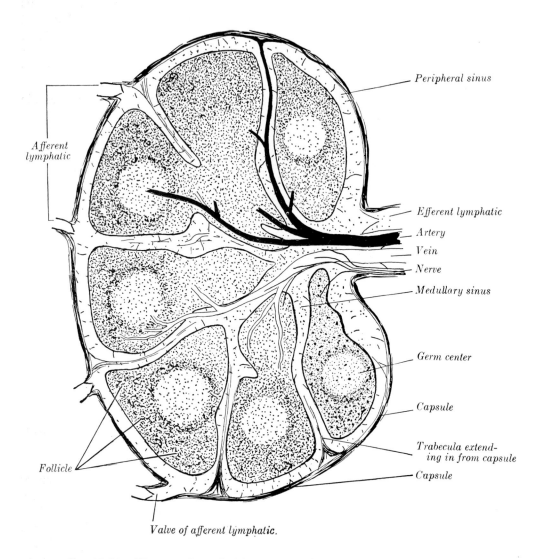

Peripheral sinus

Afferent
lymphatic

Efferent lymphatic

Artery

Vein

Nerve

Medullary sinus

Germ center

Capsule

Trabecula extend-
ing in from capsule

Capsule

Follicle

Valve of afferent lymphatic.

FIG. 14–11.—Diagram of a typical lymph node. (Finerty and Cowdry, *A Textbook
of Histology,* Lea & Febiger.)

lymphatic vessels. These lymph nodes serve as filters for the lymph and act as one of the first body defenses against infection by producing lymphocytes and antibodies.

Each lymph node is surrounded by a connective-tissue capsule that blends with the surrounding connective tissue and acts as a means of holding it in place. The capsule also sends numerous connective-tissue *septa* (or *trabeculae*) into the substance of the node. The node is divided into a *cortex* and a *medulla*, which contain large numbers of lymphocytes. Those in the cortex are arranged in dark-staining groups known as *primary nodules*. Within the primary nodules are light-staining areas called *secondary nodules* because they are located within the primary nodules. Secondary nodules are areas of rapid cell multiplication and for this reason are also called *germinal centers*. *Lymphocytes* in the medullary portion of the lymph node are arranged in cords rather than nodules.

In addition to the lymphocytes, lymph nodes also contain *plasma cells* that are sometimes classified with the connective tissue cells. Plasma cells are believed to be an important source of antibodies produced by the animal body. They are somewhat larger than lymphocytes, with dark-staining granules in the nucleus that often are arranged in the form of a cart wheel or the form of the dial of a watch. The cytoplasm is rich in RNA (ribonucleic acid) granules, suggesting extensive protein synthesis.

Immediately deep to the capsule is a space, the lymph sinus of the cortex, that communicates with other lymph sinuses located in the cortex and in the medulla.

Physiology of the Lymphatic System. —The lymph enters the sinus of the cortex and slowly percolates through the cortex and medulla, where it is filtered to emerge finally at the hilus of the node where the blood vessels and nerves enter and the efferent lymph vessels emerge.

The lymph vessels which carry lymph toward the lymph node enter through the capsule and are known as *afferent vessels*. Lymph vessels which carry the filtered lymph away from the lymph node are known as *efferent vessels*.

The terms efferent and afferent must be used in relation to a specific node since the efferent vessels from one node frequently are the afferent vessels for the next node in the channel draining a given area.

In addition to the lymph vessels, each lymph node has its own blood supply and venous drainage. The lymph nodes are scattered throughout the body, and, in general, the condition of each node reflects the health or disease of the area from which the afferent lymph vessels are derived. If an infection is present in a specific area, the lymph nodes in that area will tend to increase in size in order to fight the infection. For example, a horse with distemper, or strangles, which is an infection of the nasal cavity and pharynx, will frequently show great enlargement of the *mandibular lymph nodes*. These mandibular lymph nodes receive their afferent vessels from the nasal cavity, mouth, and pharynx. If the first lymph node is unable to stop the infection, the bacteria or other infective agent will then pass on by way of the efferent vessels to the next lymph node on the lymphatic channel. This lymph node or nodes in turn responds to the infection by increasing in size. Cancer cells as well as infections may spread throughout the body by way of the lymphatic channels. When a tumor (cancer) is removed surgically, it may be necessary to also remove the lymph node or nodes draining the cancerous area, if they are affected, to prevent further spread of the condition. The meat inspector studies the lymphatic system in order to determine whether a given part of a carcass should be condemned. For example, if a cow with a cancerous eye shows involvement of the lymph nodes of the head, neck, and thorax, the entire carcass probably will be condemned. However, if it appears that the cancerous condition has been stopped by the nodes immediately draining the eye, perhaps only the head will be condemned, and the rest of the carcass may be passed for food.

The following lymph nodes of cattle are described in USDA Circular 866:

It is attached to the stomach either directly by connective tissue as in the ruminants, where it is closely adherent to the rumen, or it is connected with the stomach by the *gastrosplenic omentum*. The shape of the spleen varies considerably from one species to another. In the chicken, the spleen is nearly spherical in shape, while in other animals it is more or less elongated. The spleen has a thick

Name of Node	*Location of Node*
Mandibular	In mandibular space about 2 inches cranial to angle of mandible
Parotid	1 inch in front of and just below external meatus of ear
Suprapharyngeal	Dorsal to pharynx close to mid-line
Atlantal	Ventral to wing of atlas
Cranial cervical	Cranial third of neck on common carotid artery
Middle cervical	Middle third of neck on course of common carotid artery
Prescapular (Post superficial cervical)	Above shoulder joint covered by brachiocephalicus muscle
Axillary	On medial side of shoulder near brachial plexus
Prepectoral (post cervical)	At entrance to thorax on each side of trachea
Popliteal	Behind stifle on gastrocnemius between semitendinosus and biceps femoris
Ischiatic	At lesser sciatic notch of pelvis
Prefemoral	In front of thigh just above stifle
Superficial inguinal (Supramammary)	Bulls—in front of external inguinal ring (Cows—above posterior part of udder)
Deep inguinal	Where circumflex iliac artery leaves external iliac artery
Sacral	Ventral surface of sacrum
External iliac	At bifurcation of circumflex iliac artery
Internal iliac	At junction of external iliac artery and aorta
Anal	Floor of pelvis lateral to anus
Lumbar	Sublumbar region along abdominal aorta
Renal	At hilus of kidney on renal artery
Gastric	On course of gastric blood vessels and between folds of stomach
Mesenteric	Along attached border of intestine between layers of mesentery
Splenic	At hilus of spleen
Hepatic or portal	At hilus of liver near vessels
Intercostal	Between ribs near thoracic vertebrae
Sternal	Dorsal surface of sternum on course of internal thoracic artery
Bronchial	On trachea near branching of main bronchi
Anterior mediastinal	Along trachea and esophagus caudal to thoracic inlet
Posterior mediastinal	Between esophagus and aorta cranial to diaphragm

Hemal lymph nodes are small dark red or black structures found in cattle and sheep. They resemble lymph nodes but are interposed on the course of small vessels.

The Spleen

The *spleen* is a lymphoid organ which is associated with the circulatory system.

capsule from which septa penetrate into the interior of the gland, forming a definite stroma.

Blood vessels enter and leave the spleen at the hilus of the organ. The splenic vein drains blood from the spleen and is a tributary to the portal vein. The spleen functions as a storage area for blood, so the size of the spleen varies from time to time even within a given individual, as well as from species to species, depending on the amount of blood present in the spleen at a given time.

The spleen is one of the *reticulo-endothelial organs*. It functions to destroy worn-out red corpuscles, releasing the iron from the hemoglobin for reuse by the body and also forming bile pigments, which are then collected by the liver.

Many lymphocytes and monocytes are formed in the spleen, and it probably is associated with antibody production. Although the spleen is a very useful organ, it is not absolutely essential in the adult, because apparently all of its functions can be carried on by other organs. The spleen can be removed without apparent damage to a mature animal.

CHAPTER 15

PHYSIOLOGY OF CIRCULATION

GENERAL

THE study of physiology of circulation can be an extremely complex subject. It involves details of all events in the cardiac cycle as well as dynamics of circulating fluid, pressure relationships, electrical and nervous activity, and chemical, physical, and engineering principles.

One of the most useful analogies is a comparison of the circulatory system with a piston-pump water system for a residence. Although the water system is extremely simple when compared with the circulatory system, many of the same problems have to be solved in each.

The heart is in reality a pump capable of receiving blood into the atrial chambers (atria) and then pumping this same blood from the ventricles to the tissues and back again. This organ contains valves which open and close in proper sequence to insure movement of the blood in one direction. The force exerted to propel the blood comes from the muscular action of the heart itself.

CARDIAC CYCLE

The *cardiac cycle* refers to the sequence of events that occurs during one complete heart beat. The events of the cardiac cycle, or the heart beat, are arranged in a specific sequence (Fig. 15–1). First the blood enters the right atrium from the periphery of the body and the left atrium from the lungs. When these chambers are full, atrial contraction occurs. Pressure is built up in the atria, and, as a consequence, the A-V valves open allowing the blood to pass into the relaxed ventricles. When most of the blood has been delivered to the ventricles, these chambers undergo contraction. Meanwhile the atria have begun to relax. Intraventricular pressures are elevated with contraction of the ventricles. This pressure elevation now causes both right and left A-V valves to close, shutting off the communication between the atria and ventricles. At the same time, the pressure within the ventricles builds up to a point where the pulmonary and aortic semilunar valves open, and the blood is ejected from the left ventricle into the aorta and from the right ventricle into the pulmonary artery.

Diastole (Gr. dia–apart; stello–send) refers to the relaxation of a chamber of the heart just prior to and during the filling of that chamber. It may be right or left atrial diastole or right or left ventricular diastole.

Systole (Gr. contraction, syn–together;

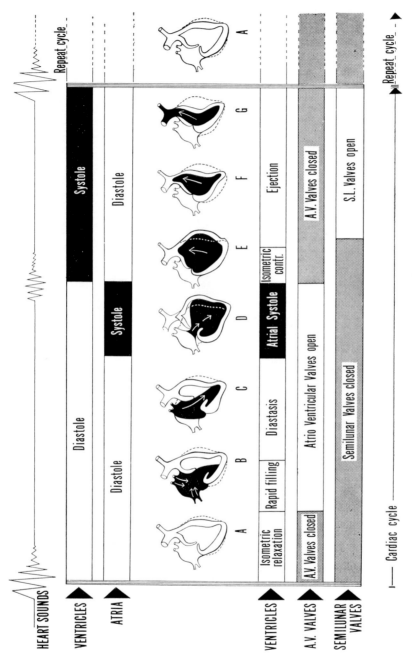

Fig. 15–1.—Events of the cardiac cycle.

stello–place) refers to the contraction of a chamber of the heart in the process of emptying that chamber. It also may be right or left atrial systole or right or left ventricular systole.

Immediately following *ventricular systole*, the A-V valves are still closed from the pressure of blood forced against them by ventricular contraction, and the pulmonary and aortic valves have just been closed by the relatively high arterial pres-

sure in the aorta and pulmonary artery produced by the elasticity of the arterial walls.

The beginning of the *ventricular diastole* is marked by a short period of isometric (same measure) relaxation, in which the heart muscle fibers are relaxing without increase in length because no blood has entered the ventricle to stretch the fibers.

The aortic and pulmonary valves remain closed because the arterial pressure

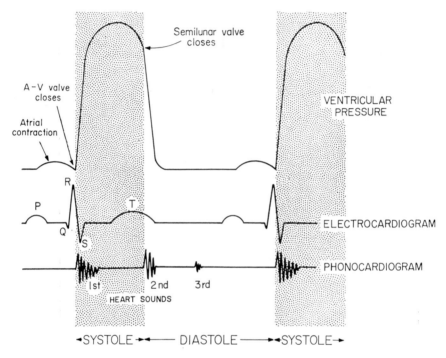

FIG. 15–2.—Relationship of ventricular pressure to the electrocardiogram and phonocardiogram during the cardiac cycle. (Guyton, *Functions of the Human Body*, courtesy of W. B. Saunders Co.)

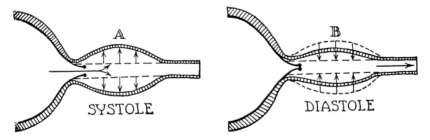

FIG. 5–3.1—Diagram to illustrate role of elastic walls of aorta in maintenance of circulation. *A*, Walls are distended as ventricular contents enter aorta. *B*, Following closure of aortic valves, elastic recoil of walls drives blood peripherally. Elastic walls serve to store energy during systole and release it during diastole. (After Rein *in* Ruch and Fulton, *Medical Physiology and Biophysics*, courtesy of W. B. Saunders Co.)

is higher than ventricular pressure. As the ventricle continues to relax, the pressure drops even more, while the pressure in the atria is increasing because of inflow of blood from the vena cava and pulmonary veins. As soon as atrial pressure exceeds ventricular pressure, the A-V valves open, and blood rushes into the ventricles. Filling of the ventricles is speeded by atrial contraction, or *atrial systole*, as the ventricles relax completely.

As *atrial diastole* begins, the pressures decrease in the atria, and the A-V valves begin to close.

Ventricular systole forces the A-V valves shut, resulting in the first heart sound. The first part of systole is a period of isometric contraction—from the time the A-V valves close until ventricular pressure exceeds the arterial pressure. Heart muscle fibers do not change in length during this period of isometric contraction, because the volume of blood in the ventricle does not change, and fluid is incompressible.

As soon as ventricular pressures exceed arterial pressures, the aortic and pulmonary valves open, and the period of ejection begins. Heart muscle fibers shorten during the period of ejection, the second part of ventricular systole. Continued strong contraction of the ventricles soon empties them.

The period of isometric relaxation again starts, arterial pressure is higher than ventricular pressure, and the aortic and pulmonary valves snap shut, producing the second heart sound.

HEART SOUNDS

If we place our ear or the receiver of a stethoscope on the wall of the thorax over the heart, two distinct sounds can be heard which are repeated indefinitely. The first sound is "lub" and the second sound is "dup." These sounds are separated by a short interval and followed by a longer pause. The slower the heart rate, the longer the pause.

The first sound, "lub," is produced by contraction of muscle fibers of the ventricles and the vibrations of the A-V valves and their chordae tendineae. It is louder, lower pitched, and of longer duration than the second heart sound.

The second heart sound, "dup," is caused by vibrations of the aortic and pulmonary semilunar valves when they close at the beginning of ventricular diastole.

VALVE DISORDERS

A valve that fails to close completely permits blood to flow through in the wrong direction and at the wrong time. This condition, called *valvular insufficiency* or *incompetence*, results in an abnormal heart sound, or *murmur*.

On the other hand, a valve may fail to open completely because of thickening or presence of scar tissue, a condition called *stenosis*. The abnormal heart sound associated with stenosis is caused by the blood being forced through an opening that is too small.

Both insufficiency and stenosis increase the work load of the heart—insufficiency, because some of the blood must be pumped twice for each beat; and stenosis, because of the greater resistance of the small opening.

Endocarditis, inflammation of the lining of the heart, is a common cause of pathological changes in heart valves. *Erysipelas* infection in hogs frequently results in endocarditis, as does *rheumatic fever* in man.

AUTOMATIC BEATING OF THE HEART

The heart beat originates in the *sinoatrial node* (*S-A node*), called the *pacemaker* of the heart. This is a collection of specialized cardiac muscle cells located at the junction of the cranial vena cava and the right atrium. The impulse from the S-A node spreads throughout the atria, causing them to contract in atrial systole. No special fibers have been demonstrated connecting the S-A node with the A-V node; only normal atrial muscle fibers have been described.

The *atrioventricular node* (*A-V node*), located in the septum between the atria, picks up the impulse from the contracting atrial muscle and conducts the impulse to the ventricular muscle by way of the *A-V bundle* (*bundle of His*) and the *Purkinje*

network, causing ventricular systole. This pathway (A-V node, A-V bundle, and Purkinje network) composed of modified muscle fibers, constitutes the only communication for impulse transmission from the atria to the ventricles.

Heart block refers to any interruption of this impulse pathway. The most common block occurs in the A-V bundle, which breaks the connection between atria and ventricles. Then the atria continue to beat at the normal rate, but the ventricular beat is much slower and completely disassociated from the atrial beat.

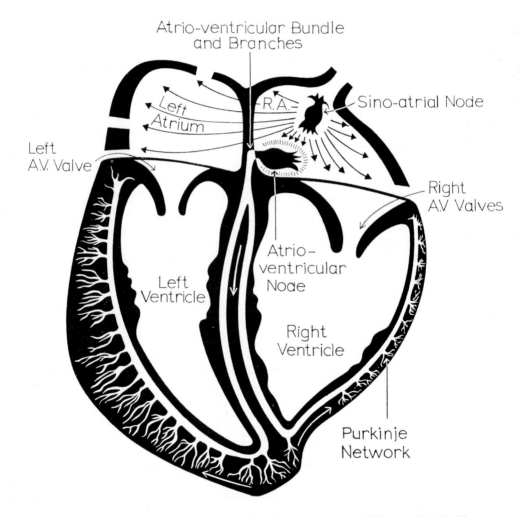

FIG. 15–4.—Conduction system of the heart. (After Carlson and Johnson, *The Machinery of the Body*, courtesy of University of Chicago Press.)

even if air is permitted to enter the pleural cavity, a condition known as *pneumothorax*. In the fetus, however, the lungs are nearly the consistency of liver, contain no air, and will sink in water. Whether the lungs will sink or float in water is a standard test to determine if a newborn animal was born dead, in which case the lungs will sink, or if it drew at least one breath, the lungs will float.

BONY THORAX

The *bony thorax* is bounded cranially by the first pair of ribs, the first thoracic vertebra, and the cranial part of the *sternum*; dorsally by the thoracic vertebrae; laterally by the ribs; ventrally by the sternum; and in the living animal the caudal boundary is the diaphragm. Movement of the lungs within the thorax is facilitated by the presence of a smooth serous membrane, the *pleura*, which consists of a single layer of mesothelial cells on the surface of a connective tissue layer.

THE PLEURA

The pleura consists of two continuous serous sacs. One sac is reflected around each lung. The junction of the two sacs near the midline of the thorax forms a double layer of pleura called the *mediastinum*. Whenever structures are interposed between these two layers of the mediastinum this area is called the mediastinal space. For example, the heart is located in the middle mediastinal space. The trachea, esophagus, lymph nodes, and most of the great vessels are also located in the mediastinal space. In other words, mediastinal pleura bounds both sides of these structures.

The pleura which lines the thorax is known as *parietal pleura*, while that pleura covering the lungs is called *visceral pleura*. The three subdivisions of pleura (parietal, visceral, and mediastinal) are covered by one continuous sheet of simple squamous epithelium known as mesothelium. The *pleural sac*, or *pleural cavity*, is a potential space between parietal and visceral pleura and between mediastinal and visceral pleura. This pleural cavity contains nothing except a small amount of serous (watery) fluid, which acts as a lubricant to reduce friction between the lungs and other structures of the thorax.

PHYSIOLOGY OF RESPIRATION

The respiratory apparatus provides an open passageway for air from the exterior to reach the smallest subdivisions of the lung (the alveoli). The thin membranes of the alveolar wall and capillaries facilitate movement of oxygen into the blood and movement of carbon dioxide into the alveolar air. This exchange constitutes external respiration, as contrasted with internal respiration, in which oxygen from the blood is given to the tissues for cellular oxidation and the resulting carbon dioxide is picked up by the blood.

External respiration is dependent on movement of air into and out of the lungs. Enlargement of the thoracic cavity reduces the already negative pressure in the pleural cavity, causing the lungs to enlarge, which results in an inflow of air into the lungs, known as *inspiration*.

During relatively quiet respiration, contraction of the diaphragm enlarges the thorax sufficiently. The *diaphragm* is a dome-shaped structure with the convexity directed cranially into the thorax. The central portion is largely tendinous, but the periphery consists of striated muscle, as do the two crura (roots) of the diaphragm, which are attached ventral to the lumbar vertebrae. The *right* and *left phrenic nerves* supply the respective sides of the diaphragm. Contraction of the muscular portion of the diaphragm forces the

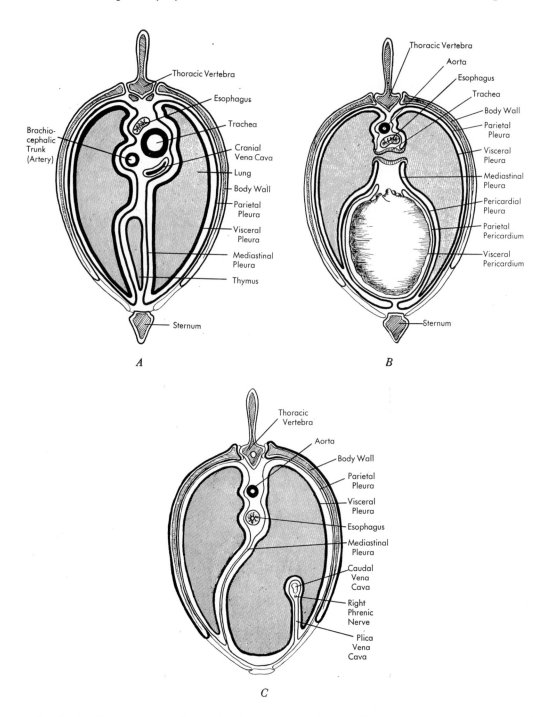

Fig. 16–6.—Cross-sections of thorax showing serous membranes. Spaces are exaggerated for ease of visualization. *A*, Section cranial to the heart; *B*, section through the heart; and *C*, section caudal to the heart. (After Ellenberger, *Handbuch der Vergleichenden Anatomie der Haustiere*, Springer.)

Abnormal lungs may produce exaggerated sounds called *rales*, or they may not produce any sound at all, depending on the condition.

Percussion involves striking the thorax to determine the type of sound produced. If the thorax is normal the sound is clear and resonant, as produced by striking a drum. However, if the lungs are solid or the thorax is filled with fluid, the sound, or percussion, will be much duller.

Epistaxis (*nose bleed*) occasionally results in any animal because of the highly vascular nasal mucous membrane. Some race horses develop nose bleed during races, perhaps because of the high blood pressure involved.

Atrophic rhinitis (*necrotic rhinitis*) is an infectious disease of pigs, in which some of the structures lining the nasal cavity may be almost completely destroyed.

Calf diphtheria is an infectious laryngitis of cattle sometimes seen in feed-lot cattle.

Pharyngitis (*sore throat*) is an inflammation of the pharynx and may involve the digestive system as well as the respiratory system.

Bronchitis is an inflammation of the bronchi (bronchial tubes). It may be an extension of tracheitis (inflammation of the trachea) and can lead to pneumonia or pleuritis or both.

Pleuritis (*pleurisy*) is simply an inflammation of the pleura. It usually is a complication of some other condition such as pneumonia, shipping fever, or injury. Pleuritis may produce a rasping sound due to the roughened surfaces rubbing together. In severe cases adhesions may form between the parietal pleura and visceral pleura. *Hydrothorax* (fluid in the pleural sac) may also result from pleuritis.

Pneumonia is an inflammation of the lung substance itself. Non-infectious pneumonia is frequently caused by inhalation of feed, water, or improperly administered medicine. Infectious pneumonia may be caused by bacteria or viruses and rarely by other living organisms, including molds, yeasts, and parasites such as lung worms. One of the most common causes of pneumonia in cattle is *shipping fever* (also called *hemorrhagic septicemia*), which is probably caused by a combination of *Pasturella bacteria* and one or more viruses.

Pulmonary emphysema (*heaves*) is due to enlargement of the alveoli of the lungs (*vesicular emphysema*) and, finally, rupture of some alveoli, with escape of air into the connective tissue between the alveoli (*interstitial emphysema*).

Heaves is more common in horses than in any other animal, although it is described in cattle. In this disease inspiration is fairly normal, but expiration is difficult and usually requires a double bellows-like movement of the abdominal muscles. The strong contraction of the abdominal muscles produces a marked ridge at the location of the costal arch with each expiration effort. Dusty or moldy hay increases the severity of heaves and often results in a characteristic dry cough.

Some type of cough frequently is associated with inflammation of all parts of the respiratory system from the larynx to the lungs but is less frequently associated with inflammation of the nasal cavity, pharynx, or guttural pouches.

CHAPTER 17

THE DIGESTIVE SYSTEM

GENERAL

THE digestive system consists of a musculomembranous tube extending from the mouth to the anus. Its functions are ingestion, grinding, digestion, and absorption of food, and elimination of solid wastes. The digestive system reduces the nutrients in the food to compounds that are simple enough to be absorbed and used for energy and building tissues.

The digestive tract consists of a tube, lined with mucous membrane, that is continuous with the external skin at the mouth and at the anus. The four layers making up the wall of the digestive tract, from within outward, are (1) the *epithelium* (stratified squamous to the glandular part of the stomach and simple columnar from there on), (2) the *lamina propria* (including the muscularis mucosae and submucosa), (3) the muscles (striated into or through the esophagus, smooth the rest of the way—usually inner circular and outer longitudinal), and (4) caudal to the diaphragm, and covering most of the digestive tract, an outer serous covering, the *visceral peritoneum*.

(254)

Portions of the digestive tract are the mouth, pharynx, esophagus (forestomachs in ruminants), glandular stomach, small intestine, large intestine, and the accessory glands, which are the salivary glands, the liver, and the pancreas.

THE MOUTH

The *mouth* is used primarily for grinding food and mixing it with saliva, but may also serve as a prehensile (grasping) mechanism and as a defensive and offensive weapon. The teeth and tongue are surrounded by lips, cheeks, and muscles to operate the jaws.

Functions of the oral cavity (mouth) and associated structures include prehension, mastication, insalivation, and bolus formation.

THE TEETH

Teeth develop from an invagination of the epithelium known as the *dental lamina*, which produces the *enamel organ*, a cap-like covering of a connective-tissue elevation called the *dental papilla*. The connec-

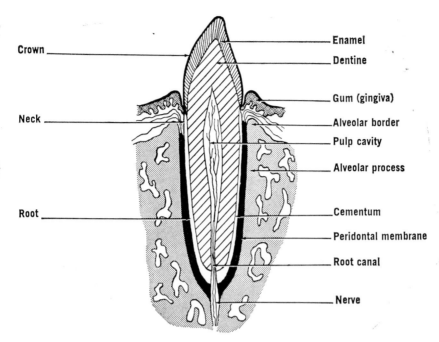

Fig. 17-1.—Structure of a tooth (longitudinal section). (De Coursey, *The Human Organism*, courtesy of McGraw Hill Book Co.)

tive tissue around the beginning tooth forms the *dental sac*. Both deciduous teeth and permanent teeth develop in the same manner from similar embryonic structures.

The outer cells of the dental papilla eventually produce the *dentine* of the tooth, and the inner cells form the *pulp*, which is invaded by the vessels and nerves that will supply the tooth.

The *enamel* of the tooth is formed by the *ameloblast* layer of the enamel organ. It is the only part of the tooth derived from epithelium and is the hardest substance in the body.

The inner layer of the dental sac forms the *cementum*, and the outer layer of the dental sac forms the *periodontal membrane* that connects the tooth to the bone of the socket (*alveolus*). It acts as a sling supporting the tooth.

Dentine makes up the major portion of the tooth. It is produced by *odontoblasts*, cells that line the pulp cavity and send processes out through the dentine. It

also contains collagenous fibrils and very fine canaliculi.

Enamel covers the crown in *brachydont* teeth. In *hypsodont* teeth of herbivores the enamel not only covers the crown but is invaginated into the longitudinal grooves and infundibula (cups) of the teeth.

Cementum is modified bone that covers the roots of brachydont teeth. In hypsodont teeth the cementum covers the root and crown and fills in the grooves and infundibula where the enamel is not in apposition with anything else.

Teeth are of the cutting or shearing type, as found in the incisors of all animals, and of the grinding type, as seen in the premolars and molars, particularly of herbivorous animals. Teeth that have a short crown are called brachydont teeth, while those with a long crown are known as hypsodont teeth.

Deciduous teeth (*milk teeth*) erupt first and are replaced by permanent teeth. This time of eruption or breaking through the

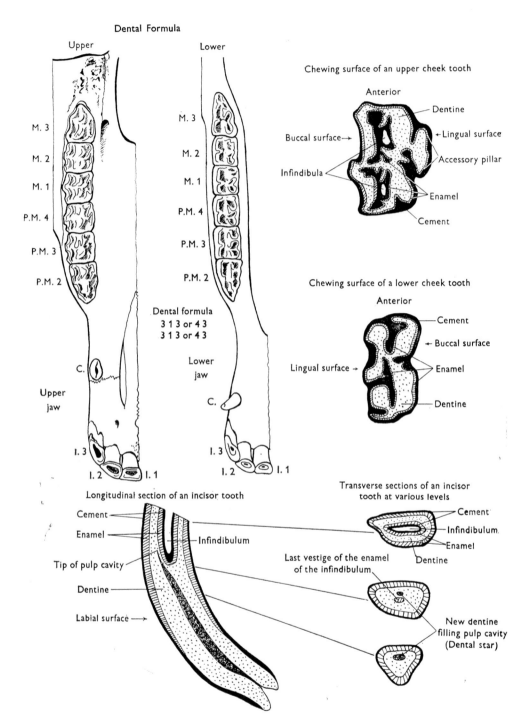

FIG. 17–2.—Dentition and dental characters of the teeth in the horse. (Taylor, *Regional and Applied Anatomy of the Domestic Animals*, courtesy of J. B. Lippincott Co.)

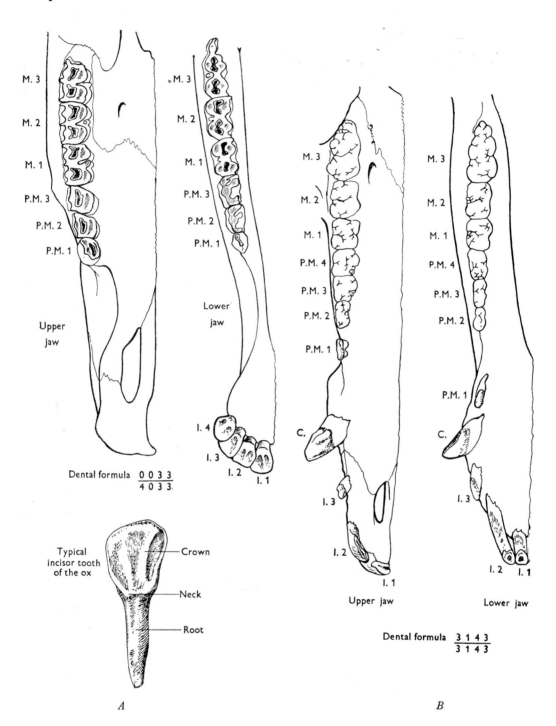

FIG. 17–3.—*A*, Dentition of the cow. *B*, Dentition of the pig. (Taylor, *Regional and Applied Anatomy of the Domestic Animals*, courtesy of J. B. Lippincott Co.)

TABLE 17–1.—FORMULAS AND ERUPTION OF DECIDUOUS TEETH

(After Sisson and Grossman, *Anatomy of the Domestic Animals*. Courtesy of W. B. Saunders Co.)

	Horse	Cow	Sheep	Pig	Dog
	Deciduous Formulas				
	3 0 3 2(DI–DC–DP–) 3 0 3	0 0 3 2(DI–DC–DP–) 4 0 3	0 0 3 2(DI–DC–DP–) 4 0 3	3 1 4 2(DI–DC–DP–) 3 1 4	3 1 3 2(DI–DC–DP–) 3 1 3
	Deciduous Eruption				
Incisors					
DI 1	Birth to 1 wk	Birth to 2 wk	Birth to 1 wk	2–4 wk	4–5 wk
DI 2	4–6 wk	" " "	1–2 "	1½–3 mo	4–5 wk
DI 3	6–9 mo	" " "	2–3 "	Birth or before	4–6 wk
DI 4	———	" " "	3–4 "	———	———
Canines					
DC1	———	———	———	Before birth	3–4 wk
Premolars					
DP1	———	Birth to few da	2–6 "	5 mo	4–8 wk
DP2	Birth to 2 wk	" " "	2–6 "	5–7 wk	4–8 wk
DP3	" " "	" " "	2–6 "	U–4–8 da	4–8 wk
DP4	" " "	———	———	U–4–8 da L–2–4 wk	———

Deciduous Incisors	DI		Day	da		Upper	U
Deciduous Canines	DC		Week	wk		Lower	L
Deciduous Premolars	DP		Month	mo			
			Year	yr			

TABLE 17–2.—FORMULAS AND ERUPTION OF PERMANENT TEETH

(After Sisson and Grossman, *Anatomy of the Domestic Animals*. Courtesy of W. B. Saunders Co.)

	Horse	Cow	Sheep	Pig	Dog
	Permanent Formulas				
	3 1 3-4 3 2(I–C–P——M–) 3 1 3 3	0 0 3 3 2(I–C–P–M–) 4 0 3 3	0 0 3 3 2(I–C–P–M–) 4 0 3 3	3 1 4 3 2(I–C–P–M–) 3 1 4 3	3 1 4 2 2(I–C–P–M–) 3 1 4 3
	Permanent Eruption				
Incisors					
I1	2½ yr	1½–2 yr	1–1½ yr	1 yr	3–5 mo
I2	3½ yr	2–2½ yr	1½–2 yr	16–20 mo	3–5 mo
I3	4½ yr	3 yr	2½–3 yr	8–10 mo	4–5 mo
I4	———	3½–4 yr	3½–4 yr	———	———
Canines					
C	4–5 yr	———	———	9–10 mo	4–6 mo
Premolars					
P1	5–6 mo	2–2½ yr	1½–2 yr	12–15 mo	4–5 mo
P2	2½ yr	1½–2½ yr	1½–2 yr	12–15 mo	5–6 mo
P3	3 yr	2½–3 yr	1½–2 yr	12–15 mo	5–6 mo
P4	4 yr	———	———	12–15 mo	5–6 mo
Molars					
M1	9–12 mo	5–6 mo	3–5 mo	4–6 mo	5–6 mo
M2	2 yr	1–1½ yr	9–12 mo	8–12 mo	6–7 mo
M3	3½–4 yr	2–2½ yr	1½–2 yr	18–20 mo	6–7 mo

Incisors	I		Day	da
Canines	C		Week	wk
Premolars	P		Month	mo
Molars	M		Year	**yr**

gums by the teeth is probably the most accurate aid to determining the age of animals, when no accurate records are available.

The front teeth are called *incisors* and are designated by the letter I. The incisor teeth are numbered from the center of the mouth, or symphysis, laterally. The first pair of incisors is called I_1 or centrals, the next pair I_2 or first intermediates, next I_3, or second intermediates, and the last and most lateral pair of incisors is called I_4 or corners. In the non-ruminants, only one pair of intermediate incisors is found.

Canine teeth are also called eye teeth, bridle teeth, tusks, and tushes (abbreviated C). Normally not more than one pair of canine teeth occur in each jaw at any given time, and canines may be completely absent in the mare, gelding, and ruminant.

Cheek teeth are called premolars, P, and molars, M. Deciduous cheek teeth are premolars and are numbered from front to back, 1, 2, 3, and 4. Molars appear caudal to the premolars and the numerical sequence is repeated, M1, M2, and M3.

The dental formula for deciduous teeth is indicated by a D preceding the key letter as DI, DC, and DP. There are no deciduous molars.

The dental formulas for cattle are

$$\text{Deciduous 2 } (DI\frac{0}{4} \, DC\frac{0}{0} \, DP\frac{3}{3})$$

and

$$\text{Permanent 2 } (I\frac{0}{4} \, C\frac{0}{0} \, P\frac{3}{3} \, M\frac{3}{3})$$

These formulas indicate the teeth found on one side of the mouth. The numerator of the fraction represents the teeth in the upper jaw, while the denominator indicates the teeth in the lower jaw. Obviously, this fraction must be doubled to include all the teeth in the mouth.

The permanent formula for cattle shows there are no incisors in the upper

jaw and four on each side in the lower jaw. There are no canine teeth in either jaw. There are three premolars and three molars on each side in each jaw. Dental formulas and time of eruption of teeth for a number of domestic animals are indicated in Tables 17–1 and 17–2.

The gums consist of a non-glandular mucosa tightly adherent to the underlying bone.

THE TONGUE

The tongue consists of a mass of muscle covered by mucous membrane. The *hyoglossus muscle* attaches to the *hyoid bone*, the *genioglossus muscle* attaches to the symphysis of the mandible (chin), and the *styloglossus muscle* attaches along the inside of the *great cornu* of the hyoid bone.

Cattle use the tongue as a prehensile organ as well as an aid to chewing and forming a bolus of the food.

The tongue is covered with stratified squamous epithelium that presents a large number of papillae, particularly on the dorsal surface of the tongue. Filiform, fungiform, and circumvallate papillae are found in all domestic animals, and foliate papillae are present in the horse, pig, and dog, but not in the sheep and cow. The filiform papillae do not bear taste buds, but all other types of papillae do have taste buds.

The *filiform papillae* are somewhat hairlike in appearance. They consist of a connective-tissue core covered by a highly cornified epithelial layer. These papillae are shorter and softer in the horse than in other domestic animals, giving the tongue of the horse its velvety feel.

The *fungiform papillae* are assumed to resemble a fungus, or low toad stool. They contain taste buds in all animals.

Foliate papillae resemble the foliage or leaves of plants. They are found in the horse, pig, and dog, where they contain taste buds and serous glands. Mucous glands are also found in the foliate papillae of the horse and dog.

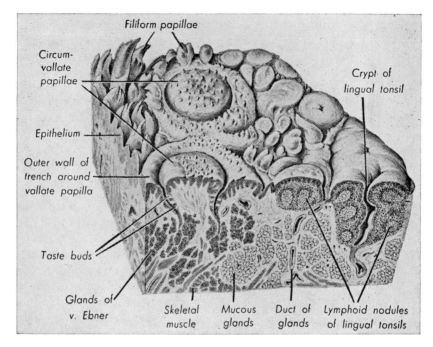

A

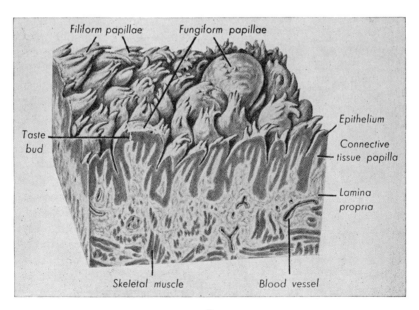

B

Fig. 17–4.—*A*, Drawing of the surface of the human tongue near the root. Magnification × 13. (Redrawn from Braus.) *B*, Drawing of the surface of the human tongue farther from the root. (Copenhaver, *Bailey's Textbook of Histology*, courtesy of Williams & Wilkins Co.)

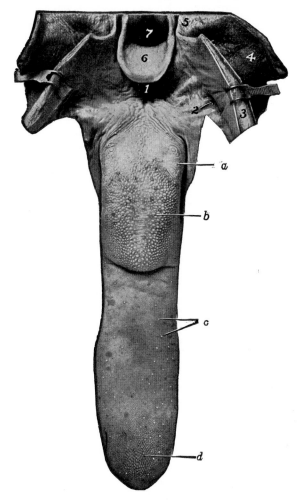

Fig. 17–5.—Tongue and fauces of cow; dorsal view. The pharynx and soft palate are cut dorsally and reflected. *a*, Vallate papillae; *b*, prominence of dorsum with broad, flattened papillae; *c*, fungiform papillae; *d*, filiform papillae of tip; *1*, glosso-epiglottic space; *2*, tonsillar sinus; *3*, cut surface of soft palate; *4*, pharynx; *5*, posterior pillar of soft palate; *6*, epiglottis; *7*, aditus laryngis. (Sisson and Grossman, *The Anatomy of the Domestic Animals*, courtesy of W. B. Saunders Co.)

Circumvallate papillae are large, circular projections surrounded by a deep groove. They contain taste buds and serous glands in all domestic animals and also contain mucous glands in the horse.

Taste buds are described in Chapter 7, p. 104.

The tongue of the cow has a transverse groove in front of a dorsal prominence, which consists largely of a thickened mucosa.

LIPS, CHEEKS, JAWS, AND HARD PALATE

Lips of sheep and horses are soft and flexible and aid in picking up food. Lips of cattle and hogs, being very stiff and immobile, serve little more than to close the mouth.

Cheeks are muscular structures covered with skin and lined with mucous membrane. They aid the tongue in positioning food between the teeth for chewing. The cow has numerous conical papillae lining the cheeks.

Jaws are closed by the powerful *masseter*, *temporal*, and *pterygoid muscles* and are opened by the *digastricus*, *occipito-mandibularis*, and *sterno-mandibularis muscles*. The pterygoid muscles contribute to grinding movements by protruding the jaw and moving it from side to side.

The *hard palate* forms the roof of the mouth and is continued caudally by the *soft palate*, which separates the mouth from the pharynx.

The lining of the oral cavity is stratified squamous epithelium that is thickened and highly cornified, particularly in areas exposed to considerable wear, such as the dental pad of ruminants, cheeks, hard palate, and the oral side of the soft palate. Glands are common in the submucosa of the mouth, except on the tip and body of the tongue, the hard palate, and the gums.

The lips are covered with skin externally and mucous membrane internally over a layer of muscle, connective tissue, and *labial glands*. As the skin joins the mucous membrane, the hair and skin glands disappear, and the labial glands begin. Relatively large conical papillae are found projecting inward on the mucosa of the lips of ruminants. The upper lip forms part of the *planum nasolabiale* of cattle and the *planum rostrale* of pigs (see Fig. 16–1). Serous glands are present on these areas as well as on the planum nasale of sheep, but not on the dog. (The moisture on a dog's nose comes from exhaled moisture or saliva from the tongue.) Tactile hairs, used as sensing probes, are present in the lips of some animals.

The cheeks have the same layers as the lips, with the skin externally, the mucous membrane internally, and the muscle, the connective tissue, and the buccal glands between. The mucosa of the ruminant cheek bears rather large cornified papillae that may aid in mastication.

The hard palate contains transverse ridges formed by thickenings of the mucous membrane. A network of veins forming *cavernous tissue* underlies the mucosa. A condition called "*lampers*" in horses is an inflammation of the mucosa of the hard palate. An empiric treatment is incision of the palate with a sharp knife, which is dangerous because of the large arteries and venous plexus in the submucosa.

The oral side of the soft palate is covered with stratified squamous epithelium overlying mucous glands in the submucosa. The pharyngeal side of the soft palate is covered with pseudostratified columnar ciliated epithelium. The submucosa and lamina propria of the mucosa both contain glands.

TONSILS

The *tonsils* are more or less circumscribed masses of *lymphoid tissue*, named according to their location.

The *palatine tonsils* in man and the dog are paired oval bodies located in pockets on the lateral wall of the pharynx ventral to the soft palate and lateral to the base of the tongue. These are the structures commonly referred to as tonsils. In the horse, cow, and sheep these palatine tonsils are located in about the same relative position, but they are in the submucosa and are completely covered by mucous membrane except for the crypts or fissures over the tonsils. In other words, the tonsils do not project into the pharynx at all in these animals. In the pig the palatine tonsils are located in the substance of the soft palate.

The *lingual tonsils* consist of accumulations of lymph follicles on the base of the tongue. These tonsils are most prominent in the horse, cow, and pig.

The *pharyngeal tonsil* is an accumulation

of lymphoid tissue in the submucosa of the dorsal pharyngeal wall of all domestic animals. Enlargement of the pharyngeal tonsil of man is called *adenoids*.

THE PHARYNX

The pharynx is a common passage for food and air, lined by mucous membrane and surrounded by muscles. Openings into the pharynx are the mouth, two posterior nares, two Eustachian tubes, the esophagus, and the larynx. Inspired air passing through the nasal cavity enters the posterior nares. The air then crosses the pharynx to enter the larynx.

Food, of course, enters the pharynx from the mouth and is forced into the esophagus by contraction of the pharyngeal muscles. Thus the paths of food and air must cross in the pharynx.

The Eustachian tubes provide free exchange of air from the pharynx to the middle ear so pressure is equalized on both sides of the tympanic membrane, or ear drums.

The nasal portion of the pharynx is lined with pseudostratified columnar ciliated epithelium, and the oral portion is lined with stratified squamous epithelium. Mucous glands predominate in the oral portion, and mixed glands are found in the nasal part, with the serous type predominating.

The muscular wall of the pharynx is continuous with the muscle of the esophagus. Pharyngeal muscles are named according to the structure where each originates. These include the *pterygopharyngeus* (from the pterygoid bones), the *hyopharyngeus* (from the body of the hyoid bone), the *thyropharyngeus* (from the thyroid cartilage of the larynx), the *stylopharyngeus* (from the styloid process of the hyoid bone), and the *cricopharyngeus* (from the *cricoid cartilage* of the larynx). All these muscles insert on a fibrous raphe (band) on the mid-line at the dorsum of the pharynx.

During swallowing, the stylopharyngeus muscles shorten the pharynx, and the rest of the pharyngeal muscles (be-

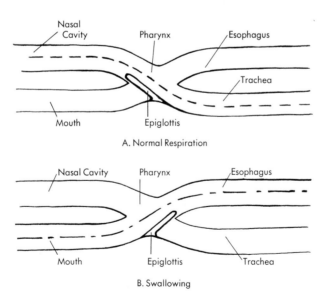

A. Normal Respiration

B. Swallowing

Fig. 17–6.—Relationship of pharynx and mouth to larynx and esophagus during *A*, normal respiration. *B*, Swallowing. (After Miller, Christensen, and Evans. *Anatomy of the Dog*; courtesy of W. B. Saunders Co.)

cause of their circular arrangement), by contracting in series from cranial to caudal, force the bolus of food from the pharynx into the esophagus.

THE ESOPHAGUS

The *esophagus*, a direct continuation of the pharynx, is a muscular tube extending from the pharynx to the *cardia* of the stomach just caudal to the diaphragm.

From the pharynx the esophagus passes dorsal to the trachea and usually inclines somewhat to the left in the neck. It again passes dorsal to the trachea, where it enters the thorax and continues caudally between the trachea and the aorta to the diaphragm. The esophagus then passes through the *hiatus esophageus* and joins the stomach within the abdominal cavity at the *cardia*. The cardia, or *cardiac sphincter*, of the stomach is so named because of its proximity to the heart.

The muscular wall of the esophagus consists of two layers that cross obliquely, then spiral, and finally form an inner circular and outer longitudinal layer. The muscle changes from striated to smooth muscle in the caudal one-third of the esophagus in the horse and just in front of the diaphragm in the pig; it is striated throughout its entire length in the dog and ruminants.

THE NON-RUMINANT STOMACH

In *non-ruminants* the stomach is located just behind the left side of the diaphragm. The diaphragm is a muscular sheet which separates the thoracic and abdominal cavities.

Viewed from the exterior, the *stomach* is subdivided into the *cardia* (entrance), *fundus, body,* and *pylorus* (termination). The cardia and pylorus are sphincters which control the passage of food through the stomach.

The cardia and pylorus are quite close together, giving the stomach a shape somewhat like a bent pear. This arrangement produces a very short concave side between the cardia and pylorus, which is known as the lesser curvature, and a much longer convex side, known as the greater curvature. The large bulge near the cardia is called the fundus, but should not be confused with the fundic gland region of the interior of the stomach.

Immediately surrounding the cardia is an area of stratified squamous epithelium called the *esophageal region.* The size of the esophageal region varies with the species and is non-glandular. Other regions of the stomach are the *cardiac-gland region, fundic-gland region* and *pyloric-gland region.*

The entire surface area of the stomach is increased many times by infolding of the epithelium into depressions called *gastric pits,* or *foveolae.*

The *lamina propria,* outside the epithelium, is very thick. It is almost filled with glands that empty into the depths of the gastric pits. Three types of glands described are the *cardiac glands,* located closest to the cardia; the *pyloric glands,* located in the region of the pylorus; and the *fundic glands (gastric glands),* found throughout the remainder of the stomach. The cardiac glands are simple or compound tubular glands that produce primarily, if not entirely, mucus. They are found in the cardiac-gland region of the mucous membrane lining the stomach, which should not be confused with the cardia of the stomach. The cardia is the location of a sphincter at the junction of the esophagus and stomach and in the ruminant is a great distance from the cardiac-gland region. The cardiac-gland region of the ruminant is poorly defined and contains cardiac, pyloric, and fundic glands (see Fig. 17–8).

The fundic-gland region occupies much more area than just the fundus of the stomach. It includes the entire area be-

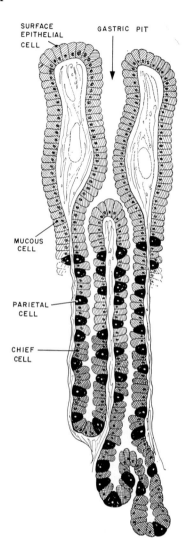

FIG. 17–7.—Gastric glands from the fundus of the stomach. (Grollman, *The Human Body*, courtesy of the Macmillan Co.)

tween the cardiac-gland region and the pyloric-gland region. A fundic gland is a simple tubular gland that consists of a mouth that opens into a gastric pit, a neck that is constricted, the main portion (called the body of the gland), and the blind extremity (called the fundus of the fundic gland). Several fundic glands may open into the same gastric pit. The neck of the gland contains mucous neck cells that produce mucus, and the neck

also contains some *parietal cells* that are involved in the production of hydrochloric acid. Parietal cells are also found in the body, where they are the most numerous, and to a lesser extent in the fundus of the gland. The *chief cells* contain an intracellular network of canaliculi which connect directly or indirectly with the lumen of the gland. The chief cells, also called *zymogen cells* because they produce enzymes, are found mainly in the body and fundus of the fundic glands. The chief cells are located close to the lumen of the glands, where they appear to crowd the parietal cells out toward the periphery of the gland. Both *pepsin* and *rennin* (not to be confused with *renin*) are produced by the chief cells.

In the non-ruminant stomach the *esophageal region* compares to the fore-stomachs of the ruminant, in that it is lined with non-glandular stratified squamous epithelium. The rest of the stomach can be more-or-less accurately divided into a cardiac-gland region, a fundic-gland region, and a pyloric-gland region (Fig. 17–8).

The esophageal region is large in the horse, small in the pig, and practically absent in the dog. The cardiac gland region is large in the pig but smaller in the horse, and the remainder of the non-ruminant stomach is divided between fundic- and pyloric-gland regions.

THE RUMINANT STOMACH

The true (glandular) stomach in the ruminant is preceded by three divisions, or diverticulae, (lined with stratified squamous epithelium), where food is soaked and subjected to digestion by microorganisms before passing through the digestive tract.

The *rumen, reticulum,* and *omasum* of ruminants are collectively known as the fore-stomachs. The cardia is located craniodorsally in the dome-shaped *atrium ventriculi*, which is common to both the

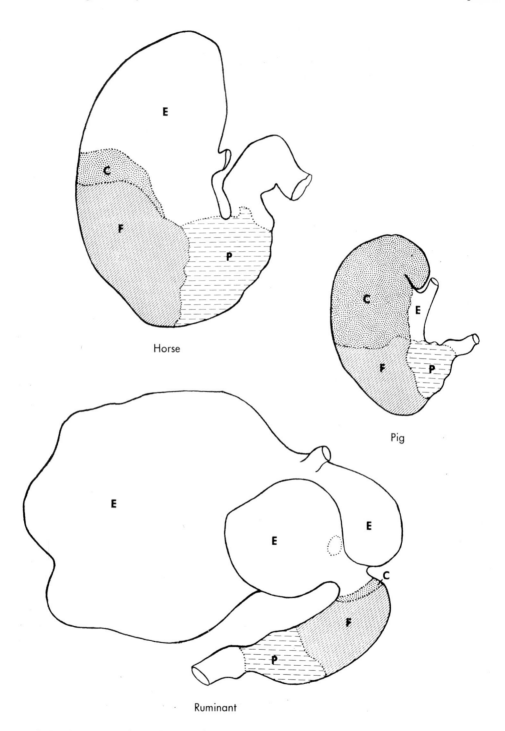

Fig. 17–8.—Stomach regions of horse, pig, and ruminant. *E*, Esophageal region; *C*, cardiac gland region; *F*, fundic gland region; and *P*, pyloric gland region.

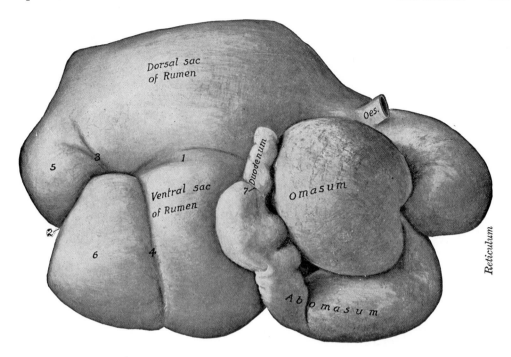

FIG. 17–9.—Stomach of cow; right view. *Oes.*, Esophagus: *1*, right longitudinal groove of rumen; *2*, posterior groove of rumen; *3*, *4*, coronary grooves; *5*, *6*, posterior blind sacs of rumen; *7*, pylorus. (Sisson and Grossman, *The Anatomy of the Domestic Animals*, courtesy of W. B. Saunders Co.)

rumen and reticulum. The *esophageal groove*, which extends from the cardia to the omasum, is formed by two heavy muscular folds or lips, which can close to direct material from the esophagus into the omasum directly, or open and permit the material to enter the rumen and reticulum.

THE RETICULUM

The *reticulum* is the most cranial compartment. It is also called the honeycomb, and as the names imply, it is lined with mucous membrane containing many intersecting ridges which subdivide the surface into honeycomb-like compartments. The surface is stratified squamous epithelium. The location of the reticulum immediately behind the diaphragm places it almost in apposition to the heart, so any foreign objects such as wire or nails that may be swallowed tend to lodge in the reticulum and are in a very good position to penetrate into the heart.

THE RUMEN

The rumen is a large muscular sac which extends from the diaphragm to the pelvis and almost entirely fills the left side of the abdominal cavity. The rumen is subdivided into sacs by muscular pillars, which appear from the exterior of the rumen as grooves. The dorsal and ventral sacs are separated by a nearly complete circle, which is formed on the frontal plane by the right and left longitudinal pillars, connected by the cranial and caudal pillars. The dorsal sac is the largest compartment. The dorsal sac overlaps the ventral sac and is continuous cranially with the reticulum over the *rumino-reticular* fold, which separates the floor of the rumen from the floor of the reticulum.

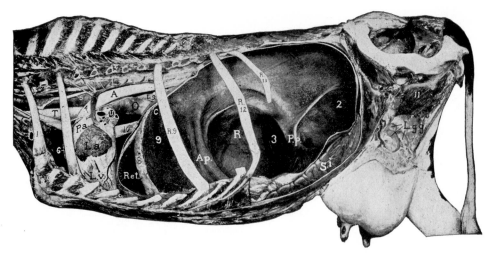

Fɪɢ. 17–10.—Deep dissection of holstein cow; left side. The lungs and pericardium have been removed. Most of the left wall of the rumen and reticulum has been cut away. *1, 2, 3,* Blind sacs of rumen; *4,* first rib (brachial vessels at left of *4*); 5, vertebral end of thirteenth rib; *A,* aorta; *Ap., P.p.,* anterior and posterior pillars of rumen; *C,* cardia; *F,* rumino-reticular fold; *G,* reticular groove; *L.a.,* left auricle; *L.g.,* posterior mediastinal lymph gland (large one); *Lgg.,* supramammary lymph glands; *L.V.,* left ventricle; *O,* oesophagus; *P.a.,* pulmonary artery; *P.p.,* posterior pillar of rumen; *R,* rumen; *Ret.,* reticulum; *R.O.,* reticulo-omasal opening; *S.i.,* small intestines; *T,* trachea; *T',* left bronchus. (Sisson and Grossman, *The Anatomy of the Domestic Animals,* courtesy of W. B. Saunders Co.)

Caudally the dorsal sac is further subdivided by the dorsal coronary pillars, which form an incomplete circle bounding the dorsal blind sac. The caudal part of the ventral sac is a diverticulum separated from the rest of the ventral sac by the ventral coronary pillars.

The mucous membrane lining the rumen is glandless stratified squamous epithelium. The most ventral parts of both sacs of the rumen contain numerous papillae up to 1 cm. in length, but papillae are almost entirely absent on the dorsal part of the rumen.

The smooth muscle of the wall of the rumen consists of two layers. The superficial layer runs largely cranio-caudally in direction and bridges most of the ruminal grooves. The fibers of the inner layer of muscle run more transversely and also make up most of the substance of the ruminal pillars.

The two muscle layers are continuous with the muscle of the esophagus. They run obliquely and cross at right angles. The wall of the esophageal groove con-

sists largely of smooth muscle. Striated muscle from the esophagus predominates at the cardia but fades out rapidly in the groove. Both transverse and longitudinal smooth-muscle fibers are found in the floor of the groove. The lips contain mainly longitudinal fibers which form a loop around the cardia at the dorsal end of the groove and enter the sphincter of the reticulo-omasal orifice at the ventral end of the groove. Most of the transverse fibers enter the wall of the reticulum. The mucous membrane of the esophageal groove resembles that of the reticulum in the ventral part and that of the rumen in the dorsal part. The lower part of the esophageal groove connects the atrium ventriculi with the omasum.

THE OMASUM

The omasum is a spherical organ filled with muscular laminae which descend from the dorsum or roof. The mucous membrane covering the laminae is studded with short, blunt papillae which

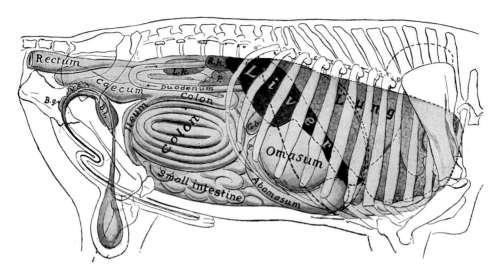

Fig. 17–11.—Projection of viscera of bull on body-wall; right side. *P,.* Pylorus; *G.b.,* gall-bladder; *R.K.,* right kidney; *L.K.,* left kidney; *P.* (above duodenum), pancreas; *Bl.,* urinary bladder; *V.s.,* vesicular seminalis; *B.g.,* bulbo-urethral (Cowper's) gland. Costal attachment and median line of diaphragm are indicated by dotted lines. (Sisson and Grossman, *The Anatomy of the Domestic Animals,* courtesy of W. B. Saunders Co.)

grind roughage before it enters the abomasum (true stomach). The omasum is located to the right of the rumen and reticulum just caudal to the liver.

The omasum is nearly filled with laminae, bearing pointed papillae arranged in such a manner that food is moved from the *reticulo-omasal* orifice, between the laminae, and on to the *omaso-abomasal* orifice. Each lamina contains three layers of muscle, including a central layer continuous with the muscle wall of the omasum, and a layer of muscularis mucosae on each side of the central muscle. The fibers of the *muscularis mucosae* run at right angles to the fibers of the central muscle.

The floor of the omasum as well as the leaves are covered with stratified squamous epithelium. At the junction of the omasum and abomasum is an arrangement of folds of mucous membrane, the *vela terminalia,* derived from the omasum in the cow, but from the abomasum in the sheep.

THE ABOMASUM

The *abomasum* (true stomach) is the first glandular portion of the ruminant digestive system. It is located ventral to the omasum and extends caudally on the right side of the rumen. The *pylorus* (terminal part of the abomasum) is a sphincter (thickening of circular smooth muscle fibers) at the junction of the stomach and small intestine.

The epithelium of the abomasum changes abruptly from the stratified squamous epithelium of the omasum to a tall simple columnar epithelium capable of producing mucus. Presumably the mucus covering the stomach epithelium prevents the digestive juices from digesting the stomach cells. In general, the gland regions of the abomasum correspond to the gland regions in the simple stomach of the non-ruminant, and the forestomachs of the ruminant correspond to the esophageal region of the simple stomach.

THE SMALL INTESTINE

The small intestine is divided into three parts, duodenum, jejunum and ileum, because of histologic or microscopic structural differences.

The *duodenum* is the first part of the small intestine. It is closely attached to the body wall by a short mesentery, the mesoduodenum. Ducts from the pancreas and liver enter the first part of the duodenum. The duodenum leaves the pylorus of the stomach and passes caudally on the right side toward the pelvic inlet. The duodenum then crosses to the left side behind the root of the great mesentery and turns forward to join the jejunum. The common bile duct from the liver and the pancreatic duct from the pancreas enter the duodenum a short distance behind the pylorus.

The *jejunum* is indistinctly separated from the duodenum. It begins approximately where the mesentery starts to become rather long. The jejunum and *ileum* are continuous, and there is no gross demarcation between them. The ileum is the last part of the small intestine. It enters the large intestine at the *ileo-ceco-colic junction.*

It is impossible to give a definite location for the jejunum and ileum, but they tend to be located toward the left ventral portion of the abdominal cavity in nonruminants. The terminal part of the ileum, however, joins the *cecum* (horse) or cecum and *colon* (other animals) in the right caudal part of the abdominal cavity.

THE LARGE INTESTINE

The *large intestine* consists of the cecum, which is a blind sac, and the colon, which terminates as the rectum and anus.

There is considerably more variation in the large intestine from one species to another than in the small intestine. Therefore, the large intestine will be described separately for each species.

The Large Intestine of the Horse

The horse has the largest and most complex large intestine of any of the domestic animals.

The cecum in the horse is a comma-shaped structure extending on the right side from the pelvic inlet to the floor of the abdominal cavity just behind the diaphragm. The base of the cecum projects caudally toward or into the pelvic inlet, while the apex is usually located over the caudal part of the sternum.

The ileum enters the concave side, or lesser curvature, of the cecum near the base, at a sphincter called the *ileo-cecal valve*, or orifice.

The first part of the large colon passes cranially along the right ventral abdominal wall toward the sternal part of the diaphragm, where it turns sharply to the left and proceeds caudally along the left ventral abdominal wall toward the pelvic inlet. These first parts of the large colon are known respectively as the right ventral colon, the sternal flexure, and the left ventral colon. They are arranged like a horseshoe with the toe forward and the branches directed caudally on either side of the apex of the cecum.

The left ventral colon turns sharply dorsally at the pelvic inlet to form the pelvic flexure. The colon then continues cranially as the left dorsal colon, located just dorsal to the left ventral colon. At the diaphragmatic flexure it continues a short distance caudally as the right dorsal colon. The right dorsal colon turns again to the left and crosses the mid-line in front of the root of the great mesentery as the transverse colon.

The *small*, or *floating*, *colon* in the horse is the direct continuation of the transverse colon. The small colon is arranged in loops within the mesocolon, much like the small intestine in the mesentery. The small colon, however, is somewhat larger in diameter than the small intestine. The small colon is usually located near

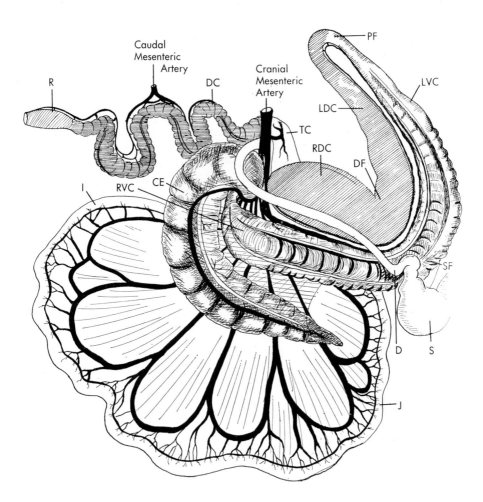

Fig. 17–12.—Gastrointestinal tract of the horse. *S*, Stomach; *D*, duodenum; *J*, jejunum; *I*, ileum; *CE*, cecum; *RVC*, right ventral colon; *DF*, diaphragmatic flexure; *LVC*, left ventral colon; *PF*, pelvic flexure; *LDC*, left dorsal colon; *SF*, sternal flexures; *RDC*, right dorsal colon; *TC*, transverse colon; *DC*, descending colon (small or floating colon); *R*, rectum. (After Nickel, Schummer, and Seiferle, *Lehrbuch der Anatomie der Haustiere*, Berlin, Paul Parey, 1960.)

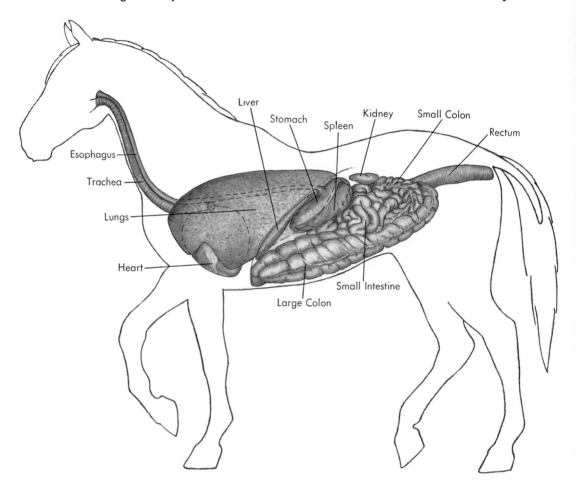

Fig. 17–13.—Viscera of the horse.

the middle of the caudal part of the abdominal cavity.

The *rectum* represents the terminal part of the small colon in the horse. The rectum is fairly straight and is readily dilated for storage of feces.

The junction of the terminal part of the digestive tract and the skin is the *anus*. The anus is closed by both smooth and striated sphincter muscles.

The Large Intestine of the Pig

The large intestine of the pig begins as usual with the cecum. The blind end of the cecum projects forward and ventrally near the mid-line. The dorsal end of the cecum is continuous with the colon at the ilio-ceco-colic junction, where the entrance of the ileum marks the division between the cecum and colon.

The colon of the pig presents a spiral arrangement of coils, giving a somewhat cone-shaped appearance. When the colon leaves this spiral, it passes forward and crosses to the left as transverse colon and then continues caudally as descending colon to the rectum. As in other animals, the rectum terminates at the anus.

The Large Intestine of the Dog

The large intestine of the dog is the shortest and simplest of all domestic

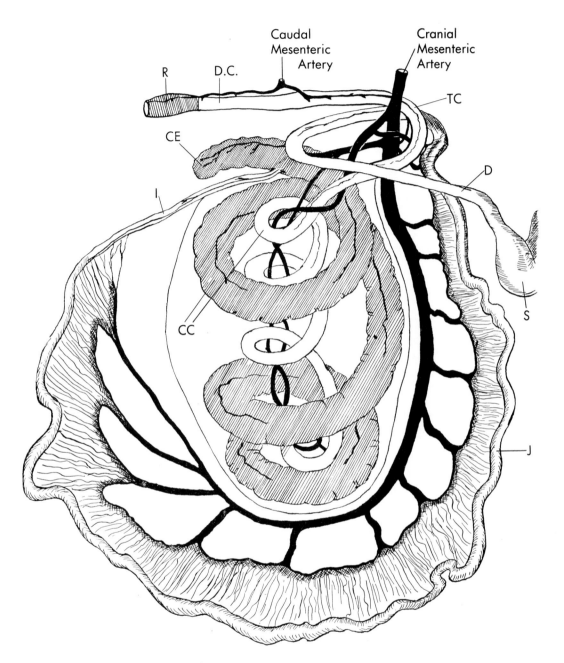

Fig. 17–14.—Gastrointestinal tract of the pig. *S*, Stomach; *D*, duodenum; *J*, jejunum; *I*, ileum *CE*, cecum; *CC*, coiled colon; *TC*, transverse colon; *DC*, descending colon; *R*, rectum. (After Nickel, Schummer, and Seiferle, *Lehrbuch der Anatomie der Hasutiere*, Berlin, Paul Parey, 1960.)

animals, consisting of a very short irregular cecum, a short ascending colon, a transverse colon, a descending colon, a rectum and an anus.

The Large Intestine of Ruminants

In the ruminant the large intestine consists of the cecum and colon. The cecum has one blind end that projects caudally. Cranially, it is continuous with the colon. This junction is marked by the entrance of the ileum at the ilio-ceco-colic orifice.

The *colon* passes forward between the two layers of mesentery which support the small intestine. Here it is arranged in coils, the *ansa spiralis*. The first portion spirals toward the center of the coils (centripetally) and the next part spirals away from the center (centrifugally). After leaving the ansa spiralis the colon

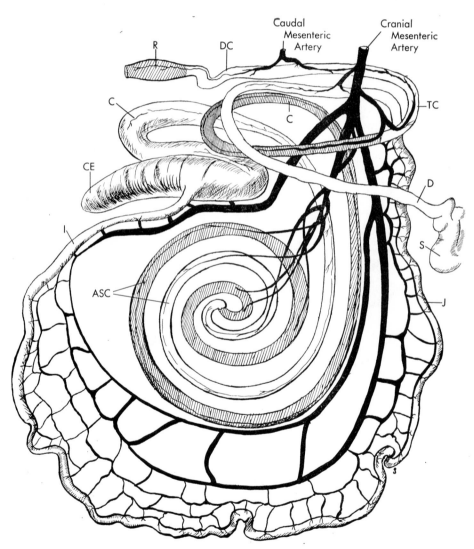

Fig. 17–15.—Gastrointestinal tract of the cow. *S*, Stomach (Abomasum: forestomachs not shown); *D*, duodenum; *J*, jejunum; *I*, ileum; *CE*, cecum; *C*, colon; *ASC*, ansa spiralis (coiled colon); *TC*, transverse colon; *DC*, descending colon; *R*, rectum. (After Nickel, Schummer, and Seiferle, *Lehrbuch der Anatomie der Haustiere*, Berlin, Paul Parey, 1960.)

crosses to the left side and continues caudally to the rectum and the anus, the terminal part of the digestive tract.

General Arrangement

The entire digestive tract is sometimes described as a tube within a tube. This concept seems most logical when considering the embryo, although the same general arrangement persists throughout life. The body wall is essentially a tube consisting from without inward (or superficial to deep) of (1) epithelial covering (the epidermis), (2) a connective-tissue layer (the dermis and superficial fascia), (3) muscle (skeletal muscles), and (4) a serous membrane lining (parietal peritoneum). (See Fig. 1–13.)

The abdominal portion of the digestive tract presents the same layers but in reverse order. From without inward the layers are (1) serosa (visceral peritoneum), (2) muscle (mostly smooth muscle), (3) submucosa (connective tissue), and finally (4) the epithelial lining of the tube (mucous membrane).

The peritoneum consists of a continuous layer of simple squamous epithelial cells called mesothelium. The peritoneum is a serous membrane which lines the entire abdominal cavity and covers all visceral organs within the abdomen.

The peritoneum lining the abdominal cavity is called *parietal peritoneum*, since it covers the wall (*parietal* refers to wall). The peritoneum covering the organs is called *visceral peritoneum*, since it covers the viscera. All peritoneum is continuous, so the parietal peritoneum is connected with visceral peritoneum by double folds of peritoneum which are named according to the organs each supports.

The *mesentery* is a double fold of peritoneum which supports the intestine and attaches it to the dorsal abdominal wall. The *mesoduodenum*, or that portion of the mesentery which supports the duodenum, is relatively short, so movement of the

18

duodenum is quite restricted. The remainder of the mesentery is much longer and permits the jejunum and ileum to move freely into any area of the abdominal cavity not occupied by other viscera.

Omentum refers to peritoneum connecting the stomach with other structures. Mesentery refers to a fold of peritoneum supporting the intestine. The mesentery may be subdivided into *mesoduodenum*, *mesojejunum*, *mesoileum*, and *mesocolon*, depending on which part of the intestine it supports.

Ligaments are folds of peritoneum which connect abdominal organs (other than the stomach or intestines) with each other or with the parietal peritoneum of the body wall. These ligaments are also named according to the structures they connect.

Blood vessels, nerves, and lymph vessels reach the various abdominal organs by passing between the two layers of the various double folds of peritoneum.

Other Structures

Throughout the intestine (both large and small) small tubular depressions, called *crypts of Lieberkühn*, are found between the villi. These crypts are directed toward the periphery of the intestine into the lamina propria. The lining cells are continuous with the epithelium covering the mucous membrane and produce a considerable amount of mucus. In the small intestine the crypts of Lieberkühn also produce *enterokinase*, which activates the pancreatic *trypsinogen*, and other digestive enzymes.

Duodenal glands, also called *Brunner's glands*, are branched tubulo-alveolar glands located in the submucosa and/or lamina propria of the first part of the duodenum. The duodenal gland zone extends a variable distance from the pylorus, depending on the animal. Its length is about 1.5 to 2 cm. in carnivores, 60 to 70 cm. in the sheep, 3 to 5 meters in the pig, 4 to 5 meters in the cow, and 5 to 6 meters in the horse. These glands are believed to secrete mucus, an amylase, and enterokinase.

Lymph nodules are also found both in the submucosa and in the lamina propria throughout the intestine. Aggregations of lymph nodules, termed *Peyer's patches*, are commonly described in the ileum.

The intestinal wall consists of the serosa (visceral peritoneum) superficially, the muscularis next, then the submucosa, and the mucosa deepest. These layers sometimes are called tunics, and the prefix "tunica" is used with the latin forms.

The *serosa* is a layer of simple squamous epithelium (mesothelium) supported by a thin layer of connective tissue. This forms a smooth covering for the intestine that reduces friction of the intestine against other structures in the abdomen.

The *muscularis* in most areas of the intestine is made up of an outer longitudinal layer of smooth muscle fibers and an inner circular layer of smooth muscle fibers. Coordinated contractions and relaxations of both sets of muscles move the ingesta through the intestine by a process called *peristalsis*.

The *submucosa* is a loose connective tissue layer between the inner circular muscle layer (of the muscularis) and the muscularis mucosae of the mucous membrane. Fairly large blood vessels travel in the submucosa, and a network of unmyelinated nerve fibers called *Meissner's plexus* or the *submucous plexus* is also located in the submucosa. These nerve fibers are largely sympathetic in origin, although a few parasympathetic fibers and ganglia are present.

The most superficial layer of the mucous membrane is the *muscularis mucosae*, which like the muscularis externa consists of an inner circular layer and an outer longitudinal layer. The muscularis mucosae, however, is much thinner than the muscularis externa.

The lamina propria is the thick middle layer of connective tissue that forms the basis of the mucous membrane. It forms finger-like projections, the villi, which protrude into the lumen of the intestine. Blood capillaries, lymph capillaries (lacteals), and smooth muscle fibers are found in the lamina propria, including the lamina propria of the villi.

The entire inner surface of the mucous membrane consists of columnar epithelial cells, some of which are modified to form goblet cells for the production of mucus. The rest of the columnar cells have a striated border on the free surface that has been shown to consist of microvilli, which increase the cell surface tremendously and presumably increase the absorptive function of the cell.

Surface area of the mucous membrane lining the intestine is increased by circular folds and by villi, both of which project into the lumen of the intestine.

ACCESSORY DIGESTIVE ORGANS

In all animals, the glands that aid digestion, in addition to the numerous small glands located in the walls of the stomach and intestine, are quite similar. These accessory glands include the salivary glands, the liver, and the pancreas.

The Salivary Glands

The salivary glands consist of three pairs of well-defined glands as well as scattered lobules of salivary tissue. The chief salivary glands are the *parotid*, *mandibular*, and *sublingual*.

The *parotid salivary gland* is located ventral to the ear in relation to the caudal border of the mandible. In most animals the parotid salivary duct, along with the facial vessels, passes ventrally and cranially on the deep face of the caudal part of the mandible and crosses the cheek superficially just cranial to the masseter muscle (the large muscle that closes the jaw). The duct then passes dorsally to penetrate the mucous membrane of the cheek near the upper third or fourth cheek tooth. The parotid duct of the dog crosses the lateral face of the jaw directly and does not follow the contour of the mandible.

The *mandibular*, or *submaxillary*, *salivary gland* is usually located ventral to the parotid gland just caudal to the mandible. The mandibular gland may be deep to part of the parotid gland and mandible. The mandibular salivary duct

TABLE 17–3.—CHARACTER OF THE SALIVARY GLANDS
(Trautmann and Fiebiger, *Fundamentals of the Histology of Domestic Animals,*
courtesy of Comstock Publishing Associates, 1957.)

Serous Glands	Mucous Glands	Mixed Glands
Parotid (contains mucous end-pieces in young carnivores and lambs)	Labial glands of sheep, goats, and carnivores	Mandibular gland
	Lingual glands, except those listed elsewhere	Sublingual gland
Ventral buccal gland of cattle and its ventral portion in sheep and goats		Marginal glands of the tongue of the horse
	Middle and dorsal buccal glands of cattle	Glandula frenularis of sheep and goat
Ebner's glands under the circumvallate and foliate papillae	Ventral buccal gland of carnivores, and its dorsal portion in sheep and goats	Glands of the root of the tongue in horse and ox
		Buccal glands of horses and swine
		All glands not mentioned under mucous or serous glands

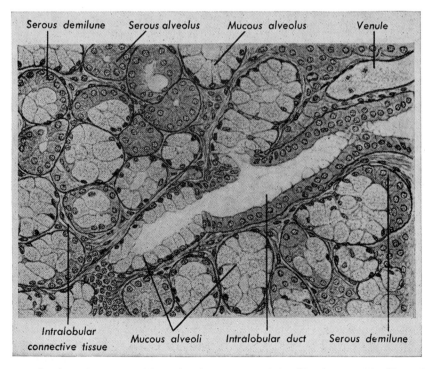

FIG. 17–16.—Section of human sublingual salivary gland. Magnification × 315. (Copenhaver, *Bailey's Textbook of Histology*, 15th ed., courtesy of Williams & Wilkins Co.)

passes forward medial to the mandible to open ventral to the tongue on a little papilla located slightly anterolateral to the *frenulum linguae* (fold that holds the tongue to the floor of the mouth).

The *sublingual salivary gland* is located deep to the mucous membrane along the ventral side of the lateral surface of the tongue near the floor of the mouth. Numerous ducts pass directly dorsally from the sublingual salivary gland to open into the floor of the mouth just ventrolateral to the tongue.

The salivary glands are classified as serous, mucous, or mixed. Serous means "whey-like." *Serous glands* secrete a watery clear fluid, as compared with *mucous glands* that secrete mucus, a thick viscid tenacious material that acts as a protective covering for the surface of mucous membranes. A mixed gland produces both mucus and serous fluids.

The cells of a serous secretory unit are somewhat pyramidal in shape (sections are wedge-shaped like a piece of pie), with the apex pointing toward the lumen of the *alveolus* (terminal unit of gland). The nucleus is round and located close to the base of the cell. Zymogen (secretion) granules are found between the nucleus and the apex of the cell, near the Golgi apparatus, and chromidial material is found near the base. There is some evidence that the cells are apocrine in nature, and some cytoplasm may be lost at the time the granules leave the cells.

Cells of mucous secretory units have flattened nuclei almost against the base of the cell. There are no zymogen granules or chromidial substance in the mucous cells, as found in serous cells. Instead there are a number of mucigen droplets which may appear as holes (vacuoles) in the usual stained section. The mucigen droplets, after leaving the cells, eventually form mucus.

Some glands contain both serous and mucous cells. They usually have mucous units associated with crescent-shaped groups of serous cells called *demilunes*. These serous cells probably secrete into the lumen of the mucous alveolus through small canals between the mucous cells.

The parotid glands are compound tubulo-alveolar serous glands enclosed in connective tissue capsules.

The submandibular (submaxillary) glands are mixed compound tubulo-alveolar glands predominantly serous in type. The capsule is well defined.

The sublingual glands are not well encapsulated. They are located deep to the mucous membrane on the floor of the mouth lateral to the tongue.

The small glands embedded in the submucosa are branched tubulo-alveolar glands, and the larger salivary glands are true compound tubulo-alveolar glands, connected with the oral cavity by one or more excretory ducts.

The secretion of mucous cells is basophilic and stains blue with common stains, such as H & E. The cytoplasm of serous cells, particularly the secretory granules, stains red, being acidophilic.

The pressure of the contents of mucous cells flattens the nuclei against the bases of the cells. Droplets of extruded *mucin* swell in water to form mucus.

Lobules of salivary glands contain intercalated ducts which join while still in the lobule to form striated tubules (salivary ducts), which continue as interlobular excretory ducts. The ducts to this level are lined by simple columnar epithelium, but larger excretory ducts are lined by two-layered columnar epithelium and then stratified columnar and finally by stratified squamous epithelium at the junction with the oral mucosa. Most if not all levels of ducts are believed to be secretory.

The Pancreas

The *pancreas* is a compound tubulo-alveolar gland which has both endocrine and exocrine portions. The exocrine por-

TABLE 18–3.—FATTY ACIDS COMMONLY FOUND IN LIPIDS

Acids	Formula	Melting Point °C.
Saturated acids:		
Butyric (butanoic)	$C_4H_8O_2$	Liquid
Caproic (hexanoic)	$C_6H_{12}O_2$	Liquid
Caprylic (octanoic)	$C_8H_{16}O_2$	16
Capric (decanoic)	$C_{10}H_{20}O_2$	31
Lauric (dodecanoic).	$C_{12}H_{24}O_2$	44
Myristic (tetradecanoic)	$C_{14}H_{28}O_2$	54
Palmitic (hexadecanoic)	$C_{16}H_{32}O_2$	63
Stearic (octadecanoic)	$C_{18}H_{36}O_2$	70
Arachidic (eicosanoic)	$C_{20}H_{40}O_2$	76
Lignoceric (tetracosanoic)	$C_{24}H_{48}O_2$	86
Unsaturated acids:		
Palmitoleic (hexadecenoic)	$C_{16}H_{30}O_2$	Liquid
Oleic (octadecenoic)	$C_{18}H_{34}O_2$	Liquid
Linoleic (octadecadienoic)	$C_{18}H_{32}O_2$	Liquid
Linolenic (octadecatrienoic)	$C_{18}H_{30}O_2$	Liquid
Arachidonic (eicosatetraenoic)	$C_{20}H_{32}O_2$	Liquid
Clupanodonic (docosapentaeonic) . .	$C_{22}H_{34}O_2$	Liquid

(Maynard and Loosli, *Animal Nutrition*, 5th ed., courtesy of McGraw-Hill Book Co., Inc.)

TABLE 18–4.—FATTY ACIDS AS A PERCENTAGE OF TOTAL FATTY ACIDS* AND
PHYSICAL CONSTANTS OF SOME COMMON FATS

	Butterfat	Lard	Coconut Fat	Soybean Fat	Corn Fat	Cotton-seed Fat
I. Saturated acids:						
Butyric	3.2					
Caproic	1.8	—	0.2			
Caprylic	0.8	—	8.2			
Capric	1.4	—	7.4			
Lauric	3.8	—	47.5			
Myristic	8.3	—	18.0	—	—	2.0
Palmitic	27.0	32.2	8.0	8.5	7.0	19.0
Stearic	12.5	7.8	2.8	3.5	2.4	2.0
Total saturated	58.8	40.0	92.8	21.1	9.4	24.4
II. Unsaturated acids:						
Oleic	35.0	48.0	5.6	17.0	45.6	20.1
Linoleic	3.0	11.0	1.6	54.4	45.0	55.5
Linolenic	0.8	0.6	—	7.1		
Melting point, °C.	28 to 36	35 to 45	20 to 35	Liquid at ordinary temperature		
Iodine No.	26 to 38	40 to 70	8 to 10	130 to 137	105 to 125	100 to 115
Saponification No.	220 to 241	193 to 220	250 to 260	190 to 194	87 to 93	190 to 200
Reichert-Meissl No.	23 to 33	—	6 to 8			

* Most of these data were taken from a compilation prepared by Verz R. Goddard and Louise Goodall, issued by the Agricultural Research Service, U.S. Department of Agriculture, May, 1959. (Maynard and Loosli, *Animal Nutrition*, 5th ed., courtesy of McGraw-Hill Book Co., Inc.)

with an alkali, a soap is formed, in a process called saponification. Since one molecule of alkali combines with one molecule of fatty acid, the larger the amount of alkali absorbed for a given quantity of fat, the more fatty acids present, and therefore the shorter the fatty-acid chains. If long-chain fatty acids make up the fat, there will be fewer acids and consequently a lower saponification number.

Unsaturated fats can be artificially saturated by adding hydrogen and breaking the double bonds. Some type of catalyst is needed for this reaction, called *hydrogenation*. Hydrogenated fats have a higher melting point and better keeping qualities than unsaturated fats of the same chain length. There is some evidence that vascular disease in man may be related to a diet high in saturated fats.

Waxes consist of a fatty acid combined with a monhydroxy alcohol (only one OH group). They are difficult to saponify and have a higher melting point than most fats.

The *phospholipids* contain phosphorus in addition to the lipid portion. They include such compounds as *lecithin, cephalins, sphingomyelins,* and *cerebrosides*.

α-Lecithin

(choline)
β-Lecithin

Sterols are unsaponifiable high-molecular-weight alcohols. They may occur free or as esters of fatty acids. *Cholesterol*, the best-known example of a sterol, has the formula $C_{27}H_{45}OH$. Plant sterols are called *phytosterols*. *Ergosterol*, found in both plants and animals, is transformed into vitamin D when it is irradiated by ultraviolet light.

MINERAL MATTER

Total mineral matter (the inorganic constituents) of plants (feed) is determined by burning a sample of feed until the ash formed contains no carbon. Although this process gives an indication of total mineral matter, it does not indicate what elements or how much of each make up the ash. Structural parts of plants, the leaves and stems, are higher in ash than is the grain portion.

The following mineral elements are accepted as essential for the animal body: *phosphorus, calcium, sodium, potassium, magnesium, iron, manganese, copper, zinc, chlorine, fluorine, sulfur,* and *iodine*. *Cobalt* probably is also essential or at least quite important in the animal body because it is a part of vitamin B_{12}, *cobalamin*. Traces of many elements are found in small amounts in the animal body. These trace elements may be essential for the animal body, but it is difficult to prove or disprove because of the small quantities involved.

VITAMINS

Vitamins include a large number of organic compounds that are, in general, chemically unrelated. They are essential for normal metabolism, but most cannot be produced by the body. However, many vitamins are formed by microorganisms in the digestive tract.

Fat-soluble vitamins are either soluble in fat or absorbed with fat. *Vitamins* A, D, E, and K are the common fat-soluble vitamins.

Water-soluble vitamins are either soluble in water or absorbed with water. Common water soluble vitamins are B_1, B_2, B_{12}, C, *niacin*, and *folic acid*. Vitamins are discussed in more detail in Chapter 21, p. 308.

CHAPTER 19

PHYSICAL FACTORS IN DIGESTION

PREHENSION AND CHEWING

THE act of bringing food into the mouth is called *prehension*. The teeth, lips, and tongue are used as prehensile organs by domestic animals. The lips of the horse, the tongue of the cow and sheep, and the snout of the pig are used extensively in obtaining food.

Mastication (chewing) usually follows prehension immediately. The type of teeth, arrangement of jaws, and chewing habits vary with the species and class of food ingested. Carnivorous animals have simple teeth and tear their food but do very little grinding. Herbivorous animals have at least some hypsodont teeth, the upper jaw is wider than the lower jaw, and chewing of the food is quite thorough. The folding of enamel, dentine, and cementum results in a ridged surface of the teeth due to differential rate of wear of the different substances. Enamel, being the hardest substance in the teeth, forms ridges and also may form sharp points. The points are on the buccal (cheek) side of the upper teeth and the lingual (tongue) side of the lower teeth. These sharp points may interfere with chewing and in horses may make the mouth extremely sensitive to the bridle.

The *lateral pterygoid muscles* and *temporal muscles* close the jaws; the *medial pterygoid muscles* produce a grinding action; and the *digastricus* and *sterno-mandibularis* muscles open the jaws.

Mastication can be controlled voluntarily, but the presence of food in the mouth will cause reflex chewing.

SALIVARY GLANDS

Sympathetic nerves go to the salivary glands by way of the cervical sympathetic trunk to the cranial cervical ganglion, where synapses occur. The postganglionic sympathetic fibers pass from the *cranial cervical ganglion* to the salivary glands with the arteries that supply the glands.

The *parotid salivary gland* receives parasympathetic nerve fibers from the *glossopharyngeal nerve*, which accompanies the auriculo-temporal branch of the trigeminal nerve.

The *mandibular* and *sublingual salivary glands* receive parasympathetic nerve fibers from the *chorda tympani* branch of the *facial nerve* that joins the lingual branch of the trigeminal nerve. The nuclei of origin of these nerves are located in the medulla oblongata.

Experiments with dogs indicate that parasympathetic stimulation of both mandibular and parotid salivary glands increases blood supply to the glands and causes secretion of generous amounts of rather thin *saliva*. Sympathetic stimulation on the other hand decreases blood supply and either inhibits flow of saliva or causes secretion of a thick mucous type of saliva.

The fact that saliva contains mucus not found as such in blood, that metabolic activity of the gland is high during secretion, and that pressure in a salivary duct caused by secretion can exceed arterial blood pressure all indicate that saliva is a true secretion actively produced and not merely a fluid transudate that passively crosses the cell membrane.

Secretion of *saliva* is a reflex act that normally is stimulated by the presence of food in the mouth. When dry food is in the mouth the saliva is watery and copious. When food is moist, only enough mucous saliva is secreted to lubricate the food during swallowing.

It is well known that the sight of food may cause the mouth to water. This is called a *psychic reflex* because it involves connection with the cerebrum. It is also a good example of a *conditioned reflex* as studied by Pavlov, the Russian scientist who did much of the initial work on conditioned reflexes. The sight, smell, or even thought of food can initiate reflex salivation. The type of saliva produced corresponds to the dryness of the food, just as occurs when a stimulus comes from food in the mouth. Psychic reflex salivation in domestic animals is absent or very limited in the horse and ruminants. It has been demonstrated in the dog and pig.

Mechanical stimulation of the ruminant cardia evokes reflex salivation. The afferent impulse is carried by way of the *vagus nerves.*

The saliva of domestic animals contains little or no *ptyalin* (also called *amylase*), the enzyme of saliva that hydrolyzes starch to maltose. Small amounts have been reported in the saliva of the dog and pig. In the ruminant, saliva functions to maintain the fluid consistency of the rumen contents, helps neutralize acids formed by rumen organisms, and may help prevent frothing.

SWALLOWING

Deglutition, the act of swallowing, is arbitrarily divided into three stages. The first stage involves passage through the mouth, the second involves passage through the pharynx, and the third consists of passage through the esophagus into the stomach.

The first stage of swallowing is under voluntary control. After the food is chewed and mixed with saliva and a bolus is formed, the food is placed on the upper surface of the tongue. The tongue then is raised, tip first, against the hard palate, moving the bolus toward the pharynx. At the same time the soft palate is raised, closing the posterior nares. The base of the tongue then acts as a plunger, forcing the bolus into the pharynx.

As the *bolus* enters the pharynx it touches sensitive areas which reflexly initiates the second stage, passage of the bolus through the pharynx. Respiration is reflexly inhibited, and the larynx is reflexly closed and pulled upward and forward. The base of the tongue folds the epiglottis over the laryngeal opening as it moves back. The pharynx is shortened, and a peristaltic (milking) action of the pharyngeal muscles forces the bolus into the esophagus.

The third stage of deglutition consists of reflex peristalsis of the esophagus, initiated by the presence of food in the esophagus. Peristalsis consists of alternate relaxation and contraction of rings of smooth muscle in the wall of the gut, coupled with regional contraction of longitudinal muscles in the area of the bolus.

Solid and semisolid food is carried through the esophagus of the horse by peristalsis at a rate of 35 to 40 cm. per second. Liquids are carried about five times as fast by a squirting action of the mouth and possibly the pharynx.

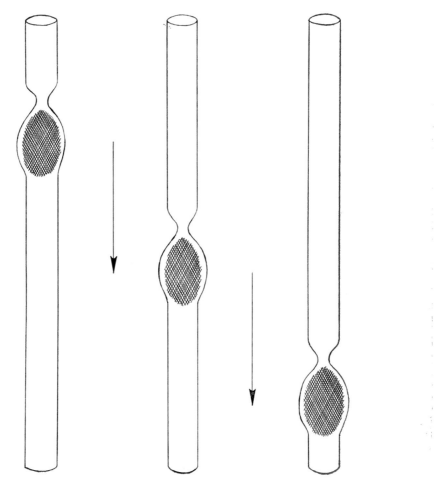

F𝗶𝗀. 19–1.—Diagram of peristalsis in the esophagus. A wave of relaxation precedes the bolus and a wave of constriction follows the bolus. (After Carlson and Cavert, *The Machinery of the Body,* The University of Chicago Press.)

STOMACH

Relaxation of the cardia is essential for food to enter the stomach. In the simple stomach as found in man, pig, horse, and dog, the first food consumed when the stomach is empty travels to the pyloric end of the stomach. Food subsequently swallowed tends to become stratified (form layers) as the stomach fills. Experiments with differentially colored foods in the horse have shown this to be correct.

Movements in the stomach are most vigorous in the pyloric region, where most of the mixing of food occurs. In man the upper half of the stomach shows mostly steady *tonic contractions*, the middle of the stomach has recurring peristaltic contractions, and the pyloric area serves to mix the food and send it into the duodenum.

Two factors that appear to control the pyloric sphincter are the acidity of the food in the stomach and the presence or absence of food in the duodenum. With the duodenum empty, as soon as the food in the pyloric end of the stomach becomes sufficiently acid, it passes through

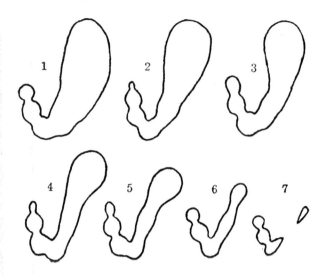

Fig. 19–2.—Changes in the shape of the stomach of a cat at intervals of an hour during the digestion of a meal, as revealed by tracings of the shadow cast on the fluorescent screen. (From Alvarez, *The Mechanics of the Digestive Tract*, Paul B. Hoeber, Inc.)

the pyloric sphincter and into the duodenum. This material, called chyme (different from chyle in the lymphatics) is a mushy, semisolid mixture of food, water, and gastric juice. The pyloric sphincter remains closed until the duodenum is empty.

The length of time food remains in the stomach varies with the type and consistency of the food and with the species.

Water may pass through a full stomach without diluting the contents to any great extent (under 10 per cent in the horse). Water ingested when the stomach is nearly empty will mix more readily with the stomach contents than if the stomach is full. In man, food leaves the stomach in the order of water, carbohydrates, proteins, and fats. The more fluid the consistency of the food, the sooner it leaves the stomach.

The stomach of carnivores will empty within a few hours, usually before the next meal. On the other hand, other animals require many hours to empty the stomach. Both the horse and pig require a full day's fast (twenty-four hours) to empty a full stomach.

In addition to the typical pattern of stomach contraction, a series of peristaltic waves travels from the cardia to the pylorus when the stomach is empty or nearly so. These contractions, known as hunger contractions, can be correlated with the sensation of hunger in man and presumably also in animals. In the horse, hunger contractions may begin as early as five hours after eating, when the stomach still contains quite a bit of food. The level of blood sugar is related to the intensity of hunger contractions. As the blood-sugar level decreases, the intensity of hunger contractions increases, along with the need for more food by the animal.

GASTRIC MOVEMENTS IN RUMINANTS

The rumen and reticulum of the adult cow normally undergo a fairly complicated sequence of contractions which are repeated at varying frequencies up to several times per minute. First the reticulum contracts sharply, forcing fluid material into the rumen. This first contraction is followed immediately by a second reticular contraction. The anterior pillar of the rumen starts to contract before the second reticular contraction is completed, thus shunting much of the material expelled from the reticulum into the anterior dorsal sac of the rumen. The ruminal contraction started at the anterior pillar passes back along the longitudinal pillars, posterior pillar, dorsal coronary pillars, and adjacent rumen wall of the dorsal sac. The ventral coronary pillars and ventral sac of the rumen contract as soon as the dorsal sac and associated pillars relax. The entire rumen contraction starting with the anterior pillar is then repeated before the reticulum contracts again to initiate a whole new cycle. Variations of the preceding pattern are quite common. Frequency of rumen contractions has been reported in cows at rest as 1.8 per minute, cows ruminating at 2.3 per minute, and cows eating as 2.8 per minute. Rumen contractions can be felt by forcing the fist into the upper left flank (paralumbar fossa). Pathologic conditions of the rumen usually result in a decreased rate or complete cessation of rumen movements.

Hyperglycemia (an increase in blood sugar level) produced by glucose injection inhibits rumen activity. *Hypoglycemia* (decreased blood sugar level) due to insulin injection stimulates rumen activity.

Rumination is a process that permits an animal to forage and ingest food rapidly, then complete the chewing at a later time. It involves regurgitation of the food (returning it to the mouth), remastication (rechewing), reinsalivation (mixing with saliva), and finally reswallowing of the food.

Regurgitation is the only step of rumination that differs markedly from the initial mastication, insalivation, and swallowing of the food. *Regurgitation* is preceded by contraction of the reticulum, which presumably brings some of the heavier ingesta into proximity to the cardia. This is followed immediately by an inspiratory movement with the glottis closed. The negative pressure produced in the thorax by this movement is transmitted to the relatively thin-walled esophagus, causing the thoracic esophagus and cardia to dilate. The lower pressure in the esophagus as compared to the rumen causes a quantity of material (semifluid ingesta) to pass through the cardia into the esophagus. Probably a reverse peristalsis in the esophagus is the major factor in moving the material up to the mouth, where excess liquid is squeezed out and swallowed.

The speed of regurgitation suggests that striated muscle rather than smooth muscle provides the active force. Apparently contractions of the esophageal groove between the cardia and the reticulo-omasal orifice, the rumen, the reticulum, and the abdominal muscles play little if any part in the actual process of regurgitation. Any opening into the trachea or thorax that interferes with the production of a negative pressure in the thorax does inhibit regurgitation.

Remastication occurs in a more leisurely manner than the initial chewing. Jaw movements of about 55 per minute during remastication compare with 94 per minute while eating grain and silage and 78 per minute while eating hay. Submaxillary salivary glands are less active during the reinsalivation than initially.

The bolus formed after regurgitation and rechewing is swallowed just as any other bolus and apparently enters the rumen rather than passing into the omasum or abomasum (true stomach) as was once believed.

The regurgitated material consists largely of roughage and fluid with little if any concentrate. It is well known that whole kernels of corn may pass through the entire digestive tract with little change in physical appearance.

Cattle average about eight hours a day ruminating, with periods of activity scattered throughout the entire day. One rumination cycle requires about one minute, of which three to four seconds is utilized for both regurgitation and re-swallowing.

Rumination appears to be largely reflex in nature, although the process can be interrupted or stopped voluntarily. Both afferent and efferent portions of the reflex probably are carried in the vagus nerves. Contact of roughage with the reticulum and more particularly near the cardia likely is the major stimulus for rumination.

CLOSURE OF THE ESOPHAGEAL GROOVE

Closure of the *esophageal groove* is of importance in young ruminants. Nursing appears to reflexly stimulate closure of the groove, which causes the milk to by-pass the rumen and reticulum and pass directly to the abomasum. The paunchiness of bucket-fed calves usually is attributed to milk entering the rumen, where it is not properly digested. The use of buckets with nipples tends to prevent appreciable amounts of milk from entering the rumen. After weaning, fluid drunk from open containers largely passes into the rumen and reticulum. This has been called a thirst pattern as opposed to a nursing pattern that involves reflex closing of the esophageal groove in young nursing calves.

Reflex closure of the *esophageal groove* has been produced with sodium salts in cattle less than two years old. *Copper sulfate* initiates reflex closure of the esophageal groove in sheep within eight seconds after it is given. The groove remains closed from one to eleven seconds.

The pharynx appears to be the location where the stimulus is effective. The afferent side of the reflex is by way of the *cranial laryngeal nerve*, and the main part of the vagus nerve carries the efferent side of the reflex.

Eventually food that has soaked enough and is finely enough divided finds its way through the reticulo-omasal orifice. It may pass directly into the abomasum by way of the omasal groove or stop in the omasum for further processing. The factors responsible for this passage are not well understood.

THE OMASUM

The *omasum* is nearly always found packed tightly with rather dry roughage in animals examined after death. The appearance of the omasal leaves studded with short horny papillae suggests a burr type of grinder. However, the amount of grinding and mechanism of grinding is still in doubt. Movement of the leaves seems quite limited and not caused by stimulation of the vagus nerve. The omasal wall undergoes strong contractions when the vagus nerve is stimulated. Some peristaltic-type contractions of the omasum have been described. Omasal contractions presumably squeeze fluid out of the ingesta, grind the solids to some extent, and move it on into the abomasum.

THE ABOMASUM

Movements of the *abomasum* resemble movements described for the simple stomach. Activity in the area of the fundus is quite limited. Contractions of the body are more marked, and peristaltic waves are seen in the pyloric portion. Activity of the abomasum depends to some extent on the contents of the duodenum. Abomasal activity is inhibited by weak hydrochloric acid and fat emulsion, but activity is stimulated by hypertonic saline solutions and emptying of the duodenum.

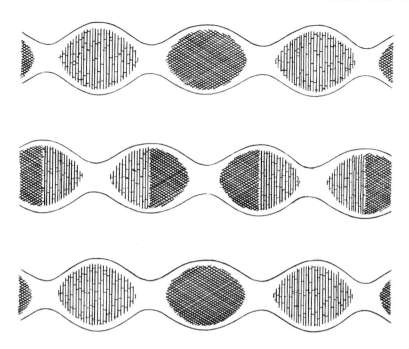

Fig. 19-3.—Diagram of rhythmic segmentation in the small intestine. Three stages in mixing of small masses of food are shown. (After Carlson and Cavert, *The Machinery of the Body*, The University of Chicago Press.)

THE SMALL INTESTINE

Movement of the intestine is similar in the non-ruminant and ruminant.

Reflex movements of the *intestine* are initiated by the stimulus of material within the lumen, stretching the intestinal wall. Intestinal movements not only propel the ingesta through the gut, but also mix it with digestive juices, bring it into contact with the intestinal wall and villi for absorption, and aid circulation of blood and lymph.

Rhythmic segmentation is a type of intestinal movement that does not move the contents along the intestine, but merely mixes it. Intermittent contractions of circular muscle fibers divide the ingesta into bead-like segments. In a few seconds the next series of contractions occurs in the muscle fibers near the middle of each of the segments, dividing it in two and thus uniting adjacent halves to form new

segments. Rhythmic segmentation facilitates absorption by bringing the ingesta into contact with the villi and by stimulating the flow of blood and lymph in the intestinal wall.

Peristalsis refers to movement that tends to propel the ingesta along the intestine in a direction toward the anus. According to Starling's law of the intestine, the presence of material in the intestine stimulates contraction of the circular muscle fibers on the oral side (in front) of the material and relaxation of the muscle fibers in the region of the material and a segment beyond the material. Some workers have been unable to find evidence of relaxation of the intestinal wall and believe the ingesta are forced into succeeding segments by contraction of appropriate circular muscles on the oral side. The peristaltic wave (whether contraction alone or contraction and relaxation) moves along the intestine at a rate between ½ and 1 inch per minute. A peristaltic rush is much faster, covering as much as 1 to 10 inches per second; otherwise the mechanism appears to be similar to that of slower peristalsis.

The normal direction of peristalsis is from oral to aboral as from the pylorus toward the ilio-cecal junction. Reverse peristalsis, also called antiperistalsis, is a movement in the opposite direction (aboral to oral). Its function in the small intestine may be to slow movement of ingesta and insure thorough mixing.

Segments of small intestine have been completely isolated and placed in appropriate fluids for study. Each segment exhibits a rhythmic contraction that is fastest near the pylorus and decreases in rate as distance from the pylorus increases. Isolated segments of intestine also possess electrical activity that can be recorded.

The villi of the intestinal wall undergo intrinsic movements such as shortening, lengthening, and swaying from side to side. These movements increase the contact with the ingesta and encourage circulation of blood and lymph in the villi.

THE LARGE INTESTINE

Isolated segments of large intestine show less tendency for automatic rhythmic contractions than do isolated segments of the small intestine.

Peristalsis, reverse peristalsis, and contractions of *sacculations* are the chief types of contractions in the large intestine. Movements of the large intestine tend to be slower and apparently less well organized than movements of the small intestine.

Peristalsis carries contents of the large intestine in the direction of the anus. Reverse peristalsis may alternate with peristalsis to move the ingesta forward and back, thus increasing the opportunity for absorption. Reverse peristalsis may also force ingesta into the cecum, from which it is emptied by contraction of the cecum.

Non-ruminant herbivorous animals display active contractions of the sacculations (*haustra*) of the large intestine which resemble pendular movements of the small intestine.

CHAPTER 20

ABSORPTION OF FOOD AND ENZYMES OF DIGESTION

ABSORPTION

No food is absorbed before it reaches the stomach, and little of the food in the stomach is in small enough units to be absorbed there even after stomach digestion. Proteins and carbohydrates are only partially digested in the stomach, and fats are only slightly hydrolyzed before the food passes into the intestine. A large amount of absorption occurs in the small intestines of all animals, particularly carnivores and omnivores.

Absorption in the large intestine is most important in simple-stomach herbivorous animals, since much digestion takes place in the colon, and these substances obviously cannot be absorbed before they are digested. Large amounts of water are absorbed from the large intestines of all animals.

The fore-stomach of ruminants (rumen, reticulum, and omasum) have been shown to absorb a number of drugs, salts of sodium and potassium, carbonates and chlorides of various substances, and end products of digestion, including glucose and short-chain fatty acids (acetic, proprionic, and butyric).

The mucosa of the intestine cannot absorb to any extent large molecules of carbohydrates, proteins, or fats. The end products (simple sugars, amino acids,

fatty acids, and glycerol), of digestion of these substances, however, pass quite readily through the mucosa and into the blood or lymph vessels.

AMINO ACIDS AND SIMPLE SUGARS

In general, the *amino acids* and *simple sugars* enter those blood vessels that are tributaries to the portal vein. The *portal vein* carries these substances to the liver sinusoids, where they may be acted upon by the liver epithelial cells. Blood from the liver sinusoids then passes into the general circulation by way of the central veins of the liver to the hepatic veins, and thence into the caudal vena cava.

FATS

Most of the fat enters the *lacteals*, small lymph vessels in the intestinal villi, and is carried as *chyle* to larger lymph vessels, which eventually empty into the *cysterna chyli* between the two crura of the diaphragm. From the cystern chyli the chyle (lymph-containing fat) passes by way of the thoracic duct to the cranial vena cava or to the jugular veins near their entrance into the vena cava and enters the venous circulation in this manner.

There has been much debate as to whether *fat* can be absorbed as neutral fat or only in the form of fatty acids and glycerol. Nor is it completely settled as to the fate of absorbed fatty acids and glycerol. They probably recombine within the epithelial cells and enter the blood as neutral fat. The fatty acids in the presence of alkali and bile salts can form soluble soaps and may be absorbed in that form.

Evidence gained with the electron microscope indicates that small droplets of emulsified fat can be absorbed directly by the epithelial cells of the intestine and pass into the lacteals in the same form.

MECHANISMS OF ABSORPTION

Contractions of the smooth muscle of the intestinal wall (lamina muscularis), of the muscularis mucosa, and of the smooth muscle within the villi all aid digestion and absorption by churning the intestinal contents and by pumping fluid (blood and lymph) from the intestinal capillaries and lacteals.

The mechanism of *absorption* appears to involve more than the usual physical and chemical forces of filtration, osmosis, diffusion, adsorption, and imbibition, although these undoubtedly are important factors in absorption.

The fact that absorption is an active process rather than merely being passive is suggested by the ability of epithelial cells to absorb selectively materials such as glucose, galactose, and fructose in unequal concentrations. Glucose is absorbed faster than galactose and galactose faster than fructose, as long as the epithelium is alive and undamaged. However, after death the three sugars pass through the mucosa at equal rates, because only passive absorption by physical forces are then involved. During absorption, the epithelial cells increase their metabolic activity, as shown by increased oxygen consumption.

ENZYMES OF DIGESTION

Secretion of *saliva* is an active process that can occur against pressure in the salivary duct that is greater than carotid arterial pressure. Material such as mucin is found in saliva but not in the blood, and consumption of oxygen and glucose also indicate metabolic activity during secretion rather than simply a transudate crossing the cell membrane.

Saliva of the dog and pig contains some *amylase* capable of digesting starch. Saliva in the cow, sheep, and goat does not contain any amylase, but saliva of the horse may contain very small amounts of amylase.

STOMACH GLANDS

Stomach glands include cardiac glands, fundic glands, and pyloric glands.

Cardiac glands produce little if anything besides mucus.

Fundic glands contain specialized cells called body chief cells, neck chief cells, and parietal cells. The body chief cells contain zymogen granules which are the precursors of gastric enzymes. The neck chief cells are mucous cells that resemble cardiac gland cells and pyloric gland cells. Parietal cells produce hydrochloric acid.

The *pyloric glands* mainly produce mucus and a small amount of proteolytic enzyme.

GASTRIC JUICE

Gastric juice contains the enzymes pepsin, rennin, and gastric lipase, as well as hydrochloric acid. *Pepsin* begins the hydrolysis (digestion) of protein in the stomach if the pH is acid. The most favorable pH range is from 1.3 to 5, depending on the protein. Digestion of protein is completed in the intestine.

Rennin is the enzyme of young ruminants which causes milk to coagulate in the presence of calcium ions. Dukes (1955) gives the following reaction: "Casein + rennin → paracasein (soluble). Paracasein + Ca → calcium paracaseinate (coagulum)." The precipitate thus formed tends to remain in the stomach longer than does the same substance in the liquid form.

Gastric lipase can hydrolyze fats that are emulsified, such as milk fat, but it probably has little effect on unemulsified fats. Most fat digestion occurs in the small intestine. Carnivores have the most gastric lipase; herbivorous animals have much less.

Hydrochloric acid, produced by the parietal cells of the fundic glands of the stomach, is found in all domestic animals. The mechanism of production has not been completely determined, but studies using the electron microscope have suggested that the smooth surface endoplasmic reticulum may be the actual site of hydrochloric acid production within the cell. The hydrochloric acid activates pepsin and rennin and aids pepsin in protein digestion. It, of course, is a major factor in lowering the pH of the stomach contents.

Stimulation of gastric-juice secretion may result from the presence of food in the mouth (the cephalic phase), in the stomach (the gastric phase), or in the duodenum (the intestinal phase).

The *cephalic phase of gastric-juice secretion* results from the act of eating, even though the food may not enter the stomach, as in experimental animals that have had the esophagus severed. Stimuli reach the stomach by way of the *vagus nerves*. Herbivorous animals do not appear to have a cephalic phase of gastric stimulation.

The *gastric phase* occurs when food reaches the stomach and gastric-juice secretion increases for a period up to several hours. Mechanical stimulation of the stomach mucous membrane may increase the flow of gastric juice reflexly or by increasing the blood supply. Substances in the food called *secretogogues* (which may be incompletely digested proteins) stimulate the stomach mucosa to produce a hormone, *gastrin*. Gastrin, produced by the pyloric cells, in turn increases the secretion of gastric juice. Some authorities believe *histamine* and gastrin are identical.

The *intestinal phase of gastric secretion* occurs when products of gastric digestion reach the duodenum. A hormone from the intestine, *intestinal gastrin*, is carried by the blood stream to the stomach, where it also stimulates secretion of gastric juice.

PANCREATIC GLAND JUICE

Secretion of pancreatic juice is largely under hormonal control by two hormones produced in the mucosa of the duodenum in response to acid from the stomach. *Secretin* increases the rate of flow and bicarbonate concentration in pancreatic juice, and *pancreozymin* increases the amount of enzyme in the pancreatic juice.

Stimulation of the vagus nerves will also cause the pancreas to secrete the juice rich in enzymes similar to that produced by pancreozymin. This neural control may be reflexly stimulated by eating.

Pancreatic juice contains sodium carbonate and sodium bicarbonate (which neutralize acid from the stomach and increase the alkalinity) and a number of enzymes that function in the hydrolysis of proteins, fats, and carbohydrates.

Proteolytic enzymes include *trypsin* and *chymotrypsin* (which are secreted as inactive precursors, *trypsinogen* and *chymotrypsinogen*), and the enzyme *carboxypeptidase*, which acts on peptides.

Trypsinogen is activated by calcium and by a substance called *enterokinase*, a constituent of the intestinal juice. Chymotrypsinogen is activated by trypsin.

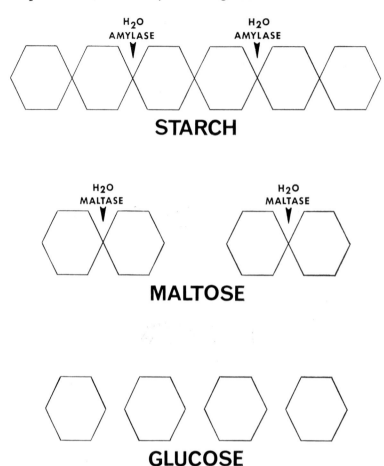

Fig. 20–1.—The hydrolysis of starch to glucose. Amylase hydrolyzes starch into maltose molecules. Maltase then hydrolyzes each maltose molecule into two glucose molecules.

These enzymes usually continue protein digestion that was started by pepsin in the gastric juice, although they can attack undigested proteins. The end products of protein digestion are amino acids, but the pancreatic proteolytic enzymes may stop digestion when the peptides reach a length of two or more amino acids. If this occurs, intestinal peptidases complete hydrolysis of the peptides to individual amino acids.

Pancreatic amylase (also called *amylopsin* and *pancreatic diastase*) can convert starch to the disaccharide sugar maltose. *Maltase,* also found in pancreatic juice, hydrolyzes maltose to glucose.

Pancreatic lipase (*steapsin*) hydrolyzes fats into fatty acids and glycerol. This action is most effective after the fats have been emulsified by bile. A pH near 8 is optimum for the action of steapsin in fat hydrolysis and for trypsin in protein hydrolysis.

INTESTINAL ENZYMES

Succus entericus, intestinal juice, is derived from intestinal glands in the *crypts of Lieberkühn,* scattered throughout the entire small intestine, and from *Brunners' glands* (*duodenal glands*), found only in the duodenum. Secretion by these glands is stimulated by the presence of food in the intestine. Presumably this is a reflex stimulation of a local nature. The presence of a hormone, *enterocrinin*, that causes release of intestinal juice, has been described, but the existence and function of such a hormone and the effect of autonomic nerves are still debated subjects.

In addition to water, salts, and mucus, a number of enzymes have been described in intestinal juice. These include the following:

Enterokinase—activates trypsinogen

Inverting enzymes—

  Maltase—hydrolyzes maltose to glucose

  Sucrase—hydrolyzes sucrose to glucose and levulose

  Lactase — hydrolyzes lactose to glucose and galactose

Peptidase—hydrolyzes peptides to amino acids

Polynucleotidase—splits nucleic acid into mononucleotides

Nucleotidase — hydrolyzes nucleotides into nucleosides and phosphoric acid

Nucleosidase—hydrolyzes nucleosides

BILE

Secretion of *bile* occurs in the hepatic cells of the liver. In all farm animals except the horse, bile is stored in the *gallbladder*. Since the horse has no gallbladder, the bile passes directly from the liver to the duodenum by way of the bile duct and its tributaries at a fairly continuous rate. The gallbladder not only stores bile for intermittent discharge into the duodenum, but also concentrates the bile, adds mucus to the bile, and serves as a relief mechanism to prevent excessive pressure in the hepatic ducts coming from the liver substance.

Emptying of the gallbladder appears to be caused by a hormone, *cholecystokinin*, produced by the mucosa of the first part of the small intestine.

Factors responsible for stimulating the liver to produce bile are not well understood. Apparently the autonomic nerves have little or no effect, so either some agent carried in the blood may be effective, or simply changes in volume and pressure of blood passing through the liver may control bile secretion.

Bile is a greenish-yellow liquid consisting largely of water, bile salts, bile pigments, and cholesterol, with smaller amounts of fats and inorganic salts. The bile salts, sodium and potassium salts of glycocholic and taurocholic acids, are the chief factors that make bile assist digestion and absorption, particularly of fats. Bile aids in emulsification of fats and increases the solubility of the long-chain fatty acids that are otherwise nearly insoluble in water. It also aids absorption of fat-soluble vitamins. Bile may also activate pancreatic lipase and accelerate the action of pancreatic amylase. The basic salts in bile aid in obtaining an alkaline pH in the intestine, and the mucin acts as a stabilizer for maintaining fat in an emulsified state.

CHOLESTEROL

Cholesterol formed in the liver is excreted in the bile whenever an excess occurs. Sometimes cholesterol precipitates from the bile in the gallbladder or bile ducts in the form of gallstones. This may occur when insufficient bile salts are produced. In man, excess cholesterol in the body has been implicated in diseases of the heart and blood vessels.

CHAPTER 21

METABOLISM

GENERAL

A TANK of gasoline under certain conditions may explode (combine with oxygen rapidly and violently), almost instantly producing a great deal of heat (energy) through oxidation of the hydrogen and carbon to water and carbon dioxide respectively. The same gasoline (hydrogen and carbon), when burned under controlled conditions in an engine or gasoline stove, will be of much more value.

In a similar way a stack of hay or a bin full of grain may burn in a matter of hours, with a complete waste of the energy resulting from rapid oxidation of the carbon and hydrogen in the carbohydrate, fats, and proteins of the feed. However, if this same material is fed to livestock, the stepwise-controlled oxidation (*metabolism*) will provide enough energy in the proper amounts to maintain a herd of livestock over a period of time.

Energy relationships within the animal body are studied under the broad classification of metabolism. That which results in building and maintaining body tissues and storage of energy is classified as anabolism. The process in which substances are broken down, with the concurrent release of energy, is classified as catabolism.

All energy available to the animal ultimately is derived from the sun. Plants utilize this energy in *photosynthesis* to combine CO_2 and H_2O in the formation of plant tissue and consequent storage of energy. Strictly herbivorous animals obtain this energy directly from plants; omnivores receive some energy directly from plants and some second-hand by eating flesh of other animals; and strict carnivores receive all of their energy second- or third-hand by consuming only other animals. Catabolism of the three major classes of foods—carbohydrates, fats, and proteins—provides the energy for all vital processes in the animal body. This energy is temporarily stored in the form of so-called "high-energy bonds" which link phosphorus and oxygen atoms in *ATP* (*adenosine triphosphate*). In the presence of the appropriate enzyme

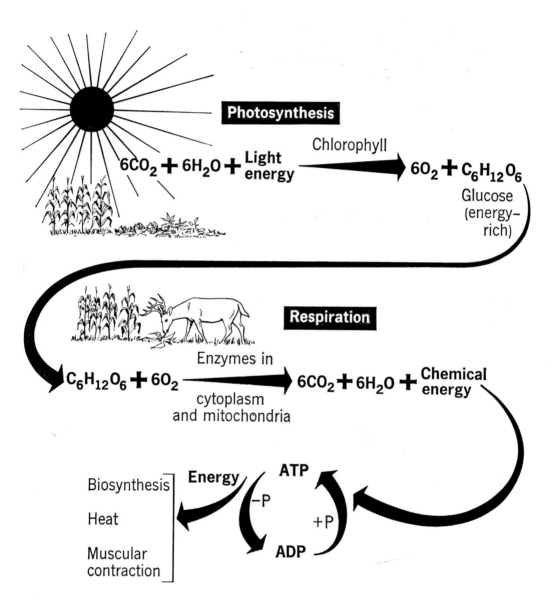

FIG. 21–1.—Energy relationships in life. (Biological Science: *An Inquiry Into Life*, courtesy of Harcourt, Brace & World, Inc. and American Institute of Biological Sciences.)

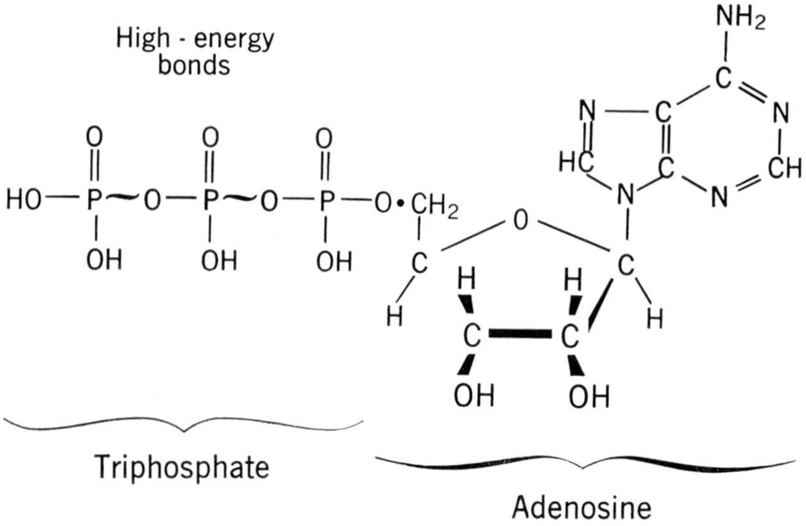

Fig. 21–2.—A diagram of a molecule of adenosine triphosphate (ATP), the substance that supplies most of the energy for the chemical reactions of a cell. Energy derived from the oxidation of foods is stored in ATP until needed for the cell's work.

(*ATPase*) one phosphate radical splits off, with the release of a great deal of available energy. The resulting compound, *ADP* (*adenosine diphosphate*) can be readily reconverted to ATP by the addition of phosphate and energy.

BREAKDOWN OF FOODS

Initial stages of chemical breakdown varies with the different foods, but the products of each enter the *Krebs cycle* (*citric-acid cycle* or *tricarboxylic-acid cycle*) at some point for the final common method of breakdown of foods (see Fig. 21–3).

As carbohydrate is broken down to *pyruvic acid*, about 10 per cent of its potential energy is released, which leaves 90 per cent of the energy to be released by oxidation of pyruvic acid by the citric-acid cycle. Fats are hydrolyzed into *glycerol* and *fatty acids*. The glycerol is transformed into *triose phosphate*, then into *phosphoglyceric acid*, and finally into pyruvic acid, which again enters the citric acid cycle for further oxidation.

The fatty acids eventually break down into a 2-carbon-atom compound, *acetyl-coenzyme A*, which enters the citric acid cycle.

Breakdown of protein is somewhat more complicated because the *amino acids* resulting from protein digestion must be deaminated (NH_2 groups removed) before further degradation can occur. Amino acids that form *glucose* and finally pyruvic acid are called *glycogenic amino acids*. Those that form *acetic acid* are called *ketogenic amino acids*. The glycogenic and ketogenic amino acids enter the citric acid cycle as pyruvic acid and as acetic acid respectively.

Oxidation reactions may involve the addition of oxygen, the removal of hydrogen, or the transfer of electrons.

CARBOHYDRATE METABOLISM

Carbohydrate metabolism involves chemical reactions and energy relationships in the utilization of *polysaccharides*, *disaccharides*, and *monosaccharides*.

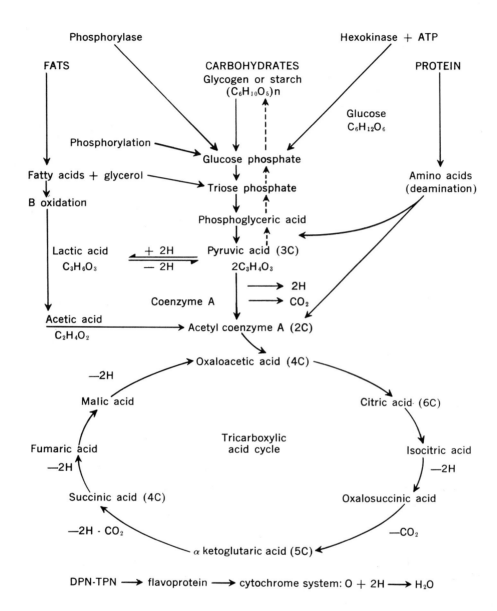

FIG. 21–3.—A simplified diagram of some of the phases of cellular metabolism including the tricarboxylic acid cycle (Krebs cycle). (DeCoursey, *The Human Organism*, courtesy of McGraw-Hill Book Co., Inc.)

Starch, glycogen, and disaccharides are hydrolyzed to monosaccharides by enzymes in the digestive tract of simple-stomach animals. More complex carbohydrates, such as *cellulose* and *pentosans,* must be digested by the organisms in the digestive tract to be of any value to the animal. This occurs to a marked degree only in herbivorous animals, where the carbohydrates are converted to fatty acids rather than to monosaccharides. In the ruminant much of the starch and sugar is also converted to fatty acids by the organisms in the rumen. These fatty acids, including acetic, *proprionic,* and *butyric acid,* are absorbed, at least to some extent, through the rumen wall.

The overall effect of carbohydrate catabolism is a release of a large amount of energy by the time the end products of CO_2 and H_2O are reached. However, just as combustion of ordinary fuel requires an initial flame, the process termed *glycolysis* requires outside energy for activation. This energy can be supplied in the form of ATP, which reacts with glucose to form *glucose 6 phosphate,* ADP, and hydrogen. The glucose 6 phosphate becomes *fructose 6 phosphate,* which reacts with more ATP to form *fructose 1, 6 diphosphate,* ADP and hydrogen. Fructose 1, 6 diphosphate, in the presence of the enzyme fructo-aldolase, splits into *glyceraldehyde 3 phosphate* and *dihydroxy-acetone phosphate.* After a series of reactions catalyzed by different enzymes, these last compounds finally yield pyruvic acid, which can then enter the Krebs cycle for continued oxidation.

One molecule of glyceraldehyde 3 phosphate forms one molecule of pyruvic acid. This process permits synthesis of two molecules of ATP (from ADP) and reduction of one molecule of *NAD* (*nicotinamide-adenine dinucleotide,* a hydrogen acceptor). The ATP formed is a ready source of energy for any biological work, including muscle contraction, glandular secretion, excretion, and active absorption.

Pyruvate in the presence of *NADH,* H^+, and the enzyme *lactic dehydrogenase* forms *lactate* and NAD. By means of the Krebs cycle, lactate can be completely oxidized to CO_2 and H_2O, with the release of a great deal of energy, largely in the form of high-energy phosphate bonds of ATP.

FATTY ACID METABOLISM

Fatty acids are oxidized through a series of reactions involving *coenzyme A* to acetyl coenzyme A, which can enter the Krebs cycle.

AMINO ACID METABOLISM

Amino acids are first deaminated to form a keto acid which may enter the Krebs cycle as pyruvic acid or may be changed to some compound that can enter the Krebs cycle at a different point.

SYNTHESIS OF GLYCOGEN, FAT, AND PROTEIN

Synthesis of *glycogen, fats,* and *proteins* may start at nearly any stage in the respective catabolic cycle. This anabolic process (synthesis) occurs wherever tissue is increased, as in growth, or when energy is stored in the form of fat or in the form of glycogen. The energy for synthesizing these compounds is derived from hydrolysis of ATP.

METABOLISM AND HEAT

In the late 1700's Lavoisier found that in a 10-hour period a guinea pig produced about the same amount of heat as produced by burning 3.3 grams of carbon, and that the carbon dioxide produced in the ten-hour period was the same volume as produced by burning 3.3 grams of carbon. Crawford had previously demonstrated the same relationship between oxygen consumption and heat production, regardless of whether carbon was burned inside the body or outside of it.

Lavoisier used an *ice calorimeter* to measure body heat produced by a guinea pig. This consisted of a chamber for the guinea pig, surrounded by another chamber filled with ice. The amount of heat produced was determined indirectly by measuring the amount of ice melted during a given period.

Metabolism of 1 gram of fat yields 9.3 calories of heat, about the same as produced by burning 1 gram of fat outside the body. One gram of carbohydrate yields about 4.1 calories when burned either outside or inside the body. Protein, however, yields 5.3 calories when burned outside the body but only 4.1 calories when metabolized. This difference in heat production by protein is due to the excretion of nitrogenous waste products from protein metabolism. The difference practically disappears when the heat equivalent of the urine and feces is added to the metabolic figure for protein.

Heat production measured by direct calorimetry (placing the animal in a calorimeter) agrees within one per cent with heat production calculated by indirect calorimetry (measurement of O_2 consumption and CO_2 production).

RESPIRATORY QUOTIENT

Respiratory quotient (*R. Q.*) is the ratio of CO_2 expired divided by O_2 inspired. The R. Q. of glucose is 1, since one molecule of CO_2 is produced for each molecule of O_2 used. This is generally true of any carbohydrate, because the hydrogen and oxygen in the molecule are in the same proportion as in water, which

leaves the carbon as the only element to be oxidized. Neither the carbon nor the hydrogen in fats is completely oxidized, so more molecules of O_2 are required than molecules of CO_2 produced. Some of the O_2 is used to oxidize a portion of the hydrogen to H_2O. This gives the R. Q. in the neighborhood of 0.71. Proteins give an R. Q. of about 0.80. The R. Q. is supposed to afford an indication of the type of food being metabolized. In animals fattened on carbohydrates, the R. Q. may be greater than 1, because a relatively oxygen-rich material (carbohydrate) is being converted to an oxygen-poor material (fat), so some oxygen that does not have to be inhaled is available for CO_2 production.

ENERGY VALUE OF FOODS

The energy value of food can be determined by the use of a *bomb calorimeter* which consists of a metal chamber surrounded by water. The chamber is loaded with a known sample of dried food and an excess of oxygen. The sample is ignited with an electric fuse and the heat produced is calculated from the rise in temperature of the water surrounding the chamber.

In physiological work the unit of heat is the large calorie (Calorie or Cal.). This is the amount of heat necessary to raise the temperature of 1 kg. of water from 15° to 16°, 1° C. This is 1000 times as much heat as the small calorie (calorie or cal.) which is the heat required to raise the temperature of 1 gram of water 1° C.

Basal metabolism refers to the amount of heat produced by a subject at complete rest twelve to fourteen hours after eating a light meal. Surface area is a more important factor than weight in influencing basal metabolism, so in man the basal metabolic rate is related to the calculated surface area of the individual.

VITAMINS

Water-Soluble Vitamins

The water-soluble vitamins function as enzymes in certain metabolic reactions. Specific dietary vitamin requirements vary considerably from species to species, depending in part on the ability of the animal to synthesize the particular vitamin and also on the presence of organisms in the digestive tract that may synthesize some of the vitamins.

Thiamine

Thiamine (vitamin B_1) functions widely as a coenzyme in *decarboxylation reactions*. Combined with ATP, thiamine forms *cocarboxylase*, which is a coenzyme for oxidative decarboxylation of pyruvic acid.

Deficiencies of thiamine cause *beriberi* in man and *polyneuritis* in birds. Ruminants and most other mammals do not ordinarily need additional thiamine in the diet because microorganisms in the digestive tract synthesize more thiamine than needed by the host animal. Accumulation of pyruvic acid and *lactic acid* in blood and tissues due to thiamine deficiency causes irritability, loss of appetite, and fatigue.

Cobalamin

Cobalamin (*vitamin B_{12}*) is a vitamin containing cobalt that is frequently seen as the cyanide derivative, *cyanocobalamin*. Vitamin B_{12} may function in protein synthesis and in metabolism of compounds containing one carbon atom. Deficiency of cobalamin causes an *anemia* because of failure of red blood cells to mature. Cobalamin can be found in most animal products such as milk, meat, and organ tissues.

Biotin

Biotin is probably involved in synthesis of *oxaloacetate*, in synthesis of protein, and in fixation of CO_2. Intestinal bacteria synthesize biotin, and egg yolk is a good source of biotin. Raw egg white contains an anti-biotin factor that inactivates the vitamin. Deficiency of biotin causes loss of hair, loss of weight, and, in chickens, high chick mortality and skeletal changes in the baby chicks.

Riboflavin

Riboflavin (*vitamin B_2 or G*) forms the *prosthetic group* for *flavoprotein coenzymes* that are necessary for oxidation reactions in normal cellular metabolism Intestinal and ruminal microorganisms synthesize riboflavin in adequate amounts for most animals. Calves will show deficiency symptoms if ruminal organisms are absent. Deficiency symptoms for riboflavin include loss of hair, skin lesions, and eye disorders. Yeast, milk products, liver, fish, and green vegetables are sources of riboflavin.

Niacin

Niacin (*nicotinic acid*) forms a part of *DPN* (*diphosphorpyridine nucleotide*), also known as *coenzyme I*, and also forms a part of *TPN* (*triphosphorpyridine nucleotide*), also known as *coenzyme II*. These coenzymes act with flavoproteins in cellular respiration (metabolism). Niacin plays a role in carbohydrate absorption and metabolism. *Tryptophan* is used in the synthesis of niacin by both mammals and microorganisms. Calves synthesize niacin even in the absence of rumenal organisms. "*Black tongue*" in dogs and *pellagra* in man result from deficiency of niacin.

Pyridoxine

Pyridoxine (*vitamin B_6*) is important in protein metabolism where *pyridoxal phosphate* is a coenzyme for *transamination* of alpha amino acids. Pyridoxine is synthesized by intestinal and ruminal microorganisms. Deficiency of pyridoxine may result in retarded growth, *dermatitis*, and *anemia*.

Pantothenic Acid

Pantothenic acid (PA) forms a part of co-enzyme A which acts in transfer of acetyl groups. This occurs in acetylation of choline to form *acetylcholine* and also occurs in the transfer of acetyl from pyruvic acid to the tricarboxylic acid cycle. Pantothenic acid is synthesized by rumen and intestinal microorganisms. Deficiencies of pantothenic acid are associated with dermatitis, loss of hair, graying of hair, and lesions of various organs.

Folic Acid

Folic acid (pteroylglutamic acid or *PGA)* functions in nucleoprotein metabolism and synthesis of *purines* and *pyrimidines*. Folic acid appears to be synthesized by intestinal microorganisms. Deficiency of folic acid seems to be associated with problems in blood formation, particularly those associated with bone marrow. Drugs such as *sulfonamides* that inhibit intestinal bacteria may cause folic-acid deficiency symptoms indirectly.

Alpha Lipoic Acid

Alpha lipoic acid (thiodic acid, or *6,8-dithio-n-octanoic acid)* is associated with thiamine in transfer of the acyl group from pyruvate. A-lipoic acid is synthesized by most animals, and the requirements have not been established.

Ascorbic Acid

Ascorbic acid (vitamin C) is not part of any known coenzyme, but it is involved in metabolism of some amino acids. Many plants and most vertebrate animals synthesize ascorbic acid. Guinea pigs, monkeys, and men, however, must receive their ascorbic acid in the diet.

Deficiency of ascorbic acid causes *scurvy,* which has symptoms of bleeding due to increased capillary fragility and presumed damage to intercellular cement.

Other Substances

Other substances that function in metabolism include *hematin* (a part of

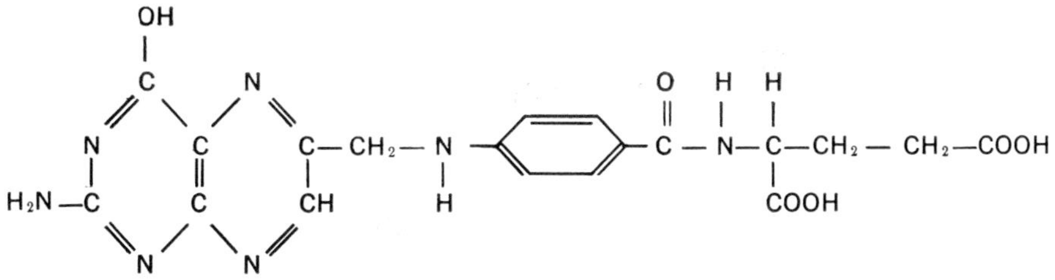

Folic acid

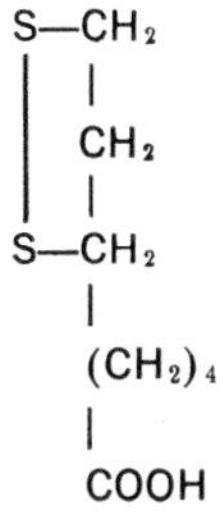

α-Lipoic acid

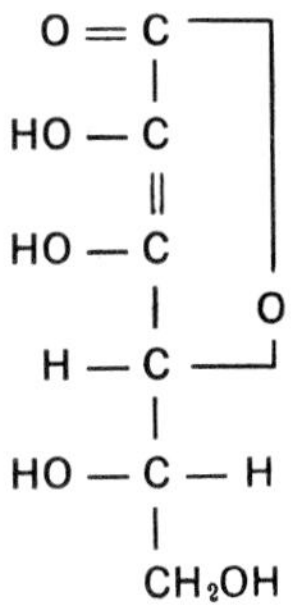

Ascorbic acid

cytochrome) and nitrogenous acids including *carnosine, anserine,* and *carnitine.* These may all be considered as vitamins for some species.

Fat Soluble Vitamins

The fat-soluble vitamins, A, D, E, and K, appear to be required by vertebrates but not by invertebrates.

Vitamin A

Vitamin A (antixerophthalmic vitamin) occurs as vitamin A_1, in higher vertebrates and salt-water fishes, and *vitamin A_2* occurs chiefly in fresh-water fishes. Several plant pigments (*alpha, beta,* and *gamma carotene,* and *cryptoxanthin*) are precursors for vitamin A. The precursors are yellow in color, but vitamin A is colorless, so no correlation can be made

between the yellow color of milk or cream and its vitamin A content. Precursors of vitamin A are converted to vitamin A in the intestine and in the liver, and the resulting vitamin A is stored both in the *liver* and in the *retina.*

Vitamin A is essential for the formation of *rhodopsin (visual purple)* needed for vision in dim light. Vitamin A is also needed for normal growth, particularly of epithelial and osseous tissues. Deficiency of vitamin A results in *night blindness,* degeneration of epithelia, excessive cornification of stratified squamous epithelium, and increased susceptibility to infections.

Vitamin D

Vitamin D (antirachitic vitamin) consists mainly of vitamin D_2 and vitamin D_3).

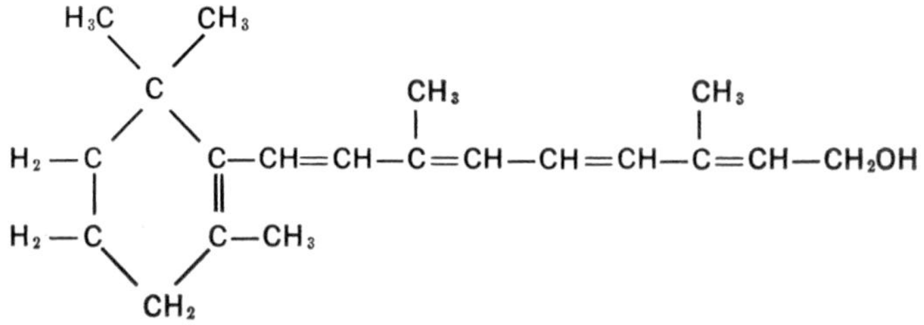

Vitamin A_1

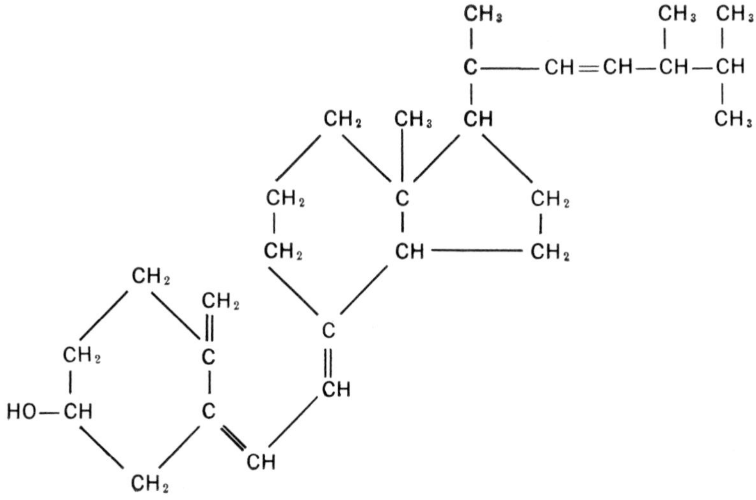

Vitamin D

TABLE 21–1.—VITAMINS

Class	Chemical Nature	Effect of Lack on Vertebrates	Cellular Function
A	Carotenoid	Growth interference, night blindness	Part of visual purple in retina; growth
D	Sterol	Bone defects	Not known; mobilizes salts in gut
E	Tocopherol	In rat, defective implantation and testis development	Unknown
B_1	Thiamine	Beriberi	Coenzyme for pyruvate metabolism
B_2	Riboflavin	Cataract	Prosthetic group of flavoprotein enzyme
Niacin	Nicotinic acid amide	Pellagra	Part of dehydrogenase coenzyme
Pantothen	Pantothenic acid	Dermatitis and spectacle eye	Part of coenzyme A
B_6	Pyridoxine	Need not demonstrated	Coenzyme for amino acid conversions
H	Biotin	Need not demonstrated	Coenzyme in CO_2 fixation in C_4 acids
Inositol	Cyclic Compound	Need not demonstrated	Unknown
Folic acid	Pteroylglutamic acid	Anemia	Coenzyme functioning in "one" carbon metabolism
B_{12}	Cyanocobalamin (tetrapyrrole with cobalt in center)	Anemia	Coenzyme of an enzyme involved in methyl transfer and nucleic acid metabolism
Protogen	Thioctic acid	Need not demonstrated	Coenzyme in pyruvate oxidation
C	Ascorbic acid	Scurvy	Maintain optimal oxidation reduction potential?
K	1,4-naphthoquinone acetate	Hemorrhage	Prothrombin formation in blood
P	A mixture of substances*	Capillary fragility	Maintains cement of capillary walls
Essential amino acids	Essential amino acids†	Failure in growth or normal function Wasting of tissue	Structure of cells, etc.
Essential fatty acids	Linoleic, linolenic and arachidonic	Failure in growth or functioning	Structure of cells, etc.
Methyl compounds	Choline, methionine	Failure in growth, etc.	Structure of cells, etc.
Sulfhydryl-containing compounds	Cysteine, glutathione	Failure in growth, etc.	Structure of cells, etc.

* Eriodictin, hesperidin, rutin.
† Tryptophan, phenylalanine, lysine, histidine, leucine, isoleucine, threonine, methionine, valine and arginine are required by the rat. The requirement is not always the same for all types of animals. (Giese, *Cell Physiology*, 2nd ed., courtesy of W. B. Saunders Co.)

Vitamin D₂ (*calciferol*) is formed by ultra-violet irradiation of *ergosterol*, and *vitamin D₃* is formed by irradiation of *7-dehydro-cholesterol* by sunlight or ultra-violet light. Since this irradiation may occur from the action of sunlight on the exposed skin, vitamin D is sometimes called the *sunshine vitamin*. Deficiency of vitamin D results in *rickets*, particularly if an imbalance of calcium and phosphorus exists in the diet. Vitamin D is important in absorption of calcium from the digestive tract. It also acts with *parathormone* (the hormone from the *parathyroid glands*) in regulation of *calcium level* of the blood and mobilization of calcium for bone formation.

Vitamin E

Vitamin E (*tocopherol*) may function as a cofactor for *cytochrome reductase* in heart muscle and skeletal muscle. In some species, at least, vitamin E is necessary for normal reproduction of both the male and female, but this apparently is not true for the horse or cow. It may also act as an anti-oxidant, preventing auto-oxidation of unsaturated fatty acids. Deficiency of vitamin E can result in degeneration of germinal epithelium in the male and resorption of embryos in the female.

Vitamin K

Vitamin K is necessary for the formation of *prothrombin* (a substance essential for blood clotting). Vitamin K is formed by microorganisms in the digestive tract and is also found in green plants and fish meal. Deficiency of vitamin K results in *hemorrhages* because of the failure of the blood to clot.

K₁ is 2-methyl-3-phytyl-1,4-naphtoquinone

CHAPTER 22

THE URINARY SYSTEM

THE urinary system consists of two kidneys, two ureters, the bladder, and the urethra.

ANATOMY OF THE KIDNEYS

The *kidneys* are organs for filtration of water and waste products from blood, and selective resorption of water and nutrients from the filtrate. With the exception of the lobulated kidneys of the cow and the heart-shaped right kidney of the horse, most domestic animals have somewhat bean-shaped kidneys. The kidneys are located in the dorsal part of the abdominal cavity on each side of the aorta and vena cava just ventral to the first few lumbar vertebrae. Details of size, shape and location are given on page 447. In the cow and sheep, particularly with a full rumen, the left kidney may be pushed to the right as far as the median plane or beyond. In these animals the left kidney may be much more loosely attached to the body wall than the right kidney, and consequently the left renal artery and vein are longer than the right vessels. Like other abdominal organs, the kidneys are *retroperitoneal*, that is, they are located outside of the peritoneal cavity. However, the kidneys are more closely attached to the abdominal wall by fascia, vessels, and peritoneum than are other organs.

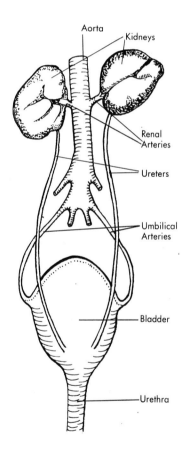

FIG. 22–1.—Dorsal view of the urinary organs. (After Sisson and Grossman, *The Anatomy of the Domestic Animals*, 4th ed., W. B. Saunders Co., 1953.)

The medial border of the kidney is usually concave and has a marked depression, the *renal hilus*, where blood vessels and nerves enter and the ureter and lymphatic vessels leave. The expanded origin of the ureter within the kidney is called the *renal pelvis*. It receives urine from the collecting tubules of the kidney. The cavity within the kidney which contains the pelvis is called the *renal sinus*. The renal pelvis has no relationship to the bony pelvis described as a part of the skeleton.

In the horse, sheep, and dog the collecting tubules empty onto a longitudinal ridge that projects into the renal pelvis.

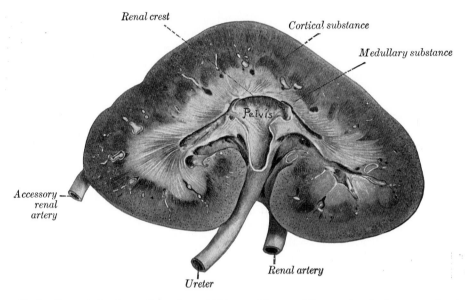

Fig. 22–2.—Frontal (horizontal) section of kidney of horse. The renal vein is removed. A large accessory renal artery entered the posterior pole. Sections of arteries in limiting layer between cortical and medullary substances are white in figure. (Sisson and Grossman, *The Anatomy of the Domestic Animals*, courtesy of W. B. Saunders Co.)

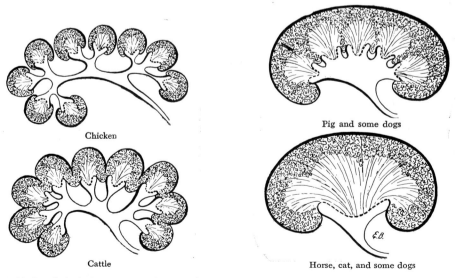

Fig. 22–3.—Lobulation of the kidney. (Elias and Pauly, *Human Microanatomy* 2nd ed., courtesy, of Da Vinci Publishing Co.)

This ridge is called the *renal crest*. In the kidney of the cow and pig individual pyramids project into minor calyces, which in turn empty into major calyces. These major calyces in the pig kidney empty into the renal pelvis and thence into the ureter. The kidney of the cow has no pelvis, so the major calyces empty into the ureter directly.

The portion of the kidney immediately surrounding the renal pelvis is the *medulla*, which appears striated because of the radially arranged collecting tubules. These tubules form the basis for the renal pyramids, which have their apices at the renal pelvis and their bases covered by the cortex. In addition to collecting tubules, the medulla also contains some *loops of Henle*. The *cortex*, located between the medulla and the thin connective tissue capsule, presents a granular appearance because of the large number of *glomeruli*. Proximal convoluted tubules and distal convoluted tubules are also located in the cortex in fairly close relation to the glomeruli and many loops of Henle.

BLOOD AND NERVE SUPPLY

The blood supply to the kidney is much more extensive than the size of the organ would suggest. The two *renal arteries* may carry as much as one-fourth of the total circulating blood. The renal artery enters the hilus of the kidney and divides into a number of relatively large branches, the *interlobar arteries*. These pass peripherally between pyramids almost to the cortex, where they bend abruptly and travel in an arched manner, suggesting the name *arciform arteries*. Each arciform artery gives off a number of interlobular arterioles of the glomeruli. Leaving the glomeruli, most of the efferent arterioles break up into a capillary network that surrounds the rest of the nephron. Those arterioles leaving glomeruli close to the medulla travel directly into the medulla

as *arteriae rectae* where they form capillary networks around the collecting tubules.

Arcuate veins drain blood from both the cortex and medulla, pass through the medulla as interlobar veins, and enter the renal vein. Lymph drains from the kidney to the renal lymph nodes. The kidneys of reptiles, birds, and amphibians receive a portion of their blood from veins which drain the body wall or hind legs. This system, the *renal portal system*, is not found as such in mammals. The pampiniform plexus of veins which drains the mammalian testicle is believed to be a remnant of the more primitive renal portal system.

The kidneys are supplied with *sympathetic nerves* from the renal plexus, which follow blood vessels and terminate largely on glomerular arterioles. Branches of the *vagus nerve* may also supply the kidneys. The success of kidney transplantation suggests the nerves do not have much to do with secretion but may only control the blood vessels. Both *vasoconstrictor* and *vasodilator* nerves are found in the kidney. The *baroceptor reflex* (responding to pressure changes) may cause vasoconstriction in the kidney; however, it also raises general blood pressure, which tends to counteract any decrease in filtration caused by the vasoconstriction.

THE URETERS, BLADDER, AND URETHRA

The ureter is a muscular tube which conveys urine from the pelvis of the kidney to the bladder. Each ureter passes caudally to empty into the bladder near its neck at an area known as the *trigone*. The manner in which the ureter passes obliquely through the wall of the bladder forms an effective valve to prevent return flow of urine to the kidney.

The *urinary bladder* is a hollow muscular organ that varies in size and position with the amount of urine it contains.

The empty contracted bladder is a thick-walled, pear-shaped structure located on the floor of the pelvis. As the bladder fills with urine, the wall becomes thinner, and most of the bladder is displaced cranially toward or into the abdominal cavity. Peritoneum covers a variable amount of the cranial portion of the bladder, depending on its fullness. The caudal part of the bladder is covered with pelvic fascia.

The neck of the bladder is continuous with the urethra caudally, and the muscle of the bladder wall is arranged in a circu-

connective tissue called the *lamina propria*. More connective tissue is found superficial to the longitudinal and circular fibers of smooth muscle. This outer layer of connective tissue, called the *adventitia*, is covered by peritoneum on the apex and body of the bladder.

The pelvic *urethra* extends from the bladder to the *ischial arch*. In the male it receives the *ductus deferens* and ducts from the accessory sex glands. It is surrounded by the striated urethral muscle, which is somewhat continuous with the *bulbo-cavernosus muscle* that partially surrounds

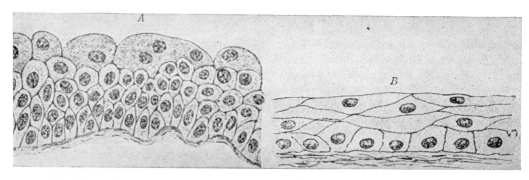

FIG. 22–4.—Drawings of transitional epithelium. (Ham and Leeson, *Histology*, 4th ed., courtesy of J. B. Lippincott Co.)

lar manner at the neck of the bladder, forming a sphincter that controls passage of urine into the urethra.

The *pelvis, ureter, bladder,* and *urethra* all are lined with transitional epithelium. This epithelial lining is useful in these areas where considerable distention of the lumen may occur. When these organs are empty the lumen is small, the walls are thick, and the lining epithelial cells are piled deeply to form a many-layered stratification. However, when the organs are distended, the lumen is enlarged, the walls are thinner, and a transition to a much lower stratification of the lining occurs. Hence the name transitional epithelium. Between the lining epithelium and smooth muscle of the organ wall is a variable amount of

the *penile urethra*. A plexus of veins forms cavernous tissue between the lining epithelium and the surrounding muscle. Around the penile urethra this cavernous tissue is well developed and is called the *corpus cavernosum urethrae*. With the exception of the *urethral bulb*, the cavernous tissue surrounding the urethra is supplied with blood from veins. The urethral bulb, located between the *crura* (roots) of the penis, receives blood from the artery of the bulb.

MICROANATOMY AND PHYSI-OLOGY OF THE NEPHRON

The *nephron* is the unit of structure of the kidney. It includes the glomerulus, Bowman's capsule, proximal convoluted

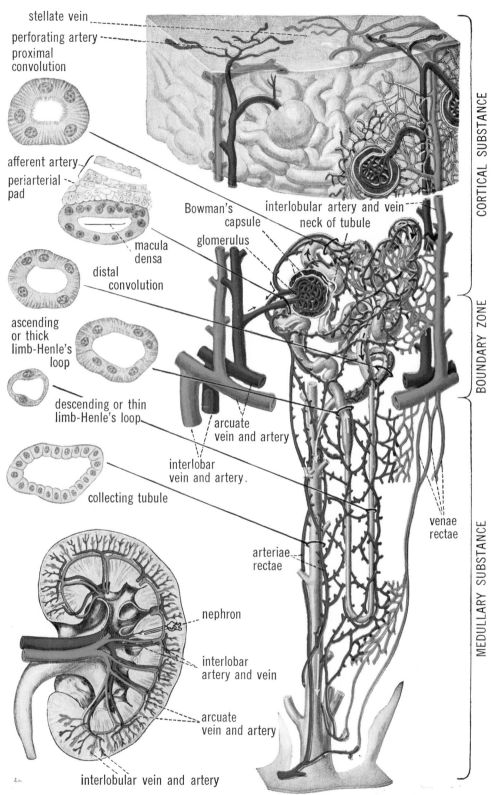

stellate vein

perforating artery

proximal convolution

afferent artery

periarterial pad

macula densa

distal convolution

ascending or thick limb-Henle's loop

descending or thin limb-Henle's loop

collecting tubule

Bowman's capsule

glomerulus

interlobular artery and vein neck of tubule

arcuate vein and artery

interlobar vein and artery.

arteriae rectae

venae rectae

nephron

interlobar artery and vein

arcuate vein and artery

interlobular vein and artery

CORTICAL SUBSTANCE

BOUNDARY ZONE

MEDULLARY SUBSTANCE

FIG. 22–5.—Diagram of a portion of kidney lobule illustrating a nephron.
(*Gray's Anatomy*, Lea & Febiger.)

tubule, loop of Henle, and distal convoluted tubule (which is continued by the collecting tubule).

The *glomerulus* is a tuft of capillaries interposed on the course of an arteriole (small artery). *Bowman's capsule* is the expanded blind end of the tubule which is evaginated around the glomerulus and almost entirely surrounds it. The visceral (inner) layer of Bowman's capsule closely surrounds the capillaries, and the parietal (outer) layer of Bowman's capsule is continuous with the proximal convoluted tubule. This complex of glomerulus and inner and outer layers of Bowman's capsule is called a *Malpighian corpuscle*. The space between the inner and outer layers of Bowman's capsule communicates with the lumen of the tubule. The Malpighian corpuscle is the major site for filtration of fluid from the blood. Approximately 100 times as much fluid passes through this filter as is eventually excreted as urine. In order that the filter might operate effectively, blood pressure within the capillaries of the glomerulus must remain relatively high. This condition is insured by the capillaries being on the course of an artery rather than between an artery and a vein, as in most capillary beds. Both the afferent arteriole entering the glomerulus and the efferent arteriole leaving the glomerulus are equipped with a smooth muscle contractile mechanism so the amount of blood entering the glomerulus and the pressure within the glomerulus can be controlled by constricting either the afferent arteriole or the efferent arteriole or both. As the afferent arteriole approaches the glomerulus, it is surrounded by a cuff of myoepithelial cells that have some characteristics of smooth muscle and some characteristics of epithelium. This cuff surrounding the arteriole is called the *juxtaglomerular apparatus*. It is believed by some to be the site of production of the substance *renin* (not to be confused with

rennin), which has the effect of increasing blood pressure.

Each human kidney contains approximately one million nephrons. Under normal conditions only about one-fourth of the nephrons of the kidneys function at a given time. Whether or not a specific nephron is functioning depends largely on the relative constriction of afferent and efferent arterioles.

In addition to the Malpighian corpuscle, the nephron consists of the proximal convoluted tubule, Henle's loop, and the distal convoluted tubule. The capillaries supplying this portion are derived from the efferent arteriole. Since the blood in the efferent arteriole has lost much of its water, it is more concentrated (has a higher osmotic pressure) and therefore is better able to reabsorb water from the tubule.

The *proximal convoluted tubule* may connect directly with the parietal layer of Bowman's capsule, or a short neck may be interposed. In any event, the proximal convoluted tubule is the longest and most winding portion of the nephron. It forms much of the tissue of the renal cortex. The cells lining the proximal segment of the tubule are columnar or cuboidal in shape and present a striated zone, the so-called *brush border*, on the free surface of the cell. The free surface is directed toward the lumen of the tubule. The brush border is similar to that of the absorptive cells of the small intestine.

The proximal segment appears to absorb most of the constituents of the glomerular filtrate that are needed by the animal body, including about seveneights of the sodium chloride and water. This action is facilitated by the concentrated blood which the capillaries around the tubule receive from the efferent arteriole of the glomerulus. In addition to selective reabsorption from the glomerular filtrate, cells of the proximal segment probably are able to concentrate and excrete waste products from the blood into the fluid passing through the lumen of the tubule.

Henle's loop is interposed between the proximal convoluted tubule and the distal convoluted tubule. It is a U-shaped tube that begins near the glomerulus as a continuation of the proximal segment. The descending limb, which is quite thin, extends a variable distance into the medulla, where it turns back upon itself as the thick, ascending limb of Henle's loop. The thin, descending segment is lined by simple squamous epithelial cells, and the thick, ascending limb is lined by cuboidal epithelial cells.

The loop of Henle may contain the most concentrated urine, with the highest concentration at the lowest part of the loop close to or within the medulla, due to the so-called *"counter current"* mechanism.

The *distal convoluted tubule* is shorter and twisted less than the proximal convoluted tubule. It extends from the termination of the ascending limb of Henle's loop to the collecting tubule.

The initial *collecting tubules*, called *arched tubules*, empty into the *straight collecting tubules* in the cortex of the kidney Each straight tubule receives several arched tubules before entering the medulla. The straight tubules unite to form papillary ducts (in the inner zone of the medulla) which empty into the pelvis of the kidney. Lining cells of the collecting ducts gradually change from cuboidal epithelium in the arched tubules to columnar epithelium in the papillary ducts.

GENERAL FUNCTION OF THE KIDNEY

The urinary system is responsible for excretion of many waste products of the body. It is also an important factor in maintenance of *homeostasis*, the relatively constant condition of the internal environment of the body. This includes regulation of such diverse factors as water balance, pH, osmotic pressure, electrolyte levels, and levels of many other substances. This control is obtained by filtering a large quantity of water and other small molecules through the glomerulus. The appropriate amounts of each substance are then reabsorbed either passively by such forces as osmosis and diffusion or actively by tubular cells.

The major factors affecting actions of the kidneys include composition of the blood, arterial blood pressure, hormones, and renal nerves.

Composition of the blood includes the relative concentration of plasma proteins and the concentration of specific individual substances. Dilution of plasma proteins generally causes diuresis (increased excretion of urine), including greater excretion of water, sodium, chloride, and bicarbonate. The resulting low osmotic pressure of blood inhibits the release of ADH (the antidiuretic hormone of the *neurohypophysis*). A high osmotic pressure of the blood usually results in decreased excretion of urine because of the release of ADH. (This will be discussed later in this chapter, p. 320.) Sodium and chloride excretion also is decreased.

The metabolic production of a substance or its injection or ingestion into the body is followed by increased urinary excretion of that substance, which maintains a relatively constant composition of the blood. In other words, an increase in the concentration of a substance in the blood tends to increase the excretion of that substance. A large increase in excretion of a substance dissolved in the blood will cause an increase in the volume of urine. This type of volume increase is called *osmotic diuresis* and may also result in loss of sodium and chloride.

Much experimental work has been done with various substances administered to animals in order to determine how the kidneys respond to them. Dramatic results may be obtained when large quantities of materials are given, but in the normal animal, small excesses of any substance usually result in little more than simple excretion of the excess.

Arterial pressure determines glomerular pressure, which is a major factor in determining quantity of fluid filtered from the blood. As discussed later, when colloidal osmotic pressure of the plasma and intracapsular pressure are subtracted from glomerular pressure, the result is the effective filtration pressure. This effective filtration pressure can be determined by attaching a tube to the ureter and measuring the height of a column of fluid in the tube. Dukes gives the average filtration pressure in the dog as 78 mm. Hg.

ADH

ADH (the *antidiuretic hormone* of the neurohypophysis) is the hormone that normally has the greatest action on the kidney. ADH is believed to exert its action on the distal tubules, where it increases the reabsorption of water. This reabsorption, called *active* or *facultative reabsorption*, may be due to increased permeability to water of the distal convoluted tubules and possibly the collecting tubules as well.

The reabsorption of water by the proximal tubules is called *passive* or *obligatory reabsorption* and accounts for reabsorption of about 85 per cent of the glomerular filtrate. The remaining 15 per cent of the glomerular filtrate may be influenced by ADH.

Osmoreceptors are structures presumed to exist in the *hypothalamus*. These structures cause the release of ADH from the posterior pituitary gland whenever the osmotic pressure of blood in the internal carotid artery becomes excessively high. This mechanism aids conservation of water by causing increased reabsorption of water, resulting in a more concentrated urine.

Stress and certain drugs also stimulate the release of ADH from the neurohypophysis. These drugs include *acetylcholine, nicotine, adrenaline,* and *barbiturates*.

Hormones of the adrenal cortex have a rather marked effect on adrenalectomized animals, but the effects are difficult to determine on normal animals because of the hormones produced by the intact animal's adrenal glands.

THE GLOMERULAR FILTRATE

The glomerular filtrate is the fluid which passes from the blood in the glomerulus through the glomerular capillary endothelium and the simple squamous epithelium forming the visceral layer of Bowman's capsule into the lumen of Bowman's capsule. Water and most molecules smaller than colloidal size may be filtered from the blood plasma to form the glomerular filtrate. Blood cells, colloidal proteins, and fats normally do not pass through the membrane.

The quantity of glomerular filtrate produced depends on filtration pressure, which is a result of differences in hydrostatic pressure (blood pressure) and osmotic pressure in the glomerular capillaries as compared with the same types of pressures in the lumen of Bowman's capsule. In man, pressure in the glomerular capillaries normally is about 57 mm. Hg., while the pressure in Bowman's capsule is about 10 mm. Hg. Colloidal osmotic pressure in the capillaries is about 28 mm. Hg., because the large molecules (mostly proteins) will not pass through the glomerular membrane. Colloidal osmotic pressure in Bowman's capsule is close to zero because colloids normally do not enter Bowman's capsule. Any osmotic pressure due to smaller molecules that pass freely through the glomerular membrane will be essentially the same in the capillaries as in Bowman's capsule, so *this* osmotic pressure does not enter into calculations of filtration pressure.

Blood (hydrostatic) pressure in the glomerulus (57 mm. Hg for example) tends to force fluid from the glomerulus into Bowman's capsule. Colloidal osmotic pressure in the glomerulus (28 mm. Hg) and the blood (hydrostatic) pressure in Bowman's capsule (10 mm. Hg) both tend to resist the flow of fluid from the glomerulus into Bowman's capsule. The net difference in pressure (57 mm. Hg minus the sum of 28 and 10 mm. Hg) equals 19 mm. Hg and is the filtration pressure forcing fluid from the glomerulus into Bowman's capsule.

The amount of glomerular filtrate is directly proportional to the filtration pressure. Any change that results in a different filtration pressure automatically affects the quantity of filtrate. An increase in general blood pressure is reflected in an increase in glomerular pressure and consequently increased filtration. An increase in glomerular pressure also occurs when the efferent arteriole is constricted and the afferent arteriole is left open. Excess water intake dilutes the blood and lowers its osmotic pressure. A reduced glomerular colloidal osmotic pressure in effect increases filtration pressure, resulting in more glomerular filtrate.

Conversely a decrease in general blood pressure, constriction of the afferent arteriole, and dehydration (resulting in increased osmotic pressure of the blood) all decrease filtration pressure, resulting in less glomerular filtrate.

CHEMICAL BALANCE

The *proximal tubules* reabsorb about 85 per cent of the water, sodium, chloride, and bicarbonate. The fluid leaving the proximal tubules has a pH of about 7.4. It contains sodium, chloride, and bicarbonate in about the same concentration as in the plasma. This fluid is approximately isotonic with the blood plasma.

Although glucose can pass through the glomerular membrane, the concentration of glucose in the blood is almost always higher than the concentration of glucose in the urine. In fact, the presence of glucose in the urine is usually abnormal. These facts imply an active transport of glucose from the lumen of the tubule back to the blood. The mechanism of this reabsorption is not well understood, but the site of transport is believed to be cells of the proximal tubule.

The *distal tubules* are the site of sodium reabsorption, which can occur without a corresponding reabsorption of water, so that concentration of the plasma sodium may be higher than the sodium concentration of the urine. Sodium ions may be exchanged for hydrogen, potassium, or ammonium ions by cells of the distal tubule. Whenever a sodium ion is reabsorbed it must be accompanied by an anion (negative ion) or exchanged for another cation (positive ion).

The ionic exchange of sodium for hydrogen or ammonium to form acid urine occurs in the distal part of the nephron. Concentration of *hypertonic urine* also occurs in the distal tubules and possibly in the collecting tubules.

The final *pH* of *urine* is dependent on the quantities of various ions in the urine. An increase of bicarbonate causes greater alkalinity of the urine. Acid urine may be produced by exchange of sodium for hydrogen and ammonium ions.

In an *acid urine* with a pH of less

than 6, titratable acid is present, ammonium ions are present, and bicarbonate ions are absent. The renal tubules may have the ability to produce ammonia (NH_3) by deamination of glutamine. The ammonia passes through the tubular wall into the lumen and becomes ammonium ions (NH_4^+) which do not readily diffuse back through the tubular epithelium. An appreciable part of the cation of acid urine is ammonium. Reabsorption of bicarbonate may be an important method of control of acidosis and alkalosis of the body.

Alkaline urine with a pH over 7 contains bicarbonate, but no titratable acid or ammonium. It also contains sodium and potassium.

Diuresis is simply an increase in quantity of urine produced. It may be caused by a raised plasma level of one or more urinary components, including water. Water diuresis occurs whenever the osmotic pressure of the plasma is reduced to a level that will not stimulate release of ADH. Excess substances other than water must be kept in solution or they cannot be excreted. This water necessary to act as a solvent produces a diuresis when added to the normal urine volume.

REABSORPTION AND SECRETION

The kidneys directly control the volume and composition of the extracellular fluid of the body and indirectly control the intracellular fluid composition. With a wide range of intake of water and solutes (dissolved substances), the composition and volume of body fluids is kept quite constant. Transporting water and these substances across the tubular cells is the chief activity of the kidney. If the materials are carried from the lumen of the tubule to the interstitial fluid, the process is called *reabsorption*. If they are carried to the tubular lumen, the process is called *secretion*. The transport may be passive when caused by such forces as diffusion or osmosis. Active transport in some unknown manner involves energy supplied by tubular cells to move the substances for either absorption or secretion.

Usually filtered substances of further use to the body are returned to the circulation, but excess amounts of these substances, and substances that are not useful, are excreted in the urine and are not reabsorbed.

Substances that normally are found in the blood in fairly definite percentages are called threshold substances, since any excess above the threshold value is excreted in the urine. All of these substances found in the glomerular filtrate up to the threshold value are reabsorbed by the tubules; only the amounts over the threshold are excreted. Threshold substances include sodium, potassium, calcium, chloride, and glucose. Non-threshold substances are not reabsorbed at all by the tubules as they are not normally found in the blood.

RENAL CLEARANCE

Renal clearance is a measure of the amount of blood plasma cleared of a given substance in one minute. The formula for calculating renal clearance is:

$$\frac{\text{mg./ml. of substance} \times \text{ml. of urine/minute}}{\text{mg./ml. of substance in the plasma}} =$$

Renal clearance of substances

Inulin is a polysaccharide that is useful for comparison of its renal clearance with other substances, since it is readily filtered through the glomeruli and is neither absorbed or secreted by the tubules. Any substance with a higher renal clearance than inulin is assumed to be secreted by the tubules as well as being filtered through the glomeruli. If the renal clearance is less than that of inulin, it is assumed that the substance is reabsorbed by the tubules. If a substance is completely reabsorbed, the renal clearance is zero. The greater the amount of a substance excreted, the higher will be its renal clearance.

MICTURITION

Micturition is the term for expulsion of urine from the bladder. It normally is a reflex activity stimulated by distension of the bladder from the constant inflow of urine by way of the ureters. The bladder adjusts to a gradual inflow of urine until the pressure becomes high enough to stimulate reflex centers in the spinal cord, which in turn cause contraction of the muscle wall of the bladder by way of sacral parasympathetic nerves. However, reflex emptying of the bladder can be prevented by voluntary control. The external sphincter surrounding the neck of the bladder may also be contracted voluntarily.

PATHOLOGY OF THE URINARY SYSTEM

Nephritis is a general term for inflammation of the kidneys. All or any part of the nephrons, the connective tissue, or the renal vessels may be affected. The course of nephritis may be acute (very rapid), or chronic (of long duration).

Nephrosis refers to kidney disease involving degeneration of the tubules, resulting in lowered albumin in the blood, albumin in the urine (*albuminuria*), and edema (excess fluid in the tissues). Nephrosis may be due to tubular damage caused by toxins such as salts of heavy metals.

Uremia (urine in the blood) may occur in kidney disease if the kidneys are unable to remove from the blood enough of the usual constituents of urine. An animal suffering from uremia develops a urinous odor of the breath and skin.

Urinary calculi, also called *urolithiasis* or simply stones, are concretions found in any part of the urinary system. They may originate in the pelvis of the kidney and obstruct passage of urine through the ureter, or they may develop in the bladder and interfere with passage of urine through the urethra. Animals with a sigmoid flexure of the penis (bull, ram, and boar) are particularly susceptible to trouble with urinary calculi because of the tendency for them to lodge in one of the sharp curves of the urethra as it follows the S shape of the penis.

Many factors have been incriminated in the study of urinary calculi. Some of these include high mineral intake in feed or water, low vitamin A level, and low water intake (as is sometimes seen in cold weather).

Acute cases of urolithiasis (also called water belly) may be treated by surgically providing a new exit from the urethra to the exterior. This operation, of course, makes an animal useless for breeding. Often this is not a problem, since more castrates than otherwise are seen with calculi lodged in the urethra.

Obstruction of a urinary passage results in *hydronephrosis* (destruction of the kidney substance and dilation of the pelvis) if maintained for a considerable period of time.

Inflammation of the bladder is called *cystitis*; inflammation of the renal pelvis is *pyelitis*; and inflammation of the pelvis and kidney is *pyelonephritis*. These inflammations usually are caused by infections which may be carried by the blood stream or may ascend from the exterior by way of the urethra.

CHAPTER 23

ANATOMY OF THE FEMALE REPRODUCTIVE SYSTEM

General
The Ovaries
The Fallopian Tubes
The Uterus

The Vagina
The Vulva
Blood and Nerve Supply of the Female Genitalia

GENERAL

REPRODUCTION in the female is a complex process that involves the entire animal body. The reproductive system itself includes the two ovaries, two Fallopian tubes and two fimbriae, the vagina, and the vulva. The ovum (or egg) is expelled from the ovary and received by the fimbria and carried to the Fallopian tube, where fertilization normally occurs during passage of the ovum from the ovary to the uterus. Within the uterus the fertilized ovum develops into an embryo and then into a fetus, and finally passes out of the uterus through the vagina and vulva as a newborn animal.

THE OVARIES

The *ovaries* are the primary (or essential) organs of reproduction in the female, just as the testes are in the male. The ovaries may be considered to be both endocrine and cytogenic (cell producing) in nature, since they produce hormones which are absorbed directly into the blood stream and also produce ova which are expelled from the gland.

The ovaries are paired glands consisting of a right ovary located behind the right kidney, and a left ovary located behind the left kidney. The distance of each ovary from the respective kidney varies with the species.

In most species, the ovaries are somewhat almond-shaped structures. However, in the mare the ovaries present a bean shape due to the presence of a definite *ovulation fossa*, an indentation in the attached border of the ovary. Ovaries of the sow usually appear quite lobulated because of the presence of *follicles*, *corpora lutea*, or both.

When palpated through the wall of the rectum, an ovary feels very solid because of the large amount of connective tissue making up the stroma of the gland. Irregularities in the surface may be cyst-like follicles about to rupture or the more substantial corpora lutea which form after ovulation

Normal size of the ovary varies considerably from species to species (Page 452), and even within a species there is some variation. For example, the ovary of a young mare may be less than 1 inch in diameter when no cysts are present, or as large as 4 inches in diameter with the presence of numerous cysts.

The medullary, or central portion, of the ovary is the most vascular part, while the majority of the cortex (outer portion) consists of dense irregular connective tissue interspersed with parenchymal

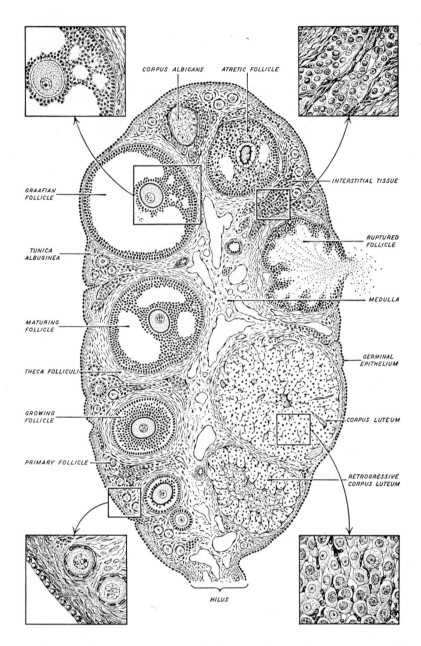

CORPUS ALBICANS   ATRETIC FOLLICLE

INTERSTITIAL TISSUE

GRAAFIAN
FOLLICLE

TUNICA
ALBUGINEA

RUPTURED
FOLLICLE

MEDULLA

MATURING
FOLLICLE

GERMINAL
EPITHELIUM

THECA FOLLICULI

GROWING
FOLLICLE

CORPUS LUTEUM

PRIMARY FOLLICLE

RETROGRESSIVE
CORPUS LUTEUM

HILUS

Fig. 23–1.—A diagram of a composite mammalian ovary. Progressive stages in the differentiation of a graafian follicle are indicated on the left. The mature follicle may become atretic (*top*) or ovulate and undergo luteinization (*right*). (Turner, *General Endocrinology*, courtesy of W. B. Saunders Co.)

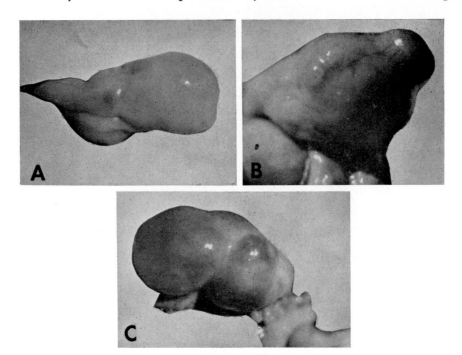

FIG. 23-2.—Bovine ovaries. *A*, Normal ovary with maturing follicle; *B*, normal ovary with well developed corpus luteum; and *C*, abnormal ovary with cystic follicles. (Belling, courtesy of *Veterinary Medicine*.)

epithelial cells which have migrated from the surface. The outer layer of cortex is a dense connective tissue capsule, the *tunica albuginea*. The outermost surface consists, in the fetus, of a single layer of germinal epithelium, the primary sex cells.

Cords of germinal epithelial cells invade the stroma of the ovary and eventually form isolated clumps of cells known as *primary follicles*. One large cell in each follicle is an *oocyte* or *ovum* surrounded by a single layer of follicular cells.

Ova in primary follicles increase in size, and the follicular cells multiply into several layers forming *maturing follicles*. A thick membrane, the *zona pellucida*, appears between the ovum and the inner layer of follicular cells of the *maturing follicle*. As soon as a fluid-filled cavity, the *antrum*, appears within the mass of follicular cells the follicle may be called a *Graafian follicle* or a *vesicular follicle*, and

the layer of follicular cells is called the *membrana granulosa*. (A double layer of cells from the stroma of the ovary surrounds the membrana granulosa, forming the theca interna and theca externa. The *theca interna* is a layer of irregularly shaped cells resembling epithelial cells. It is believed to be the source of *estrogens* (female sex hormones) found in the follicular fluid. The *theca externa* is a layer of connective tissue cells that blends on its inner surface with the theca interna and on its outer surface blends with the stroma of the ovary.)

Some of the membrana granulosa cells form a mound surrounding the ovum. This mound is called the *cumulus oophorus* (*germ hill* or *discus proligerus*). Its innermost layer, the *corona radiata*, consists of cylindrical follicular cells arranged in a radial manner over the entire surface of the zona pellucida. Cells of the corona radiata send processes through the zona pellucida to the *vitelline membrane* (cell membrane) of the ovum and presumably supply yolk material to the egg. The Graafian follicle, as it is called, after an appreciable amount of fluid forms, continues to increase in size and pushes toward the surface of the ovary, where in some species it can be palpated or observed as a cyst-like bulge.

Monotocous animals, animals not bearing litters, such as the horse and cow, normally have only one offspring per gestation. At each heat period one follicle usually develops more rapidly than the others, so that when it ruptures only one ovum or egg is released and the rest of the follicles then regress and form *atretic follicles.*

Polytocous animals, such as carnivores and swine, which normally produce two or more offspring per gestation, usually have several follicles rupture at approximately the same time. The ova may all come from one ovary, or some may come from each ovary. The immediate cause of rupture of the follicle at ovulation is not known. In most species it appears to occur as a slow oozing process that may result from local *ischemia* (lack of blood supply), followed by death of cells in the follicular wall. Immediately following ovulation the follicular cavity fills with a variable amount of blood and lymph, forming a structure called the corpus hemorrhagicum. It is relatively larger in swine than in sheep and cattle. The *corpus hemorrhagicum* is gradually reabsorbed and replaced by a corpus luteum.

Granulosa (follicular) cells mutiply rapidly to form the major part of the corpus luteum, but some cells are derived from the theca interna. The corpus luteum has a yellow color in the mare, cow, and carnivores, but is grayish white or flesh colored in the ewe and sow. The corpus luteum decreases in size and eventually leaves a whitish scar, the *corpus albicans,* as a remnant on the surface of the ovary.

THE FALLOPIAN TUBES

The *Fallopian tubes* (also called *oviducts* or *uterine tubes*) are paired convoluted tubes which conduct the ova from each ovary to the respective horn of the uterus and also serve as the usual site for *fertilization* of ova by *spermatazoa.* The portion of the Fallopian tube adjacent to the ovary is expanded to form a funnel-

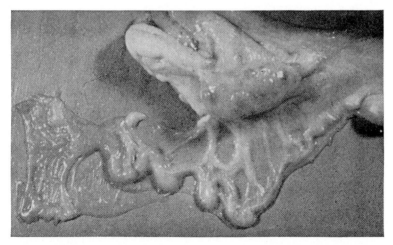

FIG. 23–3.—Oviduct (dissected away) and ovary of a cow. Note the funnel-shaped infundibulum on the left, which gradually tapers into the tortuous ampulla and thence into the portion of the oviduct that is smallest in diameter (the isthmus) and which joins with the tip of the uterine horn. (From *Physiology of Reproduction and Artificial Insemination of Cattle,* by G. W. Salisbury and N. L. VanDemark. Copyright by W. H. Freeman and Company, 1961.)

like structure called the *infundibulum*, or *fimbria*. Some authorities consider the fimbria to include the entire expanded ovarian extremity of the Fallopian tube. Other authorities use the term fimbria when referring only to the fringe-like margin of the ovarian end of the Fallopian tube and call the funnel-shaped part the infundibulum. The fimbria appears to take an active part in ovulation at least to the extent of partially or completely enclosing the ovary and directing the ovum into the abdominal opening of the Fallopian tube.

The lining of the Fallopian tubes is a highly folded mucous membrane that is covered mainly with simple columnar ciliated epithelium. During heat and before parturition the non-ciliated cells become actively secretory. The rest of the wall of the Fallopian tube includes a connective tissue submucosa, an inner circular smooth muscle layer, an outer longitudinal smooth muscle layer, and superficially a layer of connective tissue covered with peritoneum. Both the cilia and muscles function in movement of ova and possibly in movement of sperm.

THE UTERUS

The *uterus* of domestic mammals consists of a body, a cervix (neck), and two horns, or cornua. The relative proportions of each varies considerably with the species, as does the shape and arrangement of the horns. The *body of the uterus* is largest in the mare, less extensive in the cow and sheep, and very small in the pig and dog. Superficially the body of the uterus of the cow appears relatively larger than it actually is because the caudal parts of the horns are bound together by the intercornual ligament. Like most other hollow internal organs, the uterine wall consists of a lining mucous membrane, an intermediate smooth muscle layer, and an outer serous layer (peritoneum).

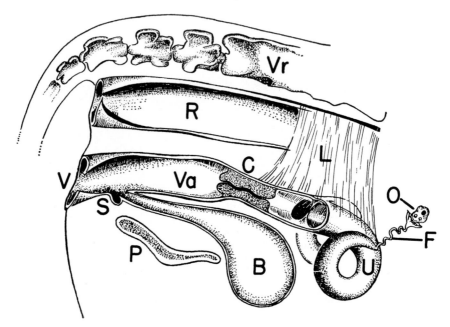

Fig. 23–4.—The reproductive tract of the cow (side view). *B*, Urinary bladder; *C*, cervix; *F*, fallopian tube; *L*, broad ligament; *O*, ovary; *R*, rectum; *P*, pelvic bone (*os coxae*); *S*, suburethral diverticulum; *U*, uterine horn; *Va*, vagina; *V*, vestibule; *Vr*, vertebral column. (Hafez, *Reproduction in Farm Animals*, Lea & Febiger.)

while the corpus luteum looks and feels solid because it actually is a tissue. If the ovum is not fertilized, the corpus luteum, which is called a corpus luteum of estrus, regresses and disappears, leaving only a scar called a *corpus albicans*.

However, if the ovum is fertilized and pregnancy ensues, the corpus luteum may last throughout the gestation period as a corpus luteum of pregnancy. The corpus luteum is in reality an endocrine gland which produces progesterone, a hormone essential for maintenance of pregnancy. Occasionally a corpus luteum of estrus fails to regress, and the animal does not come in season, thus giving the false appearance of being pregnant. This type of corpus luteum is called a retained

corpus luteum and is an important cause of temporary infertility in dairy cattle.

Sterility may also be caused by an abnormally large number of follicles developing at the same time without rupturing or regressing. This is a cystic condition of the ovary, and in the cow and horse these cysts, or abnormal follicles, can be palpated through the rectum. An animal suffering from cystic ovaries may be called a *nymphomaniac* because she appears to be in heat much of the time.

THE ESTROUS CYCLE

Domestic females come into heat at fairly regular intervals which differ rather widely between species. This interval

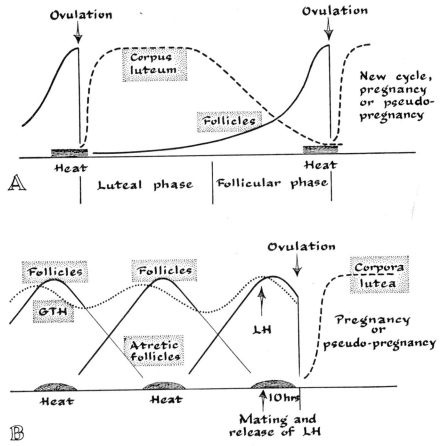

Fig. 24-2.—Comparison of estrous cyles in: *A*, Females with spontaneous ovulation and, *B*, females with induced ovulation. (*Reproductive Physiology*, by A. V. Nalbandov, courtesy of W. H. Freeman and Co., copyright 1958.)

from the beginning of one heat period to the beginning of the next is called the estrous cycle. It is controlled directly by hormones from the ovary and indirectly by hormones from the anterior lobe of the pituitary gland. The basic pattern of the estrus cycle is the same, but species differences are found in different parts of the cycle. The estrous cycle is divided into several well-marked phases called proestrus, estrus, metestrus, and diestrus.

Proestrus

Under stimulation of *FSH, Follicle-Stimulating Hormone* (and probably LH,) from the anterior lobe of the pituitary, the ovary produces increasing quantities of estrogens and possibly progesterone, which cause increased development of the uterus, vagina, and oviducts. This first phase (proestrus) of the estrous cycle is referred to as the "building up" phase. It is during this phase the ovarian follicle with its enclosed ovum increases in size primarily by increasing the follicular fluid, which contains estrogenic hormones.

Estrogens absorbed from the follicles into the blood stream stimulate increased vascularity and cell growth of the tubular genitalia, in preparation for estrus and subsequent pregnancy.

Estrus

Estrus is the period of sexual receptivity in the female, which is determined largely by circulating estrogen level. During or shortly after this time, ovulation occurs, and the corpus luteum begins to form at the time LH from the anterior lobe of the pituitary is increasing and FSH is decreasing. Just before ovulation, the follicle is large and turgid, and the enclosed ovum undergoes maturation changes. Estrus terminates about the time rupture of the ovarian follicle, or *ovulation*, occurs. At this time the ovum is expelled from the follicle to pass into

the upper part of the Fallopian tube. Follicular rupture occurs spontaneously in most animal species. However, in the cat, rabbit, mink, ferret, and a few other animals rupture is possible only if coitus occurs. Apparently some nervous reaction at this time initiates the follicular rupture. If coitus does not occur in these animals, the follicle with enclosed ovum regresses. A sterile mating frequently is followed by pseudopregnancy.

Metestrus

Metestrus is the post-ovulatory phase during which the corpus luteum functions in a non-pregnant animal. The length of metestrus may depend on the length of time *luteotrophin* is secreted by the anterior pituitary. During this period there is a decrease in estrogen and increase in progesterone formed by the ovary.

During metestrus the cavity left by the rupturing of the follicle begins to reorganize. The lining of the ruptured follicle begins to grow inward as the blood vascular supply increases within the cavity. The cells lining the cavity which have not been expelled increase in size, multiply, and become laden with fat droplets. This newly reorganized structure is called the corpus luteum, or yellow body. Progesterone secreted by the corpus luteum prevents further development of follicles and hence the occurrence of further estrous periods. Estrus does not occur so long as an active corpus luteum is present. The corpus luteum is necessary for proper implantation of the fertilized ovum in the uterus, for nourishment of the developing embryo, and for development of the alveoli of the mammary gland.

Diestrus and Anestrus

Diestrus is a relatively short period of quiescence between estrous cycles in polyestrous animals. *Anestrus* is a longer period of quiescence between the breeding seasons.

The corpus luteum, being fully developed, now has a marked influence on the uterus. The endometrial lining of the uterus thickens, uterine glands increase in size, and uterine muscles also show increased development in this stage. All the reactions are directed toward supplying a bed for nourishment of the embryo. If pregnancy occurs, these phenomena are prolonged throughout gestation, and the corpus luteum remains intact for all or most of the period.

If the ovum is not fertilized, and pregnancy does not come about, the corpus luteum regresses. During the breeding season in some species, such as the cow and the ewe, regression of the corpus luteum is followed by a new wave of ovarian follicles which initiates a new proestrous period. At the end of the breeding season, the ovaries of non-pregnant ewes become quiescent (anestrus), and the other sexual organs such as the oviducts, uterus, and vagina, deprived of hormonal influence, tend to atrophy. When another breeding season comes about, the ovary is again activated, and a new cycle is started. In the bitch, even though unmated, the corpus luteum persists throughout a period equal to the normal gestation period.

SUMMARY OF THE ESTROUS CYCLE

The estrous cycle may be summarized as follows:

A. Proestrus—Period of build-up where follicles increase in size, vaginal wall thickens, and uterine vascularity increases.

B. Estrus—Period of heat and greatest receptivity to male, rupture of ovarian follicle in most farm animals.

C. Metestrus—Formation of the corpus luteum, changes in vaginal wall and uterus.

Alternatives which may follow metestrus:

1. Diestrus—Short period of inactivity before the next proestrous period during the breeding season of polyestrous animals.
2. Pregnancy—Period of gestation.
3. Pseudopregnancy — Changes similar to pregnancy, but no fetus is present.
4. Anestrus—Long period of inactivity between sexual seasons.

Animals which have only one estrous cycle per year are called *monestrous* animals, while those that have several estrous cycles per year are called *polyestrous* animals. The period of successive estrous cycles is known as the *breeding season*, or perhaps more properly the *sexual season*, since the term "breeding season" may be used to include pregnancy and even lactation. The relatively long period of inactivity between sexual seasons in some animals is called anestrus and is not properly a part of the sexual cycle. The period of anestrus, at least in some animals, appears to be determined by seasonal changes in length of day. Stimuli from light are received by the eye and eventually reach the *hypothalamus* where they are believed to influence release of hormones from the pituitary gland.

There are two phases to the sexual cycle proper. The estrogenic phase, or follicular phase, includes proestrus and estrus. The luteal phase includes metestrus and diestrus.

The non-breeding period, or anestrus, may occupy the greater part of the year in some species such as the sheep and dog. It is followed by the breeding season when one or more estrous cycles occur.

This sequence, the estrous cycle, is repeated a number of times each sexual season in polyestrous animals if conception does not occur. If conception occurs during estrus, the next step is gestation rather than metestrus and diestrus. Gestation in turn may be followed by proestrus, initiating another sexual cycle, or by anestrus.

Pseudopregnancy, or *false pregnancy*, is a condition that may follow estrus in some species of carnivora and rodents if

next has been reported to vary in the mare from 7 to 124 days. However, the average figure reported by all investigators has been close to 21 or 22 days. The abnormally long cycles undoubtedly include a number of skipped periods or cycles.

Length of Estrus. — The average length of the estrous period in the mare is approximately 5 days, but wide variations are possible. Trum (1950) reported that thoroughbred mares at Fort Robinson,

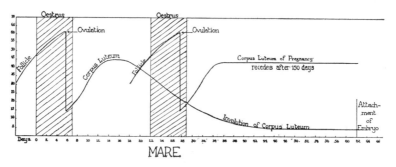

Fig. 24–3.—The estrous cycle in the mare. (Dukes, *The Physiology of Domestic Animals*, courtesy of Comstock Publishing Co.)

conception does not occur. The bitch may become pseudopregnant whether a sterile mating occurs or not, but several rodents require coitus or else artificial stimulation of the cervix to induce pseudopregnancy. Corpora lutea remain in the ovary, and changes in the uterus resemble those in pregnancy. The mammary glands become active and may secrete milk at the end of the pseudopregnancy, which is approximately equal in length to a normal gestation, or somewhat shorter.

Estrous Cycle of the Mare

Puberty begins between 10 and 24 months, with an average onset at about 18 months.

Length of Estrous Cycle. — The length of time elapsed from the beginning of one estrous period to the beginning of the

Nebraska, showed estrous periods as follows: 11 per cent, 2 to 3 days; 61 per cent, 4 to 6 days; 28 per cent, 7 to 9 days; and 5 per cent, over 10 days. Heat periods tend to become shorter from spring to midsummer. The shorter heat periods appear to be correlated with increased fertility. Early in the breeding season, through March and April, heat periods tend to be irregular and long, frequently with no ovulation occurring. From May to July the periods become shorter and more regular, with ovulation as a normal part of the cycle. Ovulation usually occurs from 1 to 2 days before the end of estrus.

Time of Breeding. — Fertility rises during estrus to a peak 2 days before the end of estrus, then falls off abruptly. Mares with heat periods of 1 to 3 days should be bred on the first day. Mares with longer heat periods should be bred

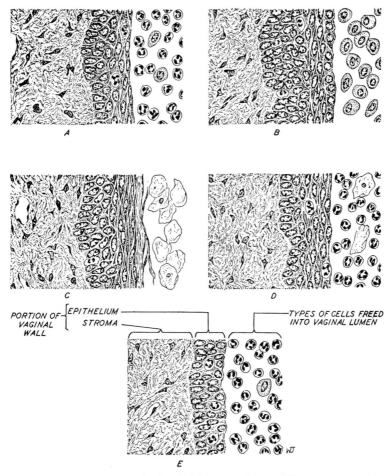

Fig. 24–7. Sections through the vaginal wall of the rat during different stages of the estrous cycle showing types of cells which appear in vaginal smears. *A*, Diestrus; *B*, proestrus; *C*, estrus; *D*, metestrus) and *E*, adult animal spayed for six months. (Turner, *General Endocrinology*, courtesy of W. B. Saunders Co.;

and in severe cases lactation, nest building, and adoption of objects or other animals may occur.

HORMONES OF FEMALE REPRODUCTION

Hormones produced in the ovary include estrogens from the follicles and progesterone from the corpora lutea. Secretory activity of the ovary is under control of the *gonadotrophic hormones* of the anterior lobe of the pituitary gland, and these in turn are at least partially controlled by ovarian hormones through the classical feedback mechanism described in Chapter 32, pages 423–432.

Estrogens

The term *estrogen* refers to any of a group of compounds that act as female sex hormones and stimulate female accessory sex glands. *Estrone, estradiol* (17B and 17A) and *estriol* are natural estrogens produced by the mammalian ovary or placenta. Others are produced by different organs and by different species. *Diethylstilbestrol* is the most common of a

TABLE 24-1.—FEMALE REPRODUCTION[1]

Animal	Onset of Puberty	Av. Age First Service	Length Estrous Cycle	Length Estrus	Gestation Period
Mare	18 mo. (10 to 24 mo.)	2 to 3 yrs.	21 days (19 to 21 days)	5 days (4½ to 7½ days)	336 days (323 to 341 days)
Cow	4 to 24 mo.	14 to 22 mo.	21 days (18 to 24 days)	18 hrs. (12 to 28 hrs.)	282 days (274 to 291 days)
Ewe	4 to 12 mo. (1st fall)	12 to 18 mo.	16½ days (14 to 20 days)	24 to 48 hrs.	150 days (140 to 160 days)
Sow	3 to 7 mo.	8 to 10 mo.	21 days (18 to 24 days)	2 days (1 to 5 days)	114 days (110 to 116 days)
Bitch	6 to 24 mo.	12 to 18 mo.	6 to 12 mo.	9 days (5 to 19 days)	63 days (60 to 65 days)

Animal	Time of Ovulation	Optimum Time for Service	Advisable Time to Breed after Parturition
Mare	1 to 2 days before end of estrus	3 to 4 days before end of estrus or the second or third day of estrus	About 25 to 35 days or second estrus. About 9 days or first estrus only if normal in every way.
Cow	10 to 15 hours after the end of estrus	Just before the middle of estrus to the end of estrus	60 to 90 days
Ewe	12 to 24 hours before the end of estrus	18 to 24 hours after the onset of estrus	Usually the following fall
Sow	30 to 36 hours after the onset of estrus	12 to 30 hours after the onset of estrus	First estrus 3 to 9 days after weaning pigs
Bitch	1 to 2 days after the onset of true estrus	2 to 3 days after onset of true estrus; or 10 to 14 days after onset of proestrous bleeding	Usually the first estrus or 2 to 3 months after weaning pups

[1] Data compiled from standard references including Dukes, Payne, Roberts, and Spector.

group of synthetic estrogens. It is used in hormonal treatments, as a feed additive for fattening animals, and to produce abortion in some domestic animals (bitches and feed-lot heifers). A number of plants also produce substances having estrogenic activity. In addition to the ovary, the *adrenal cortex, testes,* and *placenta* are natural sources of estrogens in the mammal.

The action of estrogens on accessory sex organs usually can be correlated fairly well with behavior typical of estrus (heat). Estrogens stimulate muscular activity of the Fallopian tubes and uterus and sensitize both of these organs for the action of progesterone. Other uterine changes stimulated by estrogen include increases in water content, *DNA* (*deoxyribonucleic acid*), *RNA* (*ribonucleic acid*), protein synthesis, and enzyme activity.

The epithelium lining the vagina and vulva is stimulated by estrogens and in some species becomes cornified during estrus. An increasing level of estrogen is undoubtedly an important factor in development of *libido*, the sex drive associated with receptivity to the male by the female in heat.

Estrogens also sensitize the pregnant uterus to the action of *oxytocin* from the posterior lobe of the pituitary gland.

Secondary sex characteristics associated with femininity to a large extent result from the actions of estrogens. In the domestic mammals, secondary sex characteristics are associated with development of the mammary gland and less massive skeleton and lighter muscling. In the human, distribution of hair, distribution of fat, and pitch of voice are observable secondary sex characteristics.

Progesterone

Progesterone is produced mainly by the corpus luteum, but is also found in the adrenal cortex, placenta, and testis. In general, progesterone acts on tissues that have been primed (prepared) by estrogen, although it may act synergistically (at the same time as estrogens); in large quantities progesterone and estrogens may be antagonistic in their actions. Progesterone is known as the hormone of pregnancy, because it causes thickening of the endometrium and development of uterine glands prior to implantation of the fertilized ovum. It inhibits excessive uterine motility during the period of implantation and during the period of gestation. Apparently a change in ratio of estrogen and progesterone may sensitize the uterus to oxytocin and possibly trigger parturition. The initiating cause of parturition, however, is still in doubt. The importance of progesterone in maintaining pregnancy is suggested by the fact that spontaneous abortion occurs in some animals if the ovaries are removed during the gestation period, with the consequent reduction in progesterone.

During pregnancy, progesterone suspends ovulation, possibly by its feedback inhibition of LH from the anterior pituitary. LH is necessary in small amounts for maturation of the follicle and for ovulation to occur.

Progesterone acts on the mammary gland that has previously been primed by estrogens. It promotes complete development of the alveoli of the mammary gland. Progesterone also tends to raise the body temperature, and this fact is used in the human in an effort to determine the time of ovulation. A temperature rise is presumed to be correlated with ovulation and the subsequent release of progesterone from the corpus luteum.

Other Hormones

Relaxin is a water-soluble, non-steroid hormone that is presumed to be formed by the ovaries. It can also be extracted from corpora lutea, the endometrium, and the placenta. In rodents relaxin causes relaxation of the pelvic symphysis and pelvic ligaments. It may have a similar action in other species and is believed to be a factor in relaxation of the cervix at parturition.

Both the pituitary gland and ovaries appear to be essential in all species for the events leading to conception and implantation. There is considerable species variation in the need for the pituitary gland and ovaries in later stages of pregnancy. Some animals abort immediately if either the pituitary gland or ovaries are removed, but others appear to tolerate either or both operations without fetal loss. In these latter animals, the placenta presumably secretes sufficient gonadotropins, estrogens, and progesterone to maintain pregnancy.

Chorionic gonadotrophins, predominantly FSH in nature, are found in *pregnant mare serum* (*PMS*) and in the urine of pregnant women, where they are called *human chorionic gonadotrophin* (*HCG*) predominantly LH in nature. These gonadotrophins are the basis for pregnancy tests in the mare and the human.

By the last third of pregnancy, estrogens and progesterones have stimulated essentially complete mammary gland development, so that the remaining hormone necessary to initiate lactation is sufficient *prolactin* (*LTH*) (*luteotrophic hormone*) from the anterior pituitary. Immediately following parturition, the anterior pituitary gland is released from progesterone-produced inhibition. Prolactin then is released, and milk secretion begins. The suckling reflex is believed to be important in maintenance of prolactin secretion in addition to stimulating reflexively release of oxytocin (milk letdown factor) from the posterior pituitary gland. Sensory impulses caused by nursing are carried to the hypothalamus, causing the pituitary gland to release prolactin and oxytocin.

The primordial follicle apparently can develop in the absence of pituitary hormones, but maturation of the follicle, including the development of the *thecae* and *antrum* requires a combination of FSH and LH, with the proper balance and timing of each. As the follicle releases increasing amounts of estrogen, FSH is inhibited by this estrogen, which simultaneously in some manner enhances LH production. When the correct ratio

TABLE 24–2.

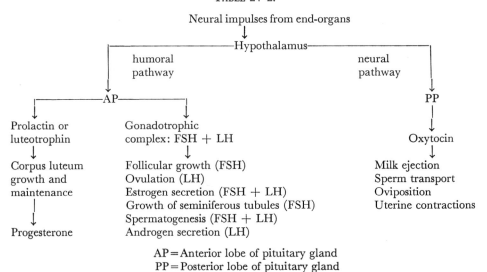

AP = Anterior lobe of pituitary gland
PP = Posterior lobe of pituitary gland

(*Reproductive Physiology*, by A. V. Nalbandov, courtesy of W. H. Freeman and Co., copyright 1958)

of FSH and LH is reached, ovulation occurs.

In some animals (rat, mouse, and sheep) LTH is reported to maintain the corpus luteum and cause secretion of progesterone. It is possible that a luteotrophic substance from the placenta may also stimulate secretion of progesterone by the corpus luteum. The control of hormones associated with reproduction is extremely complex and is not completely understood. The classical feedback mechanism undoubtedly is an important means of hormonal control, in which the level of a circulating hormone in some manner indirectly either stimulates or inhibits further production of the same hormone.

In addition to the control of endocrine glands by other hormones, the nervous system is involved in control of some endocrines by serving as the afferent limb of a neurohormonal reflex. In most instances the nerve impulses eventually reach the hypothalamus, causing release of pituitary hormones, and in this manner indirectly control release of other hormones. Ovulation following coitus in the rabbit and cat and the release of prolactin and oxytocin during nursing are examples of this neuroendocrine reflex mechanism.

CHAPTER 25

PREGNANCY AND PARTURITION

PREGNANCY

PREGNANCY refers to the condition of a female while young are developing within her uterus. This interval, the gestation period, extends from fertilization of the ovum to the birth of the offspring. It includes fertilization, or union of the ovum and sperm; nidation, or implantation of the embryo in the uterine wall; placentation, or the development of fetal membranes; and continued growth of the fetus.

Normal *gestation periods* vary greatly from species to species, and there is considerable variation between individuals within each species. Average gestation periods are: mare, 336 days, about 11 months; cow, 282 days, a little over 9 months; ewe, 150 days, about 5 months; sow, 114 days, or 3 months, 3 weeks, and 3 days; and bitch, 63 days, about 2 months. If the young are carried throughout a normal gestation period, it is a full-term pregnancy. Abnormally early termination of pregnancy is called abortion, or premature birth. In domestic animals, premature birth is nearly always fatal to the fetus.

Penetration of the ovum by the *spermatozoon* stimulates formation of the *second polar body* (see Chapter 24, p. 333) and also contributes one-half of the chromosomes of the new individual. Physical or

chemical stimuli can also stimulate division of the ovum. The mechanism of sperm penetration is still in doubt, as is the reason only one sperm usually penetrates the ovum. However, occasionally several spermatozoa are found in the perivitelline space (between vitelline membrane and zona pellucida), and sometimes more than one is found inside the ovum.

Time of *fertilization* appears to be quite important. There is some evidence that sperm must remain in the female reproductive tract, probably the *Fallopian tube*, for a certain period in order to fertilize ova effectively. This is called *capacitation of the spermatozoa*. Ova in unmated animals gradually lose their covering of cells and begin to disintegrate as they pass down the Fallopian tube. It is believed that ova that stay in the Fallopian tubes too long before exposure to sperm may have a lowered fertility and possibly result in a high percentage of abnormal and dead embryos.

Both ciliary action and muscular contractions probably are involved in movement of the fertilized ova through the Fallopian tubes into the uterus.

Polytocous animals, those giving birth to several offspring at one time, have a definite spacing of the *blastocysts* (developing embryos) in the uterus. It has been suggested that the implantation of one blastocyst in some way produces a surrounding refractory area in the *endometrium* that inhibits further implantation in the immediate vicinity. There is some evidence that the embryos near the Fallopian tubes are slightly more advanced in development than those near the cervix. Blastocysts of the rabbit are evenly distributed in the uterus by seven days after mating. Uterine contractions probably are involved in movement of the blastocysts, as there is no evidence they move in any but a passive manner.

the *zona pellucida*, and a variable amount of granulosa cells making up the *corona radiata* outside the zona pellucida. The zona pellucida is believed to be a product of the innermost layer of granulosa cells (corona radiata), which was a part of the *cumulus oophorous* of the follicle. Microvilli from the vitelline membrane of the ovum penetrate into the zona pellucida, as do processes from the follicular cells. The zona pellucida is believed to be a semipermeable membrane that helps protect the ovum. In some instances a coat of

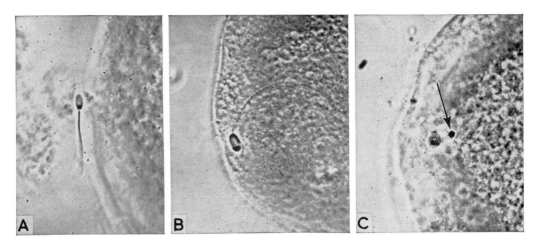

Fig. 25–1.—Different regions of a single pig ovum, 8 hours *post coitum*. ($\times$ 450). *A* shows a non-fertilizing sperm in the zona pellucida; *B* shows the penetrating sperm which has entered the vitellus (note its swollen head); *C* shows the nuclear apparatus of the ovum, with the recently formed nucleus of the 2nd polar body to the left, and the presumptive female pronucleus (arrowed) to the right. (Hafez, *Reproduction in Farm Animals*, Lea & Febiger.)

Fertilization

A large amount of work has been done in the study of *fertilization* but much of it has been with invertebrates, and many of the studies of mammalian fertilization have dealt only with the rat, mouse, and rabbit. There is little general agreement on many points to be discussed, and even where there is agreement there is no assurance that what is true for one species necessarily is true for others.

Immediately following ovulation, the ovum within the *vitelline membrane* (cell membrane of ovum) is surrounded by a heavy mucopolysaccharide membrane,

mucus is applied to the ovum outside the zona pellucida as it travels down the oviduct. This may aid attachment of the ovum to the uterine wall later.

There is a great variation in the amount of cumulus cells surrounding the zona pellucida in different animals. A well-defined corona radiata has been described in the dog and some other animals but is believed to be absent in the cow, sheep, pig, and horse. The question is still unsettled as to whether the corona radiata and cumulus cells inhibit sperm penetration and therefore must be dispersed by *hyaluronidase* or whether they aid sperm penetration by acting as a base for the sperm flagellum to push against.

The ovum usually has formed the *first polar body* before fertilization takes place, and it may be found in the perivitelline space between the ovum and the zona pellucida if it has not disintegrated.

Implantation

Many facts are known about *implantation (nidation)* of the blastocyst, but much is yet to be learned. The *zona pellucida* is shed by the blastocysts, but how much effect secretions from the Fallopian tubes and uterus have is disputed. The *endometrium* proliferates and becomes more vascular just before implantation and secretes a fluid called *uterine milk* that presumably nourishes the embryo before and during implantation. There is evidence that both physical and chemical factors are involved in stimulation of the uterus to accept the embryo. The presence of foreign material such as lint or beads will stimulate the formation of *deciduomata* (areas of maternal placentation) in the rat. Both carbonate and *histamine* have been suggested as chemicals that may be involved in the phenomenon of implantation. The connective tissue beneath the endometrium appears to react to the presence of a blastocyst even before the endometrium does.

The relationship between the endometrium and the developing fetal membranes is complex and varies from one species to another. Some of these differences are discussed on page 351.

Failures of Reproduction

Casida (1953) estimates reproductive failures in domestic animals from fertilization failure and embryonic death at approximately 50 per cent of the potential production of bred animals. Results reported with a group of normal sows were: loss due to fertilization failure

and tubal obstruction, 2.3 per cent; loss from no apparent reason, 9.5 per cent; embryonic death, 32.4 per cent; and young born at term (no loss), 55.8 per cent. A group of repeat breeding cows, those that did not conceive on the first service, showed a much poorer survival percentage, with ovulation failure and tubal obstruction, 6.0 per cent; no apparent reason, 39.3 per cent; embryonic death, 32.5 per cent; and normal embryos at 34 days, 22.2 per cent. In cattle, chances of successful conception decrease rapidly with each rebreeding. Possible causes of embryonic death include inherited lethal factors, infections, nutritional deficiencies, disturbance of endocrine functions, and defects in the egg or sperm before fertilization.

Placentation

As the embryo increases in size, the process of diffusion which nourishes the zygote becomes inadequate to maintain life and continued growth. The extraembryonic membranes, or *placenta*, develop as a means of meeting this increasing need for more nutrition. This process is known as placentation.

The placenta consists of an arrangement of membranes such that nutrition from the dam can reach the fetus and, in turn, waste products from the fetus can be excreted by the dam. In domestic animals, the terms fetal membranes and placenta are used interchangeably, although technically the fetal membranes are known as the fetal placenta. In some species a portion of the endometrium is shed at parturition. This is called the maternal placenta, or *decidua*. The fetal placenta includes the chorion, allantois, amnion, and vestigial yolk sac.

The *chorion*, the outermost membrane, is in contact with the maternal uterus. The *amnion* is the innermost membrane, closest to the fetus. The *allantoic* sac, a space formed by two layers of *allantois*,

At 5 to 7 months of pregnancy, the uterus drops over the brim of the pelvis and stretches the cervix taut. Ovaries and fetus become difficult to palpate, but the caruncles on the uterus are definite and large. From this stage onward the calf can usually be bumped in the right flank. This technique, known as ballottement, is accomplished by gently forcing the fist into the lower right flank of the cow in a reciprocating manner so that the fetus rocks from side to side. Then the fist is forced into the flank and held until the calf bumps into the fist. The calf is the only solid object that can be palpated through the right flank of a pregnant

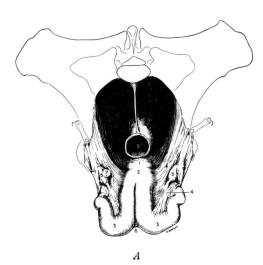

A

Nonpregnant uterus in the cow.

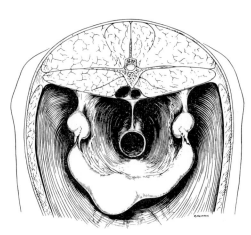

B

Uterus of a cow 60 to 70 days pregnant.

1, Cervix; *2*, body of uterus; *3*, horn of uterus; *4*, oviduct; *5*, ovaries; *7*, corpus luteum; *8*, intercornual ligament; *9*, rectum.

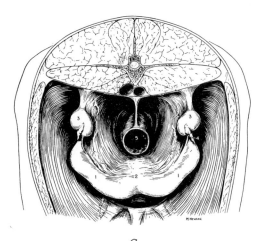

C

Nonpregnant uterus in the mare.

D

Uterus of a mare 60 days pregnant.

1, Uterine horns; *2*, body of uterus; *3*, ovary; *4*, ovarian ventricle; *5*, rectum.

Fig. 25-5.—(Roberts, *Veterinary Obstetrics and Genital Diseases*, courtesy of Edward Brothers.)

cow. From 8 to 9 months the fetus can again be palpated through the rectum and various parts of the fetus may be identified.

In the mare, pregnancy diagnosis by rectal palpation is more difficult than in the cow. The bulge of the amniotic sac surrounding the fetus is the earliest diagnostic feature. It increases in size approximately as follows:

Days of Pregnancy	Size of Bulge
30	2″ diameter by 3″ length
45	3″ diameter by 4½″ length
60	5″ to 6″ length
90	5″–6″ diameter by 8″–9″ length
100–150	Fetus palpable

Use of X-ray.—Diagnosis of pregnancy with x-ray film is of limited value in domestic animals. Horses, cattle, and sheep are too large for satisfactory abdominal x-ray procedure. In dogs and cats, x-ray pictures may be used effectively to determine pregnancy after the fetal bones have begun to calcify.

Chemical and Biological Tests.—The discovery that pituitary-like *gonadotrophins*, hormones which stimulate the ovaries and the testes, are secreted by the placenta during pregnancy, has led to a means of diagnosing pregnancy in several species. In mares of about 50 to 84 days pregnancy, gonadotrophic substance is found in the blood. The test is conducted by using 10 cc. of blood serum ollected from a mare between 50 and 84 cays after breeding. The serum is injected into the ear vein of a mature, nonpregnant female rabbit which has been isolated from all male rabbits for at least 30 days. A positive test showing that the mare is pregnant is indicated by dark red follicles, *corpora hemorrhagica*, in the ovaries of the rabbit 48 hours after the injection. The ovaries of the rabbit may be examined during a surgical exploratory operation, and the rabbit may then be saved

for future use, or the rabbit may be butchered and the ovaries examined at that time.

Although placental gonadotrophins probably are secreted by all domestic animals during pregnancy, the quantities are insufficient except in the mare to produce a reaction in the ovaries of test animals.

In the human, other tests for pregnancy depend upon the fact that the placenta also produces appreciable quantities of estrogenic hormones that are excreted in the urine. The *estrogen* output by the placenta is highest in the latter part of pregnancy.

When urine containing the estrogens is injected into ovariectomized rats, there is cornification of the test animal's vaginal epithelium. A smear of the vaginal wall is made and the cellular changes observed with the aid of a microscope.

A chemical test for pregnancy which utilizes the estrogens found in urine is called the *Cuboni test*. An extract of the urine is made with benzene. When sulfuric acid is added, a greenish fluorescent color occurs if the test is positive. In the mare this test is accurate after 140 days of pregnancy. For unknown reasons, in the sow the test can be used only from the 20th to the 32nd day and again after the 75th day.

PARTURITION

Parturition, or labor, which is the act of giving birth to young, marks the termination of pregnancy. It is customary to divide the act of parturition into three stages. The *first stage* consists of uterine contractions which gradually force the water bags against the uterine side of the cervix, causing it to dilate. This stage lasts 2 to 6 hours in the cow and ewe, 1 to 4 hours in the mare, and 2 to 12 hours in the sow and bitch.

In the *second stage* actual delivery of the fetus occurs. Passage of parts of the fetus through the cervix into the vagina along with rupture of one or both water bags reflexly initiates actual straining, or contraction of the abdominal muscles. The combination of uterine contraction and abdominal contraction forces the fetus through the birth canal.

The *third stage* of *parturition* consists of delivery of the placenta, which normally follows the fetus almost immediately.

There is some question as to what factors actually initiate parturition. However, it is well known that the oxytocic principle of the posterior pituitary gland causes uterine muscle to contract. In fact, extract of the posterior pituitary is used extensively to stimulate contractions of the fatigued uterus during prolonged labor.

Signs of Approaching Parturition

As well as the obvious enlargement of the abdomen, the mammary glands enlarge and begin to secrete a milky material within a few days of parturition. There may be some edema (swelling) of the ventral abdominal wall about the same time as the mammary gland secretion begins, particularly in the first pregnancy. The vulva swells and usually discharges a thick mucus. Other signs include relaxation of the abdominal wall with sinking of the flanks, dropping of the belly, and sinking of the rump on both sides of the tail head.

As the time of parturition becomes imminent, the animal becomes restless, usually seeks seclusion, lies down and gets up frequently, attempts to urinate

23

often, and then begins actual labor. The bitch and sow usually try to build a nest before starting labor.

Normal Presentation

The calf is normally presented front feet first with the head extended and the nose between the front feet. The dorsum of the calf is in contact with the sacrum of the dam. This position, called anterior presentation, takes advantage of the natural curvature of the birth canal of the dam and the curvature of the fetus. A posterior presentation with the hind feet first, hocks up, occurs frequently enough in cattle to be considered normal.

Contractions of the uterus force the *fetal placenta* (water bags) against the cervix of the uterus. This constant pressure causes the cervix to dilate gradually so the fetus can pass through into the pelvis of the dam. When the water bags break, the uterus contracts more strongly upon the fetus. About the same time, the abdominal muscles begin to contract forcefully to expel the fetus through the birth canal.

The contraction of abdominal muscles, called straining, apparently is a reflex response to stimuli from the presence of parts of the fetus within the vagina and vulva of the dam. Straining is readily evoked by an operator inserting his hand and arm into the vulva and vagina of a cow when attempting to deliver a calf, unless the cow has received an appropriate local anesthetic.

The uterus of the sheep is very similar to that of the cow, so nearly everything said about pregnancy in the cow applies to the sheep except gestation period and the fact that multiple births are much more common in sheep than in cattle.

The legs of a colt are relatively longer than those of a calf, and the colt is carried to a larger extent in the body of the uterus, while a calf is carried almost entirely in one horn of the uterus. Presenta-

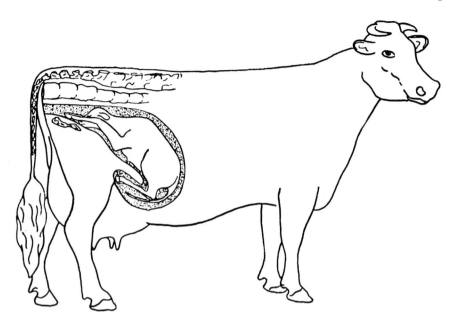

Fɪɢ. 25–6.—Position of the calf in the uterus after it has been oriented for normal delivery. (From *Physiology of Reproduction and Artificial Insemination of Cattle.* Copyright by G. W. Salisbury and N. L. VanDemark. Copyright by W. H. Freeman and Company, 1961.)

tion of the foal is essentially the same as that of a calf.

With pigs and dogs, the young are carried in both horns of the uterus and may be presented either anteriorly or posteriorly with equal facility.

Usually the placenta or after-birth is delivered a short time following birth of the young, but it may accompany the fetus or, very rarely, precede it. The placenta is considered to be pathologically retained if an abnormally long period of time elapses between birth of the young and delivery of the placenta.

Normally the placenta of the cow and ewe should be delivered within 24 hours following parturition. Since the mare is quite susceptible to *metritis*, or infection of the uterus, any retention of the placenta over two or three hours is a cause for concern. In the pig and dog, each placenta normally is still attached to the fetus and may completely surround it at birth. Immediate removal of the pla-

centa from the nostrils of the newborn is essential for life and is usually done by the dam.

Manual removal of retained placenta from the cow is the most common method of treatment. While this operation, commonly called "cleaning," is relatively simple for a skilled person, it may be dangerous to the cow and also to the operator if proper precautions are not observed. Cows infected with *Brucella abortus (Bang's disease)* often show a high incidence of retained placenta. Treatment of a retained placenta with *stilbestrol*, a synthetic female sex hormone, is sometimes used with varying degrees of success.

Retained placenta in species other than the cow may be more serious and often endangers the life of the animal. Early treatment of these cases requires not only removal of the placenta, but local treatment of the infected uterus and systemic treatment of the dam as well.

Dystocia—Difficult Birth

Normal parturition with no complications is by far the most common situation in domestic animals. However, there are occasions when the dam has difficulty giving birth to young and may need some assistance.

From the onset of actual labor, a cow should calve within a maximum of 8 hours, or intervention likely will be necessary. The ewe should complete lambing within 1 to 2 hours. If a mare does not foal within 1 to 3 hours after starting labor, a veterinarian should be called. Pigs and dogs should average one offspring at least every hour or else intervention may be necessary.

Improper presentation is a common cause of obstetrical trouble. Other causes

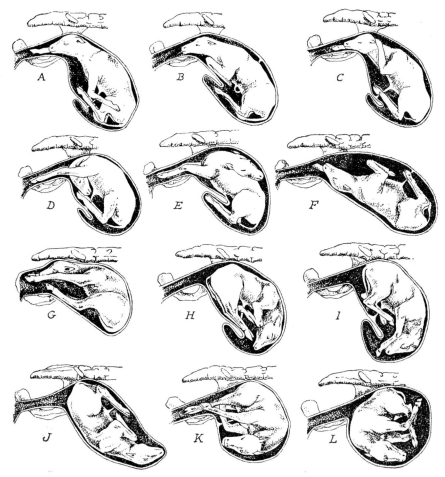

Fig. 25–7.—Abnormal presentations of the calf for delivery. (Redrawn from *Diseases of Cattle*, U.S.D.A. Special Report, 1942.) (from *Physiology of Reproduction and Artificial Insemination of Cattle* by G. W. Salisbury and N. L. VanDemark. Copyright by W. H. Freeman and Company 1961.)

A, Anterior presentation—one foreleg retained. *B*, Anterior presentation—forelegs bent at knee. *C*, Anterior presentation—forelegs crossed over neck. *D*, Anterior presentation—downward deviation of head.

E, Anterior presentation—upward deviation of head. *F*, Anterior presentation—with back down. *G*, Anterior presentation—with hind feet in pelvis. *H*, Croup and thigh presentation.

I, Croup and hock presentation. *J*, Posterior presentation—the fetus on its back. *K*, All feet presented. *L*, Dorsolumbar presentation.

include disparity of size of dam and fetus (too large a calf or too small a birth canal), and some pathological condition of dam or fetus.

Abnormal Presentations

Any deviation from the anterior presentation or posterior presentation as described is considered to be abnormal and usually requires correction before the fetus can be delivered. Figure 25–7 shows some of the many abnormal presentations that may be encountered.

Correction of any of these abnormal presentations requires returning the calf to an anterior or posterior presentation. In most instances this involves repelling the fetus into the uterus away from the pelvic inlet in order to have room for manipulation of the calf. An *epidural anesthetic* administered by a veterinarian will stop all straining by the cow and make the operation much easier on both the cow and the operator. A detailed description of abnormal presentations and their correction may be found in *Diseases of Cattle*, Atkinson *et al.*, (1942) and in most standard textbooks of veterinary obstetrics.

Other Causes of Dystocia

Excessive size of the fetus in relation to the size of the birth canal of the dam presents a very difficult problem. Even though the presentation may be normal, excessive traction in delivering the newborn will likely be very damaging to both the fetus and the dam.

Treatment of Dystocia

Cesarean section (surgical removal of the calf) is the safest treatment for this type of dystocia and is quite safe for both fetus and dam if the operation is performed by a skilled veterinarian before complications occur. The other alternative is *embryotomy* (cutting the fetus into pieces which are small enough to remove through the birth canal). This procedure may save the life of the dam.

Pathological conditions of the fetus which cause difficulty in parturition include such things as *hydrocephalus* (water on the brain), *ankylosed* (fused) *joints*, shortened tendons, *Siamese twins*, and monstrosities such as calves with two heads or extra appendages.

Pathological conditions in the dam that can interfere with parturition usually involve the birth canal. Such things as fracture of the pelvis, tumors of the genitalia, and excess fat in the pelvis, all decrease the size of the birth canal, thereby interfering with passage of even a normal size fetus. In addition, torsion, or twisting, of the uterus, rupture of the uterus, or rupture of the prepubic tendon, which is the insertion of the *rectus abdominis* muscle, will seriously impair or prevent normal parturition. Again, the best treatment for the preceding conditions is cesarean section, with embryotomy a second choice.

CHAPTER 26

ANATOMY OF THE MALE REPRODUCTIVE SYSTEM

GENERAL

EMBRYOLOGICALLY the reproductive system is closely related to the urinary system. Often both are considered together under the title urogenital system. The *urethra* is used as a passage by both the urinary system and the male reproductive system.

The male reproductive system of farm mammals consists of two testes (or testicles) contained in the scrotum, accessory organs including ducts and glands, and the penis, which is sometimes referred to as the external genitalia. The testes produce *spermatozoa* (the male sex cells also called *sperm*) and *testosterone* (the male sex hormone). The scrotum provides the favorable environment of a lower temperature for the production of spermatozoa. The remaining structures assist the spermatozoa to reach their ultimate goal, the ovum of the female, in a condition conducive to fertilization of the *ovum*. These structures include the epididymis and vas deferens for each testicle, accessory sex glands (seminal vesicles, prostate, and bulbo-urethral glands), and the urethra and the penis.

TESTICLES

The *testicles* vary somewhat from species to species as far as shape, size, and location is concerned, but the essential structure is the same. Each testicle consists of a mass of *seminiferous tubules* surrounded by a heavy fibrous capsule called the *tunica albuginea*. A number of fibrous septa, or *trabeculae*, pass inward from the tunica albuginea to form a framework, or stroma, for support of the seminiferous tubules.

In all domestic animals except the horse, these trabeculae unite near the center of the gland to form a fibrous cord, the *mediastinum testis*.

The *cells of Leydig*, which secrete the male hormone, testosterone, are located in the connective tissue between seminiferous tubules.

SPERMATOGENESIS

The germinal epithelium containing primary male sex cells makes up the periphery of the seminiferous tubules. These primary sex cells are constantly dividing, and as new cells form they

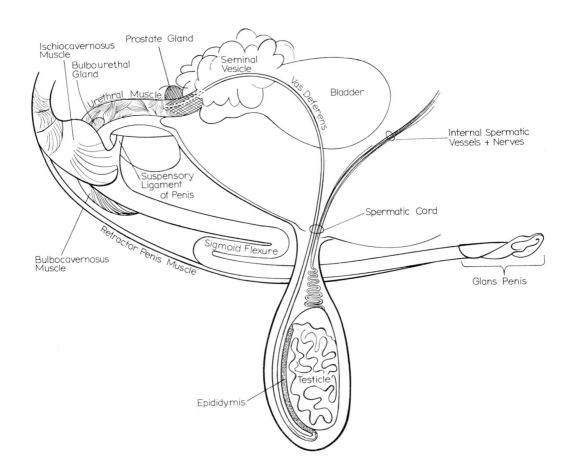

FIG. 26–1.—Genitalia of the bull.

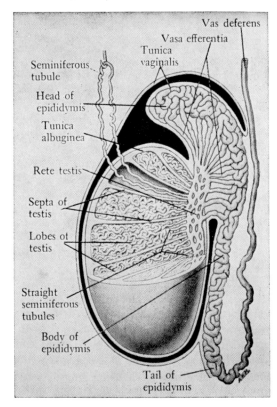

Seminiferous tubule

Head of epididymis

Tunica albuginea

Rete testis

Septa of testis

Lobes of testis

Straight seminiferous tubules

Body of epididymis

Vas deferens

Vasa efferentia

Tunica vaginalis

Tail of epididymis

FIG. 26–2.—(Borrowed by Steen & Montague [Barnes & Noble] from Hamilton, *Textbook of Human Anatomy*, 1957, St. Martin's Press and The Macmillan Co.)

migrate toward the lumen (interior) of the tubules, develop tails, and become free-swimming *spermatozoa*.

Spermatogenesis is the process by which primary sex cells in the testicle produce spermatozoa (Figs. 4–7 and 26–3).

During spermatogenesis the number of chromosomes is reduced to one-half the number normally found in the somatic (body) cells of each species. *Chromosomes* are the structures in the nucleus of each cell that carry *genes*, the hereditary determiners, which are transmitted from one generation to the next. They are the units responsible for inheritable characteristics of animals and man. The manner in which each of these characteristics is inherited depends on the location of its gene on a chromosome and the relation

of that gene to other genes on the same chromosome.

Spermatogenesis involves a series of steps in the formation of spermatozoa:

1. *Spermatogonia*, generalized cells at the periphery of seminiferous tubules, increase in number by *mitosis*, a type of cell division in which the daughter cells are nearly identical with the mother cell.

2. *Primary spermatocytes*, produced by spermatogonia, migrate toward the center of the tubule and undergo *meiotic division*, in which the chromosomes unite in pairs and then one chromsome from each pair goes to each of the two secondary spermatocytes. Thus, the chromosome number is halved in the secondary spermatocytes.

3. The two *secondary spermatocytes* formed from each primary spermatocyte divide by mitosis to form four *spermatids*.

4. Each spermatid undergoes a series of changes (*spermiogenesis*) from a nonmotile cell to a motile cell (cell with movement) by developing a flagellum (tail) to form a spermatozoon.

5. *Spermatozoa* are the germ cells which, after maturing by passing through the epididymis, are capable of fertilizing an ovum. They become actively motile when exposed to the material secreted by the prostate gland. Of the four sperm cells developed from each primary spermatocyte) two cells contain the Y chromosome to produce male offspring (XY), and two contain the X chromosome to produce female offspring (XX) when united with the ovum, which contains the X chromosome.

Sertoli's cells, also called *sustentacular cells*, or *nurse cells*, are found scattered among the sex cells within the seminiferous tubules. The Sertoli's cells apparently supply nutrition to the maturing spermatids and possibly produce *estrogen*. In cases of Sertoli's cell tumors, the affected animal often develops feminine

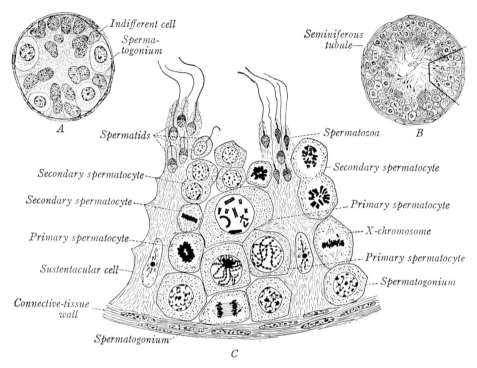

FIG. 26-3.—Drawing of a transverse section through a seminiferous tubule of a mammal. (Arey, *Developmental Anatomy*, courtesy of W. B. Saunders Co.)

characteristics such as enlarged mammary glands and a feminine pattern of fat distribution.

EPIDIDYMIS

The spermatozoa pass from the seminiferous tubules by way of the *vasa efferentia* to the head of the *epididymis*. The epididymis is a very long convoluted tube which connects the vasa efferentia of the testicle with the vas deferens, or ductus deferens.

The *head of the epididymis* attaches to the same end of the testicle that the blood vessels and nerves enter. The *body of the epididymis* parallels the long axis of the testicle, and the *tail of the epididymis* continues as the *vas deferens*, which doubles back along the body of the epididymis to the region of the head, where it enters the spermatic cord. The epididymis serves as a place for spermatozoa to mature

prior to the time they are expelled by ejaculation. Spermatozoa are immature when they leave the testicle and must undergo a period of maturation within the epididymis before they are capable of fertilizing ova.

VAS DEFERENS

The *vas deferens* (*ductus deferens*) is a muscular tube which, at the time of ejaculation, propels the spermatozoa from the epididymis to the ejaculatory duct in the prostatic urethra.

The vas deferens leaves the tail of the epididymis, passes through the *inguinal canal* as a part of the spermatic cord, and at the internal inguinal ring turns caudally, separating from the vascular and nervous parts of the cord. As the two vasa deferentia approach the urethra, they converge and continue caudally dorsal to the bladder, enclosed in a fold of

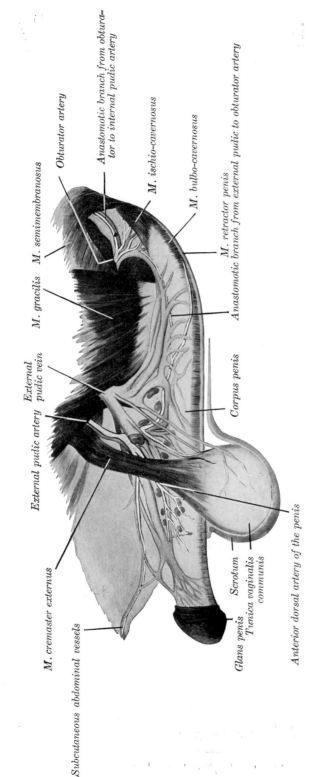

Obturator artery

Anastomotic branch from obtura—
tor to internal pudic artery

M. seminembranosus

M. ischio-cavernosus

M. gracilis

M. bulbo-cavernosus

M. retractor penis
Anastomotic branch from external pudic to obturator artery

External
pudic vein

Corpus penis

External pudic artery

M. cremaster externus

Subcutaneous abdominal vessels

Scrotum
Tunica vaginalis
communis

Glans penis

Anterior dorsal artery of the penis

Fig. 26–7.—Penis of horse; lateral view, showing circulation. The superficial inguinal glands are shown in the meshes of the plexus dorsalis penis. (Sisson and Grossman, *The Anatomy of the Domestic Animals*, courtesy of W. B. Saunders Co.)

the dorsum of the penis with the dorsal veins and dorsal nerves of the penis. The blood supply to the penis of the horse is more extensive, with the deep artery and the caudal part of the dorsal artery supplied by the *obturator artery*, which passes through the *obturator foramen* of the pelvis. The cranial part of the dorsal artery of the penis comes from the *external pudic artery* after it passes through the inguinal canal.

The *dorsal nerve of the penis* is a continuation of the *pudic nerve*, which is derived from ventral branches of sacral nerves. It crosses the ischial arch and passes along the dorsum of the penis to ramify in the glans penis. Sensory fibers from the glans provide the afferent side of reflexes for erection and ejaculation. The reflex centers for erection and ejaculation are located in the lumbar portion of the spinal cord.

CHAPTER 27

PHYSIOLOGY OF MALE REPRODUCTION

ERECTION

Erection of the penis is essentially an increase in the turgidity of the organ caused by a greater inflow of blood than outflow, with resultant increase in pressure within the penis. Both vasodilation of the arteries (caused by stimulation of the *nervi erigentes* from the pelvic plexus) and a decrease in the venous drainage from the penis are factors in producing erection. The decrease in venous drainage is caused at least in part by compressing the *dorsal veins of the penis* between the ischial arch and the body of the penis when the *ischio-cavernosus muscles* contract.

When the penis of the horse or dog erects, a considerable increase in diameter as well as increase in length occurs because of the relatively large amount of erectile tissue, or cavernous tissue, in comparison with the quantity of *tunica albuginea* and other connective tissue.

The *penis* of ruminants and swine erects

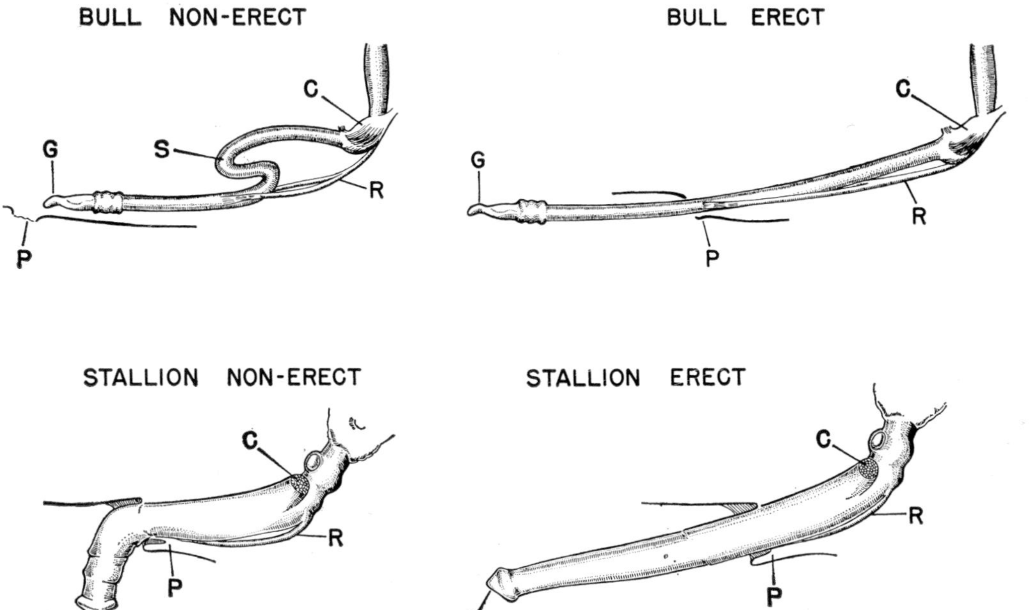

BULL NON-ERECT

BULL ERECT

STALLION NON-ERECT

STALLION ERECT

FIG. 27–1.—Penis of bull and stallion in non-erect and erect condition. *C*, ischiocavernosus muscle; *G*, glans; *P*, pruce; *R*, retractor penis muscle; and *S*, sigmoid flexure. (Redrawn from Hafez, *Cornell Vet*, in Hafez, *Reproduction in Farm Animals*, Lea & Febiger.)

chiefly by straightening of the sigmoid flexures. Although the turgidity increases, the length and diameter of the penis remains nearly the same as in the relaxed condition because there is relatively little erectile tissue in comparison to the amount of connective tissue.

The *glans penis* of the horse erects later than the body because the glans receives much of its blood supply from veins of the prepuce. This arrangement requires entrance into the *vagina* of the mare before complete erection of the glans occurs, particularly in small or virgin mares.

A somewhat similar situation is present in the dog, with the *bulbus glandis* portion of the penis erecting after entrance is made into the vagina of the bitch. This engorgement of the bulb, plus the clamping of sphincter muscles of the vulva and vagina of the bitch, prevent separation of the dogs during the "tie" until the penis of the male becomes flaccid following ejaculation.

EJACULATION

Ejaculation is a reflex emptying of the epididymis, urethra, and accessory sex glands of the male. The reflex most commonly is caused by stimulation of the glans penis, either during natural service or by an artificial vagina used for collecting semen for examination or artificial insemination. Ejaculation can also be produced by manual massage of the accessory sex glands through the rectum or by the use of an electric ejaculator. Figure 27–2 illustrates the nervous pathways involved in erection and ejaculation in man and presumably in other animals.

HORMONES OF MALE REPRODUCTION

The endocrine function of the testes consists mainly of production of *testosterone*, the male sex hormone, by the *cells of Leydig* (also called the *interstitial cells*).

Hormones such as testosterone with masculinizing effects are known as *androgens*. The testes are the chief source of androgens, but they are also produced by the *adrenal cortex*, the *ovaries*, and the *placenta*. Some of the actions of testosterone were known for centuries before the word hormone was coined and applied to products of internal secretion, because the practice of castration of both male animals and man goes back into early history. Lack of *libido* (sex drive) and inability to produce offspring are two of the most obvious effects of castration and the resultant lack of testosterone. However, animals castrated after attaining sexual maturity may continue to mate for some time if they had sexual experience before castration. If an animal is castrated before puberty, many of the masculine secondary sex characteristics fail to develop, and the castrate animal tends to resemble the female of the species. In addition, the accessory sex glands fail to develop normally if castration occurs early in life, and they regress and become non-functional if castration occurs after sexual maturity. Lack of development of accessory sex glands, the penis, and the urethra may be a contributing factor in obstructions caused by urinary calculi in feed-lot steers and wethers.

Actions of testosterone have been determined largely by using it as replacement treatment in castrated experimental animals. Testosterone promotes the development and function of accessory sex glands, causes development of secondary sex characteristics, and is necessary for mating activity, including sex drive, erection of the penis, and ejaculation. Testosterone promotes protein anabolism, resulting in increased body size as compared to the female. The skeleton also responds to testosterone, with the bones becoming larger and thicker.

Spermatogenesis is initiated by *FSH* (*follicle-stimulating hormone*) from the *anterior pituitary gland*, but testosterone is

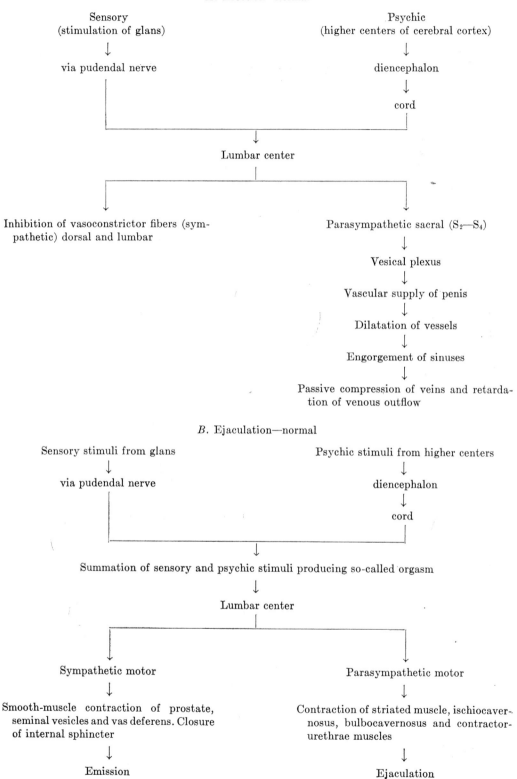

A. Erection—normal

Sensory
(stimulation of glans)
↓
via pudendal nerve

Psychic
(higher centers of cerebral cortex)
↓
diencephalon
↓
cord

↓

Lumbar center

Inhibition of vasoconstrictor fibers (sympathetic) dorsal and lumbar

Parasympathetic sacral (S_2—S_4)
↓
Vesical plexus
↓
Vascular supply of penis
↓
Dilatation of vessels
↓
Engorgement of sinuses
↓
Passive compression of veins and retardation of venous outflow

B. Ejaculation—normal

Sensory stimuli from glans
↓
via pudendal nerve

Psychic stimuli from higher centers
↓
diencephalon
↓
cord

↓

Summation of sensory and psychic stimuli producing so-called orgasm
↓
Lumbar center

Sympathetic motor
↓
Smooth-muscle contraction of prostate, seminal vesicles and vas deferens. Closure of internal sphincter
↓
Emission

Parasympathetic motor
↓
Contraction of striated muscle, ischiocavernosus, bulbocavernosus and contractor-urethrae muscles
↓
Ejaculation

Fig. 27–2.—The probable neural pathways involved in *A* erection and *B* ejaculation. (Whitelaw and Smitherick, courtesy of New England J. Med.)

(377)

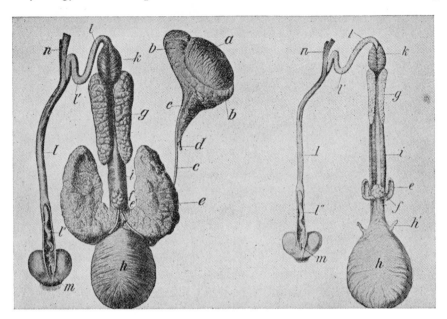

Fig. 27–3.—Genital organs of a normal and a castrated boar. (From *Handbuch der vergleichenden Anatomie der Haustiere* by permission of the Springer Verlag, Heidelberg.)

a—testis	*g*—bulbo-urethral gland	l'—sigmoid flexure
b—epididymis	*h*—bladder	l''—twisted portion of penis
c—vas deferens	*h'*—ureter	*m*—orifice of preputial pouch
d—spermatic cord	*i*—urethral muscle	*n*—retractor penis muscle
e—seminal vesicle	*k*—cavernous muscle	
f—prostate gland	*l*—penis	

necessary for completing the process. The pituitary directly controls germ-cell mitosis and meiosis and indirectly controls maturation of *spermatids* (*spermiogenesis*). Inasmuch as Leydig cells are stimulated to produce testosterone by *ICSH* (*interstitial-cell-stimulating hormone,* or *LH*), the testosterone acts in a feedback mechanism to inhibit further production of ICSH.

The testicle produces an appreciable amount of estrogen (female sex hormone), presumably from the *Sertoli's cells* in the *seminiferous tubules*. The function of estrogen in the male is obscure, but it may act to inhibit FSH from the anterior pituitary.

SEX DETERMINATION

Sex of mammals normally is determined by the genetic makeup of the individual embryo, with the dam contributing an *X chromosome* and the sire contributing either an *X* or *Y chromosome*. The embryo with XX chromosomes will become a female, and the embryo with the XY chromosomes will become a male. Although this concept of sex determination has been accepted for some time, there is evidence that the genetic mechanism may be more complex, and a genetic balance exists between the sexes, and genetic gradations are possible between maleness and femaleness. An interesting finding in *somatic cells* is the presence of a small clump of chromatin material adherent to the inner surface of the nuclear membrane. This sex chromatin is found in 60 to 80 per cent of the somatic nuclei of females and not over 10 per cent of the somatic nuclei of males. The presence or absence of the sex

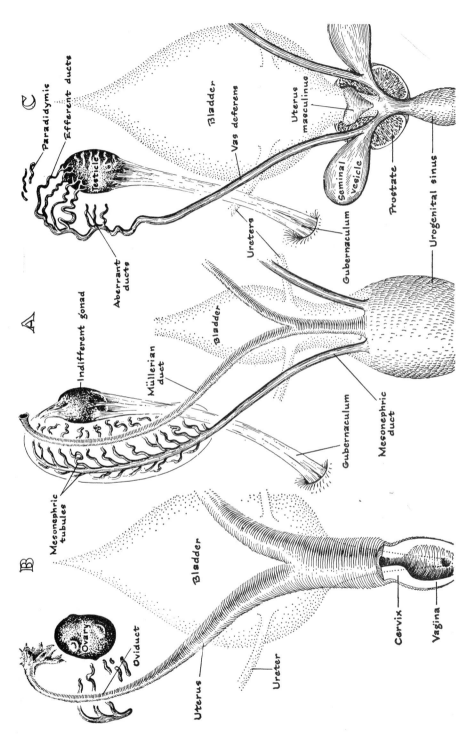

FIG. 27–4.—The indifferent reproductive system A and its modification into the female B and male C reproductive systems. Note that in A the duct systems of both sexes are present. In phenotypic males Müller's duct disappears (except for the uterus masculnus): in females the mesonephric duct disappears (except for oviducal appendages). (Modified and redrawn from Blom and Christensen, 1947, Skandinavisk Veterinaztidskrift in A. V. Nalbandov, *Reproductive Physiology*, courtesy of W. H. Freeman and Co., copyright 1964.)

chromatin is accepted as a presumptive test for genetic sex of the individual.

The understanding of *hermaphrodites*, males with female characteristics and females with male characteristics, was aided considerably by the study of *freemartins* in cattle. A freemartin is a female calf that develops in the same uterus with a normal male twin and with a common blood supply for both twins. If the placentas and blood supply are separate, a normal female calf will develop. The freemartin usually has female external genitalia but may have nearly any degree of masculinization of the internal genitalia. The amount of masculinity appears to be correlated with the amount of vascular connection between the twins and presumably with the stage of development at which the connection was established. The conclusion that the abnormal development of the female twin is due to a hormone from the testes of the male calf that is carried to the female calf by way of the common circulation has been well accepted, although attempts have been made to incriminate an antigen-antibody reaction. To test a heifer calf born with a bull twin, a blunt instrument such as a small test tube may be inserted into the vagina of the suspected calf. If the tube can be inserted several inches without difficulty, the heifer probably is normal, but if the passage is blocked within an inch or so of the opening, the heifer is likely to be a freemartin, and she cannot be used for breeding.

The term freemartin is applied exclusively to cattle, but similar intersex females have been reported in pigs and have been suspected in sheep, with apparently the same mechanism of formation as in cattle.

Regardless of the genetic sex of an embryo, it is possible to produce a functioning animal of the opposite sex by the use of the right amounts of the right hormones administered to the embryo in the indifferent stage and continued for the proper length of time. Every vertebrate embryo goes through an indifferent stage in which all embryonic structures needed for the development of either sex are present as definite structures. Both *Müllerian* and *Wolffian ducts* are present in the embryo. With normal male hormonal stimulation the Wolffian ducts become tubular portions of the male reproductive system, and the Müllerian ducts regress. Under normal female hormonal stimulation the Müllerian ducts become tubular portions of the female reproductive system, and the Wolffian ducts regress. In case of the freemartin, the testes of the male twin develop before the ovaries of the female twin, and the male hormone adversely affects the development of the female genitalia.

THE SPERMATOZOA

Each spermatozoon, or sperm cell, consists of a head, mid-piece, and tail. A nucleus extending the entire length of the *head* contains the genetic material needed in fertilization of the ovum. The fact that a sperm nucleus contains half as much *DNA* (*deoxyribonucleic acid*) as the diploid nucleus of a corresponding somatic cell is good evidence that DNA is responsible for transmission of heritable characteristics. The actual amount of DNA in the nucleus of one bull spermatozoon has been calculated to be 3.3×10^{-9} mg. Sperm from infertile individuals tends to have less DNA than normal. *RNA* (*ribonucleic acid*) is also present in the nucleus of the spermatozoon, but in very small quantities (about 0.1×10^{-9} mg. in one bull spermatozoon).

The *mid-piece* has been described as the power plant of the sperm, since the *mitochondria* are concentrated in this area. Mitochondria are believed to contain the enzyme systems associated with metabolic activity and thus provide energy for sperm mobility.

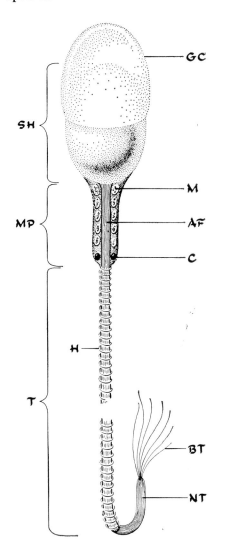

Fig. 27–5.—Details of mammalian sperm cell structure as seen under the electron microscope (composite of several published pictures).

SH—sperm head
MP—midpiece
T—tail
GC—galea caput
M—mitochondria
AF—axial filaments, which begin in midpiece, extend through tail, and emerge as a brush (BT) at tip of tail
C—ring centriole
H—helix, which coils round surface of tail but does not extend to tip of tail (NT)
(*Reproductive Physiology*, by A. V. Nalbandov, courtesy of W. H. Freeman and Co., copyright, 1958.)

The sperm *tail* resembles a flagellum of ciliated cells. Two *centrioles* are located in the mid-piece. From here fibrils similar to those of cilia extend into the tail. There are two central fibrils surrounded by a ring of nine peripheral pairs of fibrils. These fibrils are presumed to produce movement of the sperm tail in some manner as yet unknown.

When examined with the electron microscope, the cell membrane of a *spermatozoon* looks identical to the cell membrane of a spermatid.

Although spermatozoa experimentally removed directly from the testes may have the ability to fertilize ova, their capacity for fertilization is greatly enhanced by maturation. As the spermatozoa pass through the epididymis the following changes occur and are known collectively as maturation. A cytoplasmic structure of unknown function called the *kinoplasmic* droplet disappears, there is a decrease in water content and an increase in specific gravity, and there are some changes in ionic concentrations in the spermatozoa.

Movement of Spermatozoa

The movement of spermatozoa through the male reproductive tract must be entirely passive, because the spermatozoa motility becomes apparent only on exposure to oxygen at the time of ejaculation. Currents of fluid within the seminiferous tubules have been suggested as a means of moving spermatozoa from the tubules to the efferent ducts and then to the epididymis. Contractions of Sertoli's cells and contractions of smooth muscle may also aid movement of spermatozoa. Peristaltic movements of the epididymis probably are the major factor in movement of spermatozoa within and through the epididymis. A spermatozoon can move through the epididymis of a ram in about 9 to 14 days. Most spermatozoa are stored in the tail of the epididymis, where they may survive for an unknown length of time, probably a matter of weeks or months in the immotile state. Unejaculated spermatozoa may eventually be reabsorbed by the epididymis. Presumably resorption must occur in vasectomized animals.

At the moment of ejaculation, spermatozoa suddenly become motile because of access to oxygen. Under normal conditions survival time of activated spermatozoa is only a matter of hours. Length of fertility in the female tract is given as: sheep, 30 to 48 hours; cow, 28 to 50 hours; and horse, 144 hours. Although motility usually is equated with fertility, motility may last somewhat longer than fertility (the ability to fertilize an ovum).

Even though spermatozoa are motile following ejaculation into the female genital tract, the major factor in movement of spermatozoa to the *Fallopian tubes* is believed to be muscular activity of the tubular genitalia following insemination. Semen appears to be deposited in the uterus of the sow and mare during normal service, but in the vagina in the cow, ewe, and bitch. *Oxytocin* appears necessary for transport of spermatozoa, and it is released in the cow both during natural mating and during artificial insemination.

Based on the calculated speed of bull spermatozoa swimming under their own power (about 100μ per second), $1\frac{1}{2}$ hours would be required for a spermatozoon to swim directly to the Fallopian tubes. Actually the elapsed time in a natural mating is about $2\frac{1}{2}$ minutes for spermatozoa to reach the Fallopian tubes. In both artificial insemination and natural mating, the time ranges from 2 to 4 minutes. This extremely short time suggests very strongly that sperm is transported by the female genitalia to the Fallopian tubes rather than traveling under their own power. There is evidence that even within the Fallopian

tubes sperm transport is largely a matter of tubal contractions. The fact that cilia of the Fallopian tubes beat mainly in a direction toward the uterus is generally accepted and may serve to orient the spermatozoa because they tend to swim against the current. This ciliary action probably is a factor in moving the fertilized ovum into the uterus.

Hyaluronidase, an enzyme present in mammalian spermatozoa, has the ability to disperse the cells surrounding the ovum by dissolving the hyaluronic acid present. This has been believed to be important in fertilization and has been suggested as a reason for the tremendous numbers of spermatozoa found in normal ejaculates. However, one ejaculate of a bull can be divided into as many as 500 portions, and if properly handled, each portion can result in conception. Another objection to the so-called swarm of sperm being necessary for fertilization is the relatively small number of spermatozoa found in the Fallopian tubes following mating. Possibly the large number produced is needed to insure some spermatozoa reaching the ovum, or it may be a carry-over from the random fertilization outside the body of lower forms of life.

PRODUCTION OF SPERMATOZOA

Daily production of spermatozoa is large in normal male animals. The number has been calculated as 4.4×10^9 in the ram and 2.0×10^9 in the bull. Eight ejaculations of a bull within an hour reduced the volume of semen from 4.2 ml. at the first collection to 2.9 ml. at the eighth collection and the number of sperm per ml. was correspondingly reduced from 1664 million to 98 million.

ACCESSORY SEX GLANDS

The *accessory sex glands* function only in production of seminal fluid, which, however is not absolutely essential for fertilization. In experimental situations spermatozoa removed from the testicle and from the epididymis, when mixed with artificial media, can produce conception.

Functional activity of the accessory sex glands depends on *testicular androgens*. Androgens from the adrenal cortex do not appear able to maintain function of accessory sex glands in castrated males.

Smooth muscle fibers in the accessory glands empty them at the time of ejaculation in response to stimuli carried by way of autonomic nerves, including the parasympathetic *nervi erigentes* and the sympathetic *hypogastric nerve*.

CHAPTER 28

THE SKIN AND ASSOCIATED STRUCTURES

THE SKIN

THE skin consists of two layers: a superficial covering of stratified squamous epithelium, the *epidermis*, and a deeper layer of dense irregular connective tissue, the *dermis* (also known as the *corium*). This general arrangement of two layers of the skin is found throughout the body, including areas of modified epidermal structures such as hair, horns, hooves, chestnuts, and ergots.

THE EPIDERMIS

The epidermis is stratified squamous epithelium that in most areas can be divided into a deep growing layer, the *stratum germinativum*, and a superficial hornlike layer, the *stratum corneum*. The stratum germinativum follows the contour of the underlying papillary layer of the dermis to which it is closely applied. The cells range in shape from cuboidal or columnar cells undergoing mitosis in the deepest layers of epidermis to spindle-shaped cells of the *stratum granulosum* just deep to the stratum corneum.

Cells in the deepest layers of the stratum germinativum undergo active mitotic division, which pushes the more superficial layers still farther from the blood vessels in the corium. As distance from nutrients increases, the cells flatten and die. The drying and hardening of the superficial cells, a process called both *keratinization* and *cornification*, probably is related to the decreased nutrition of these cells.

The stratum corneum actually appears as stratified squamous epithelium since the cells are flat and plate-like. These keratinized cells with degenerate nuclei are constantly in the process of flaking off the surface of the skin in the form of *dandruff*. The thickness of the stratum corneum is greatest in those areas subjected to considerable wear, such as ordinary calluses and the foot pads of dogs.

The rate of cell division in the deeper layers of the epidermis increases under the influence of a number of different factors. Increased blood supply to the dermis from any cause will stimulate production of epidermal cells. Irritation or pressure will also stimulate increased cellular production, as seen in *callus* formation.

Modified epidermal structures produced by specialized areas of the stratum

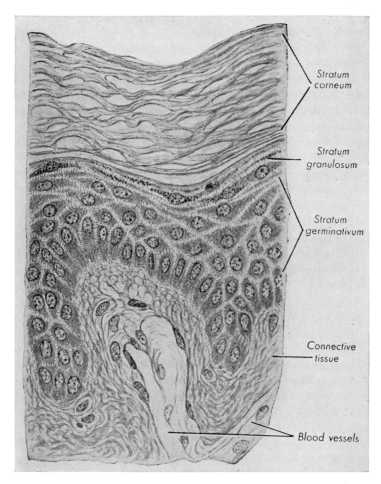

Fig. 28–1.—Vertical section through the skin. Stratum corneum, stratum granulosum, and stratum germinativum form the epidermis. Connective tissue and blood vessels are in the dermis. (*Bailey's Textbook of Histology*, 12 ed., courtesy of The Williams & Wilkins Co.)

germinativum, including hair, hooves, and horns, are described later in this chapter.

THE DERMIS

The dermis, also known as the corium, can be subdivided into a papillary layer immediately deep to the epidermis and consisting of ridges and nipple-like projections, and a deeper reticular layer that makes up the major part of the dermis.

Arteries, veins, capillaries, and lymphatics of the skin are concentrated in the dermis. Sensory nerve fibers, in addition to supplying the dermis, also extend a short distance into the epidermis. Hair follicles, especially those of tactile hairs, are well supplied with sensory nerves. Sympathetic nerves from the gray rami communicans of the spinal nerves supply sweat glands, sebaceous glands, and arrector pili muscles in the dermis.

COLOR OF SKIN

Color of skin is due to the presence of pigments within the cells of the epidermis. In some of the lower forms of life where color change is possible, it seems to be under the influence of the hormone *intermedin* from the intermediate lobe of the pituitary gland. However, higher vertebrates do not have this ability to change color readily. Absence of pigment in the skin may be very dangerous in that it makes the animal much more susceptible to the effects of sunlight, particularly after ingestion of certain feeds, including *buckwheat* and *alsike clover*. This condition, in which the unpigmented areas of the skin become edematous (filled with fluid) and may even slough off, is called *photosensitization*. Lack of pigment in the iris as well as lack of pigment in the skin surrounding the eye may cause extreme sensitivity to light; this condition appears in *albinos*. Cattle with white skin surrounding the eyes are much more susceptible to cancer of the eye than cattle with dark skin surrounding the eyes.

THE HYPODERMIS

In nearly all areas of the body the dermis is separated from underlying structures such as bone and deep fascia by a layer of loose (areolar) connective tissue. This areolar connective tissue, known as the *superficial fascia*, or *hypodermis*, is extremely important because it permits movement of the skin without tearing. It is also of importance in permitting a layer of fat to be interposed between the skin and deeper structures. This is not possible if the skin is adherent to these structures, as in the case of a tie where the dermis is attached to one or more vertebral spinous processes.

HAIR

Hair covers almost the entire body of most domestic animals, but many variations in hair structure exist between species and in different areas of an individual animal. A *hair follicle* develops first as a thickening and then as an ingrowth of epidermis into the corium of the skin. This forms a column of epithelial cells with a bulbous enlargement on the deep end, into which a connective tissue papilla is invaginated. The hair follicle consists of a connective tissue sheath surrounding a double-layered epithelial sheath. The internal epithelial root sheath intimately covers the root of the hair and is continuous with the epithelial cells covering the papilla. The external epithelial root sheath surrounds the internal-root sheath, is continuous with the epidermis, and gives rise to the sebaceous glands that are associated with hair follicles. The epithelial cells covering the papilla actually

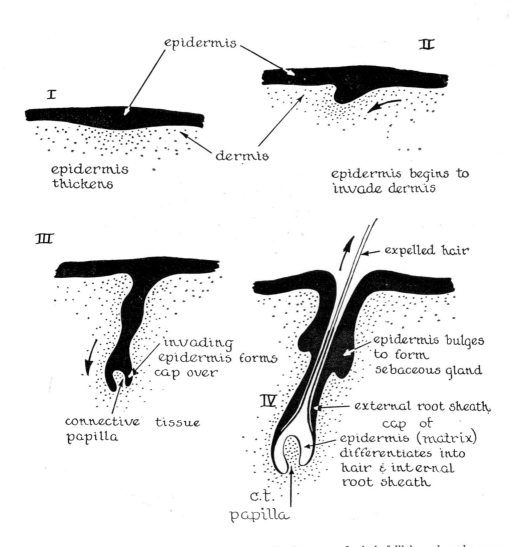

epidermis

II

I

dermis

epidermis
thickens

epidermis begins to
invade dermis

III

expelled hair

invading
epidermis forms
cap over

epidermis bulges
to form
sebaceous gland

IV

external root sheath

cap of
epidermis (matrix)
differentiates into
hair & internal
root sheath

connective tissue
papilla

c.t.
papilla

Fig. 28–2.—Sketches illustrating the embryological development of a hair follicle and a sebaceous gland. (Redrawn and slightly modified from Addison: *Piersol's Normal Histology*, J. B. Lippincott Co.)

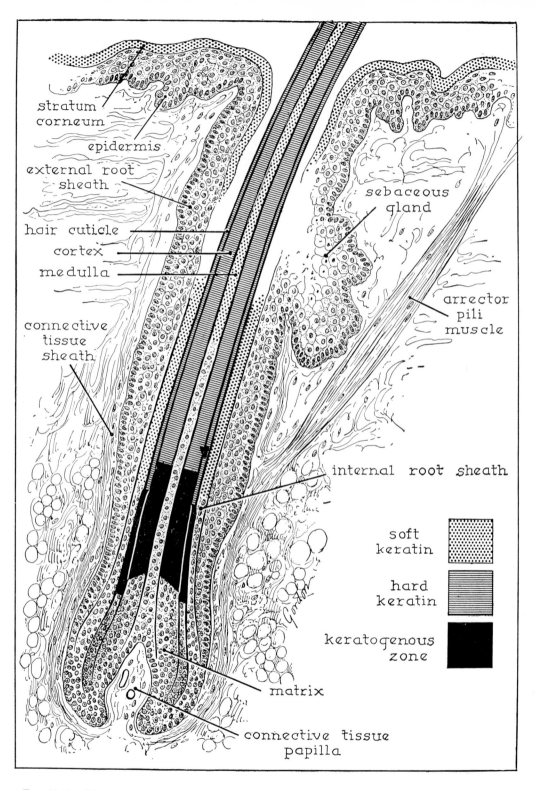

stratum corneum

epidermis

external root sheath

hair cuticle

cortex

medulla

connective tissue sheath

sebaceous gland

arrector pili muscle

internal root sheath

soft keratin

hard keratin

keratogenous zone

matrix

connective tissue papilla

FIG. 28–3.—Diagram of a hair follicle, showing the distribution of soft and hard keratin and the keratogenous zone in which hard keratin is produced. (Based on C. P., Leblond: Ann. New York Acad. Sc., *53*, 464.)

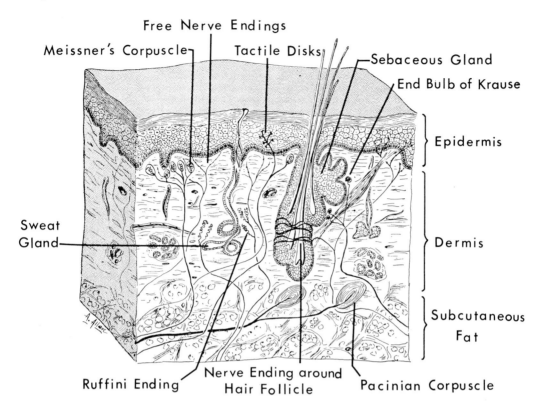

Free Nerve Endings

Meissner's Corpuscle   Tactile Disks

Sebaceous Gland

End Bulb of Krause

Epidermis

Sweat Gland

Dermis

Subcutaneous Fat

Ruffini Ending   Nerve Ending around Hair Follicle   Pacinian Corpuscle

Fig. 28–4.—Schematic representation of the nerve supply to the skin. (Modified after Woolard *et al.* 1940, and Gardner, 1963. (In Miller, Christensen, and Evans, *Anatomy of the Dog*, courtesy of W. B. Saunders Co.)

form the hair itself. Growth and multiplication of these cells extrudes the hair from the follicle, causing it to grow.

When a hair is ready to shed, the epithelial cells over the papilla stop multiplying and become cornified. The papilla atrophies and the hair may fall out, be pulled out, or be pushed out by a new hair that develops from epithelial sheath cells in a manner similar to the hair formation just described.

A typical hair consists of an inner *medulla*, an outer *cortex*, and a thin covering, the *cuticle*. The medulla may contain pigment which has little effect on hair color, but air between medullary cells is believed to give a white or silver color to the hair if the cortex lacks pigment. The major part of the hair is the cortex, which

consists of several layers of cornified cells. The amount and type of *melanin* in cortical cells determines whether the hair will be black, brown, or red. The cuticle is a single layer of thin, clear cells covering the surface of the cortex.

In addition to regular cover hair, domestic animals have wool hairs and tactile hairs. *Wool* forms the fleece of sheep. It is crimped (wavy) and lacks a medulla, and the connective-tissue portion of the follicle is sparse. Tactile hairs, used as probes or feelers, are also called *sinus hairs* because a large blood sinus is located in the connective-tissue portion of the follicle. Sinus hairs are particularly well supplied with sensory nerve endings that are sensitive to the slightest movement of the hairs.

25

COAT COLOR IN HORSES

A study by Gremmel (1939) gave most of the following information about *coat color* in horses. Hair color is due to only one pigment, and differences in color are caused by variations in the amount and location of the pigment. The pigment was never found scattered diffusely throughout the hair but always as clusters of granules. Scattered small smooth clusters of granules permit light to pass through the hair and produce a light color coat such as light chestnut. Densely packed, large, irregular clusters of pigment permit no light transmission, giving a black color to the hair. Variations in pigment clusters between these extremes were found in intermediate coats, including liver chestnuts and mahogany bays. The diluted appearance of dun horses was believed to be caused by a greater concentration of pigment on one side of the hair shaft than on the other. A lack of pigment clusters in the superficial part of the cortex was seen in hairs from brown or white muzzles of dark horses.

Standard colors of horses include black, brown, bay, chestnut, ysabella, dun, gray, roan, pinto, and possibly albino.

Black consists of uniformly black hairs including the mane and tail. Brown is a modification of black, with reddish hair on the muzzle, on the flanks, and under the eyes.

Bay is a reddish coat with black mane and tail. Chestnut varies from somewhat golden to red with mane and tail of about the same color.

Ysabella, which includes *palomino*, varies from a golden to red coat, but the mane and tail are flaxen or silver.

Dun resembles a diluted bay or chestnut with black mane and tail and a dark stripe on the dorsal mid-line.

Gray consists of an approximately equal mixture of white and black hairs. Gray horses are usually born black, and the proportion of white hairs to black hairs increases with age.

Roan is a mixture of white hairs with some other color. Blue roan consists mostly of white and black hairs with possibly a small amount of some other color.

Strawberry roan consists of a mixture of white hairs and chestnut hairs. Other colors may be mixed with white to give the respective roan color.

Pinto (paint) has irregular white areas alternated with colored areas. If the colored areas are black, the coat is called *piebald*, but if they are any color except black, the coat is called *skewbald*.

In all colors except *albino*, the skin is pigmented, but the true albino lacks pigment both in the skin and in the hair.

ARRECTORES PILORUM MUSCLES

Arrectores pilorum muscles are bundles of smooth muscle fibers that extend from the deeper portion of the hair follicle at an angle toward the epidermis. Hair follicles usually are at an angle to the surface of the skin other than 90°, and the arrectores pilorum muscles are attached to the side of the follicle forming an obtuse angle with the surface of the skin so that contraction of the muscle will straighten the hair. This action has the obvious advantage of increasing the insulating value of the coat during cold weather and may also be used by some animals immediately preceding and during battles, presumably as a means of bluffing the opponent by increasing the apparent size of the animal. These arrectores pilorum muscles are supplied by sympathetic nerves.

SEBACEOUS GLANDS

Sebaceous glands are classified as holocrine glands because the secretory products are produced by disintegration of epithelial cells within the glands. The glands derived from hair follicles are located in the triangle between the hair follicle, the surface of the skin, and the arrector pili muscle and empty into the hair follicle. Contraction of the arrector pili muscle compresses the glands and aids in emptying them. Sebaceous glands that open directly onto the skin surface include sebaceous glands in the ear canal, tarsal sebaceous glands of the eyelid, sebaceous glands around the anus, sebaceous glands on the penis, prepuce, and labia vulvae, and, in the sheep, sebaceous glands in the infraorbital pouches and inguinal pouches. Sebaceous glands of sheep produce the product called *lanolin*.

With a few exceptions, sweat glands (tubular skin glands) can be found over the entire bodies of farm animals, including the horse, cow, sheep, pig, and dog. However, the horse is the only farm animal that sweats readily. The nose of the dog lacks sweat glands, but the *planum nasolabiale* of the cow, *planum nasale* of the sheep, and *planum nasale* of the pig (all areas of the muzzle) have

tubular glands that are not generally classed as sweat glands. Modified epithelial structures including hooves, horns, and foot pads lack sweat glands.

MODIFIED EPIDERMIS

Much of the modified epithelium is based on a connective-tissue corium (dermis) that is in the form of papillae or in the form of laminae (sheets). In many places this corium is directly continuous with the underlying *periosteum*. Although the corium is often called the sensitive portion of the foot or horn, implying that it produces the corresponding insensitive structures, the insensitive portion actually represents the stratum corneum and is produced by the deepest layer of the epidermis, the stratum germinativum.

THE FOOT OF THE HORSE

The foot of the horse has a bony base which consists of the distal one-half of the second phalanx, the entire third phalanx

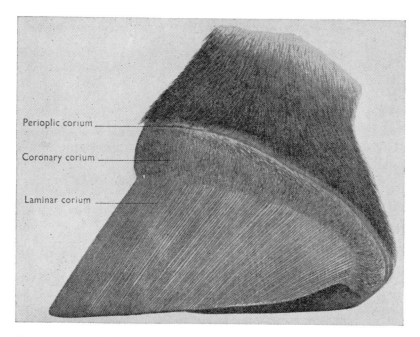

Fig. 28–5.—The corium of the foot in the horse from the lateral aspect. (Taylor, *Regional and Applied Anatomy of the Domestic Animals*, courtesy of J. B. Lippincott Co.)

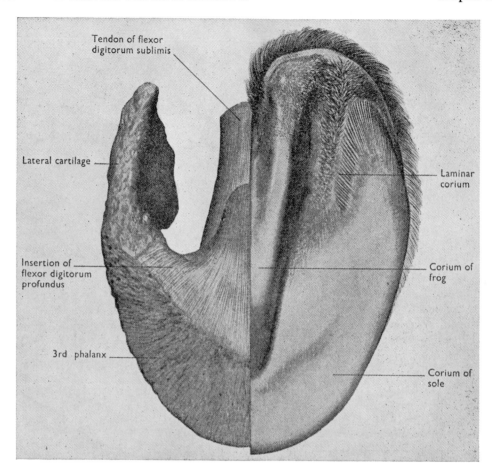

Fig. 28–6.—A solar view of the foot in the horse. Flexor digitorum sublimis is superficial digital flexor and flexor digitorum profundus is deep digital flexor. (Taylor, *Regional and Applied Anatomy of the Domestic Animals*, courtesy of J. B. Lippincott Co.)

and the distal sesamoid (navicular) bone. Covering the bone is a highly vascular modified dermis called the *corium of the foot*. The corium is regionally named according to the insensitive structures it underlies and includes the periopic corium, laminar corium, corium of the sole, and corium of the frog.

The *hoof* is the insensitive cornified layer of epidermis covering the distal end of the digit. Corresponding sensitive structures underly all insensitive structures, and pigmentation of the germinating (sensitive) layer determines the color of the hoof proper. White hooves are found where the hair at the upper margin of the hoof is also white, and dark hooves are associated with dark hair in this area. Black hooves are much tougher and stronger than non-pigmented (white) hooves, which tend to be somewhat brittle and chalky.

The insensitive structures of the hoof include the periople, wall, bars, laminae, sole, and frog. Each is produced by a corresponding sensitive structure consisting of the germinating layer of epidermis closely applied to the underlying corium of the same name, which is well supplied with vessels and nerves. With the excep-

in the proper functioning of the foot in pumping blood away from the foot. Ossification of the cartilages is a condition called sidebones.

The primary function of the foot can be summed up in the word "locomotion." A secondary function is that of standing support. As an aid to efficient locomotion, the foot absorbs concussion and provides leverage for muscles that insert on bones of the foot and produce the drive.

Support in standing is provided by both the stay apparatus and the check apparatus of the foreleg and the stay apparatus and the reciprocal apparatus of the hind leg.

THE STAY APPARATUS

The *stay apparatus* forms a flexible and somewhat elastic support of the fetlock and is essentially the same in both the front leg and in the hind leg. Structures making up the stay apparatus include the suspensory ligament, the intersesamoidean ligament between the two proximal sesamoids, and the distal sesamoidean ligaments of the proximal sesamoids. These ligaments together with the proximal sesamoid bones form a sort of sling across the caudal surface of the fetlock that helps prevent excessive hyperextension (settling) of the fetlock. The collateral ligaments of the fetlock and the collateral sesamoidean ligaments are sometimes included as a part of the stay apparatus because they help hold the fetlock and sesamoid bones in position and prevent lateral or medial deviation of the segments.

THE CHECK APPARATUS

The check apparatus also helps support the fetlock and permits the forelegs to maintain a standing position with relatively little muscular effort. With the exception of the long head of the *triceps muscle* all structures of the check apparatus are either completely tendinous or

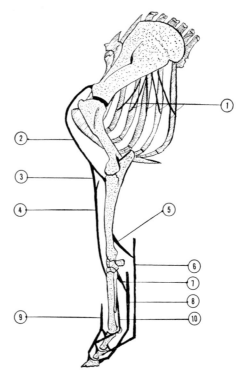

Fig. 29-3.—Check apparatus.

1. Serratus ventralis
2. Biceps brachii tendon
3. Attachment of biceps to extensor carpi radialis
4. Extensor carpi radialis
5. Superior check ligament
6. Superficial digital flexor tendon
7. Inferior check ligament
8. Deep digital flexor tendon
9. Common digital extensor tendon
10. Suspensory ligament

(Adams, *Lameness in Horses*, Lea & Febiger.)

are tendinous portions of certain foreleg muscles. Tendinous parts of the *serratus ventralis muscle* form a sling to support the trunk between the two scapulae, even with the muscular portion relaxed. The *biceps brachii* muscle has a tendon running throughout its length from the scapula to the front of the radius. When the elbow is extended by the triceps, the tension on the distal end of the biceps will tend to keep the shoulder joint extended also. A part of the biceps brachii tendon also connects to the fascia covering the *extensor carpi radialis* muscle and in this way indirectly maintains extension of the carpus. The common digital extensor tendon has no action as long as the horse remains standing without moving the foot.

The *superior check ligament* (also called the radial head of the superficial digital flexor) is a heavy ligamentous structure that attaches to the caudal side of the distal end of the radius and to the tendon of the superficial digital flexor. The *inferior check ligament* has a proximal attachment to the distal row of carpal bones and to the proximal end of the large metacarpal (cannon) bone. Distally it joins the tendon of the deep digital flexor. Both the superior check and inferior check ligaments assist the suspensory ligament in support of the fetlock even if the muscular portions of the digital flexors are relaxed.

THE RECIPROCAL APPARATUS OF THE HIND LEG

The hind leg has no check apparatus but does have a stay apparatus similar to that of the front leg. The hind leg has a *reciprocal apparatus* not found in the foreleg. The reciprocal apparatus consists of the *peroneus tertius muscle* on the front of the leg, extending from the femur to the tarsus, and the superficial digital flexor muscle on the back of the leg extending from the femur to the tuberosity of the calcaneus (point of the hock). Both of these muscles are almost entirely tendinous and contain little if any actual muscle tissue in the horse. These two muscles, in combination with the distal end of the femur and the tarsus, form a parallelogram, with the *stifle joint* and *hock joint* acting as pivots. This arrangement forces the hock joint and the stifle joint to move in unison; when the stifle extends, the hock extends, and when the stifle flexes, the hock also flexes. In other words, both joints must extend and flex at the same time. Thus, if the stifle is maintained in extension, the leg distal to the

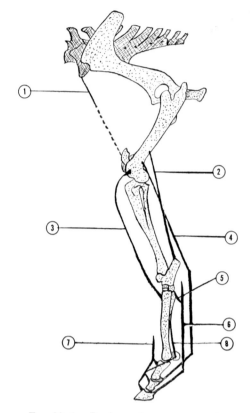

Fig. 29–4.—Reciprocal apparatus and additional structures.

1. Tensor fasciae latae
2. Fibrous band of gastrocnemius
3. Peroneus tertius
4. Superficial digital flexor continuation (also attaches to point of hock)
5. Inferior check ligament
6. Deep digital flexor tendon
7. Common digital extensor tendon
8. Suspensory ligament
   (Adams, *Lameness in Horses*, Lea & Febiger.)

stifle will bear the weight of the horse with little additional muscular effort. The part of the superficial digital flexor that passes from the point of the hock to the digit has no effect on the stifle and therefore does not function as a part of the reciprocal apparatus.

CONCUSSION-ABSORBING MECHANISMS

A large part of the *mechanism* for *absorbing concussion* depends on angulation of the joints of the limbs at the time of impact and immediately following contact of the foot with the ground. The muscles, tendons, and ligaments act as springs that absorb the shock of impact by permitting some flexion of all the limb joints except the fetlock joint, the pastern joint, and the coffin joint, which hyperextend on bearing weight. The elasticity of the ligaments and tendons of the digits also aids propulsion by helping straighten the digit before it leaves the ground thus adding impetus to the drive.

The hoof and its contents absorb concussion because of the elasticity of the hoof wall, the lateral cartilages, the digital cushion, and the frog. As the frog strikes the ground, both the digital cushion and the *frog* are compressed between the phalanges and the ground. This causes them to become wider and thinner. Pressure on the bars, the lateral cartilages, and the wall spreads the heels and also forces blood out of the vascular bed of the foot. The direct cushioning effect of the frog and digital cushion is enhanced by the resiliency of the wall and the hydraulic shock-absorbing effect of the blood confined within the hoof wall. At the same time the hoof is expanded by frog pressure, blood is forced out of the vascular sensitive structures of the foot against some resistance, which not only absorbs concussion but also pumps blood out of the foot and into the veins of the leg against gravity. This pumping action of the foot is an important means of returning venous blood from the foot to the general circulation.

ELASTICITY OF THE HOOF

Elasticity of the hoof is associated with moisture content of the horn material. Smith (1912) gives moisture content of the wall as 24.735 per cent, of the sole 37.065 per cent, and the frog 42.54 per cent. The frog is more elastic than the sole or wall. There is an increasing elasticity of

the wall from the toe to the heel that is correlated with the decreasing thickness of the wall in this direction and with the decreasing age of the hoof from the toe to the heel. The young thin wall of the heel is more elastic than the older thick wall at the toe. To take full advantage of this elasticity, the shoe should be nailed only as far back as the quarters.

CONSIDERATIONS IN SHOEING

So-called *physiological horse shoeing* maintains normal function of the foot by interfering as little as possible with most structures of the foot. The ground surface of the hoof wall is leveled in a manner to maintain the normal axis of the foot without lowering either the heels or toes excessively. To preserve moisture in the hoof, the outside of the hoof wall should be rasped only below the nails to form a groove for the clinches, and the surface of the sole should be left intact to prevent loss of moisture. To maintain frog pressure, the frog should never be lowered; only loose strands of tissue should be removed. After the hoof wall is leveled, the shoe should be fitted to the foot rather than fitting the foot to the shoe. The heel of the shoe should be about $\frac{1}{4}$ of an inch longer than the heel of the foot and should be about $\frac{1}{8}$ of an inch wider at the heel ($\frac{1}{16}$ of an inch on each side) than the foot to permit weight bearing during expansion of the heels when the foot bears weight. The nails should be started at the white line with the bevel toward the inside of the shoe so the nail will bend away from the sensitive structures of the foot. It is desirable to have the nails emerge in an even line about $\frac{3}{4}$ of an inch above the junction of the hoof and shoe.

Contraction of the heels, because of lack of frog pressure, is a common result of shoeing that does not follow physiological principles.

CHAPTER 30

THE MAMMARY GLANDS

GENERAL

THE mammary glands are modified sudoriferous (sweat) glands. They develop along the so-called milk line of the embryo, which is a line on each side of the abdominal wall parallel to the mid-line. In the bitch and the sow the mammary glands are found over the entire length of the milk line. However, in most domestic animals only the inguinal mammary glands develop. The most caudal group,

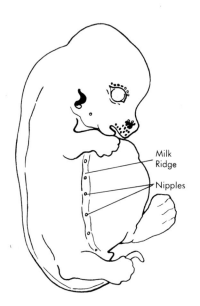

FIG. 30–1.—Drawing($\times$ 515)of 20mm. pig embryo. (After Minot.). Showing milk ridge (Milk line).

(404)

either a pair or four mammary glands develop. In the anthropoids and the elephant, the pectoral mammary glands are the only ones that develop.

MAMMARY GLANDS OF THE COW

The *mammary glands* or *udder of the cow* consist of four quarters. The skin of the udder is covered with fine hair; however, the teat is completely hairless. As far as the gland tissue is concerned, each quarter is a separate entity. The right half and the left half each consists of a craniaf (front) quarter and a caudal (hind) quarter, each of which is more or less of an entity. Each half is almost completely independent from the other half of the udder as far as blood supply, nerve supply, and suspensory apparatus is concerned.

Ventrally the separation of halves of the udder is marked by a longitudinal furrow, the intermammary groove. Occasionally a transverse furrow is located ventrally between the two quarters of each half. One half of the udder can be removed surgically without damaging the other half. The two quarters of the hall are separate as far as the gland tissue and duct system are concerned. They more or less resemble two trees close together,

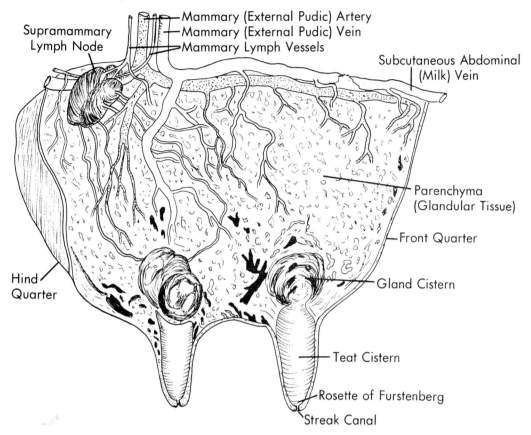

Fig. 30–2.—Sagittal section of udder of cow.

in which the branches intermingle but each retains its own identity. Thus all the milk from one teat is produced by the glandular tissue of that respective quarter.

However, the blood supply, nerve supply, venous drainage, and lymphatic drainage are all pretty much common to both quarters. The parenchyma (epithelial tissue) of the mammary gland to some extent resembles the lung tissue, or, in other words, a bunch of grapes with the alveoli representing the grapes and the various orders of ducts representing the stems of the grapes. The alveoli are the chief structures for actual milk production. The various orders of ducts converge to form larger ducts which eventually empty into a large basin, the *lactiferous sinus*. The lactiferous sinus may be divided into a large cavity within the

quarter proper, the *gland cistern*, and a smaller cavity within the teat called the *teat cistern*.

The term lactiferous sinus is also sometimes used as a synonym for teat cistern and also as a synonym for gland cistern.

Within the quarter the gland cistern is the cavity located above the base of the teat and is continuous with the teat cistern. The demarcation between gland cistern and teat cistern frequently is marked by a circular ridge that contains a vein and some smooth muscle fibers.

The wall of the empty teat cistern contains numerous overlapping longitudinal and circular folds that are obliterated through expansion of the wall when the teat is full of milk. There may also be diverticula (pockets) in the wall of the teat cistern.

The teat cistern is continuous with the exterior of the teat through a narrow opening in the end of the teat, the streak canal. The streak canal is about 8.5 mm. long, and the lumen normally is closed by a number of epithelial folds which project inward from the wall of the streak canal, leaving only a star-shaped potential opening. At the junction of the teat cistern and streak canal, the lining of the teat is arranged in a group of radial folds called the *rosette of Fürstenberg*. There are usually about eight primary folds and a number of secondary folds, all of which are effaced through expansion of the wall during milking by pressure from milk in the teat cistern.

The *streak canal* at the end of the teat is surrounded by a sphincter composed of circular smooth-muscle fibers. In hard milkers this sphincter is too tight. In cows that tend to leak milk, the sphincter is not tight enough. A tight sphincter can be corrected surgically, but *mastitis* is always a possible sequel to operations on the udder or teat.

SUSPENSORY APPARATUS

The suspensory apparatus of the udder consists of the *medial suspensory ligament* and the *lateral suspensory ligament* of the udder. The medial suspensory ligament contains a considerable amount of yellow elastic tissue because it is derived from the abdominal tunic, which is an elastic modification of the fascia (connective tissue) covering the superficial surface of the *external abdominal oblique* muscle. This medial suspensory ligament passes down between the two halves of the udder. One layer of the ligament intimately covers the medial side of each half of the udder. The two layers of the ligament can be readily separated since they are joined only by a small amount of loose areolar connective tissue. Practically no vessels or nerves pass through the medial ligament from one half of the udder to the other. Each ligament covers the medial side of the respective half of the udder; It passes around the front quarter to about the middle of the cranial side of the quarter, and it passes back around the hind quarter to about the middle of the caudal side of the hind quarter. The medial suspensory ligament is continued laterally by the cranial and caudal portions of the lateral suspensory ligament.

The *lateral suspensory ligament* is largely composed of white fibrous tissue, making it much less elastic than the medial sus-

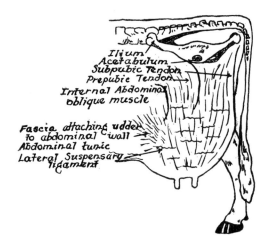

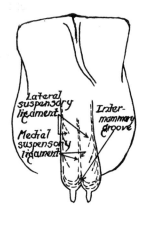

Fig. 30-3.—Suspensory apparatus of the udder. (From Espe in Turner, *The Comparative Anatomy of the Mammary Glands*, courtesy of Columbia, Missouri, University Cooperative Bookstore.)

pensory ligament. The lateral suspensory ligament is derived in a large measure from the *subpelvic tendon*. The subpelvic tendon is a medial vertical sheet of connective tissue that attaches to the *symphysis pelvis* and the *prepubic tendon* (the tendon of insertion of the *rectus abdominis muscle*) and in part gives origin to the medial muscles of the thigh, including the *gracilis* and the *adductor* muscles. From the *subpelvic tendon* the lateral suspensory ligament passes outward, downward, and forward around the lateral side of each half of the mammary gland to meet the medial suspensory ligament at the front and back of each half. A number of connective-tissue laminae are given off of both the lateral suspensory ligament and the medial suspensory ligament to enter the mammary gland. These laminae subdivide the gland into large compartments, the lobes, and these lobes into smaller compartments, the lobules, to form the stroma (framework) of the mammary gland. Both the medial suspensory ligament and the lateral suspensory ligament cover their respective portions of the surface of the udder, but they stop at the base of the teat. An additional lamina from the lateral suspensory liga-

ment sometimes is described as joining the connective tissue on the medial surface of the thigh. Some fibers may also be derived from the aponeurosis of the external abdominal oblique muscle to aid in forming the lateral suspensory ligament of the udder.

Blood Supply

The blood supply to the udder is largely by way of the *external pudic artery* (also called *mammary artery* in the cow). This artery comes from the *prepubic artery*. It passes downward through the inguinal canal in a more-or-less tortuous manner and divides into several branches which supply the front and hind quarters on the same side as the artery. A small artery that may be single or may be paired (as determined simply by chance) is the *perineal artery* which continues from the internal pudic artery and passes downward from the vulva just deep to the skin on the median line. The perineal artery usually supplies a small amount of blood to the caudal part of both halves of the udder.

The venous drainage from the udder is largely by way of a venous circle at the base of the udder, where it attaches to the

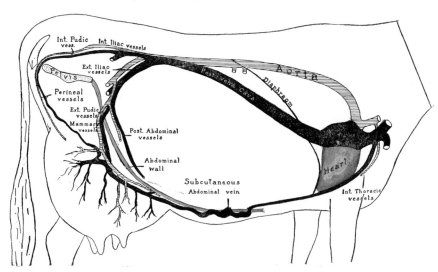

Fig. 30–4.—Diagram of circulation of udder of the cow. (Sisson and Grossman, *The Anatomy of Domestic Animals*, courtesy of W. B. Saunders Co.)

abdominal wall. This venous circle is formed from the main veins that drain the udder. The *external pudic vein* of each side receives blood from both the cranial and caudal quarters of the same side. Cranially each external pudic vein is continuous with the *subcutaneous abdominal (milk) vein* and caudally with the *perineal vein*. An anastomosis between the two *subcutaneous abdominal veins* just at or in front of the udder completes the venous circle. Each subcutaneous abdominal vein is a large tortuous vein in high-producing dairy cows. It passes forward in a sagittal plane lateral to the mid-line on the ventral abdominal wall. The subcutaneous abdominal vein passes through a foramen in the rectus abdominis muscle (the milk well) and joins the *internal thoracic vein*. Some authorities include the perineal vein as one of the veins draining the udder. Other authorities believe it carries blood toward the udder. The perineal vein may be single or paired (according to chance), and is a satellite of the perineal artery. It joins the *internal pudic vein*.

Innervation

According to St. Clair (1942) sensory and sympathetic nerves reach the udder by way of the *inguinal nerves* (from *2, 3, 4, lumbar nerves*), ventral branches of the first two *lumbar nerves* (portions not in the inguinal nerves), and the *perineal nerve* (from *2, 3, 4 sacral nerves* by way of the *pudic nerve*). There apparently are no secretory nerves in the udder, and the nerves to vessels (vasomotor nerves) do not follow the arteries to the udder but go by way of the spinal nerves. As will be described in the next chapter, secretion of milk is largely under hormonal control.

Lymphatic Vessels

The lymphatic vessels draining the udder show up rather well superficially just under the skin, particularly in high-producing cattle. They drain from the entire udder, including the teat, to the *superficial inguinal (mammary or supramammary) lymph nodes* located near the external inguinal ring above the caudal part of the base of the udder.

MICROANATOMY OF MAMMARY GLAND

The mammary gland is classified as a compound tubulo-alveolar gland. It consists of a stroma (connective tissue framework), parenchyma (epithelial portion), ducts, vessels, and nerves.

The surface of the teat is covered with stratified squamous epithelium which is continuous into the streak canal as the same type of epithelium (stratified squamous).

Surrounding the streak canal are a large number of smooth muscle fibers. Most of these fibers are arranged in a circular (annular) fashion around the streak canal to form a sphincter. Some muscle fibers close to the lining of the streak canal are arranged longitudinally parallel to the lumen of the streak canal. At the junction of the streak canal and the teat cistern, the location of the rosette of Fürstenberg, the epithelial lining changes abruptly to a stratified columnar epithelium that is usually two cells thick. This stratified columnar epithelium lines both the teat cistern and gland cistern. The lining of the larger lactiferous ducts is the same as the lining of the gland cistern. As the ducts branch and become smaller, the epithelial lining changes first to simple columnar and then to secretory epithelium in the alveoli. The height of the alveolar epithelium varies considerably with the activity of that particular portion of the gland.

The mammary gland differs from most other exocrine glands in that the secretory portion is not limited to the terminations of the smallest ducts, but milk-

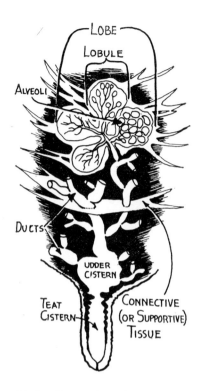

FIG. 30–5.—Connection of the ducts with the lobule-alveolar system (Hendren). (Turner, The Mammary Gland I. *The Anatomy of the Udder of Cattle and Domestic Animals*, courtesy of Lucas Bros.)

secreting structures empty directly into the larger ducts and also directly into the gland cistern and the teat cistern.

Turner classifies the ducts in increasing size as *intralobular, interlobular, intralobar,* and *interlobar.* A group of alveoli surrounded by a connective tissue septum form a more or less distinct unit called a lobule. The alveoli making up the lobule empty into small ducts within the lobule, the intralobular ducts. These intralobular ducts drain into a central collecting space, from which the interlobular ducts emerge. A group of lobules within a connective tissue compartment form a lobe. Within the lobe the interlobular ducts unite to form a single intralobar duct which is called an interlobar duct as soon as it emerges from the lobe. The interlobar duct may enter the gland cistern directly or it may join one or more other interlobular ducts before entering the gland cistern. Many of the ducts have numerous dilatations that act, in addition to the lactiferous sinus, as collecting spaces for milk.

The alveoli and ducts are surrounded by contractile *myo-epithelial cells,* which

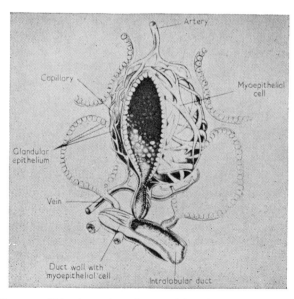

FIG. 30–6.—Diagram of blood vessels and myoepithelial cells surrounding an alveolus.
(After Hendren from Turner.)

are also called *basket cells*. These cells resemble smooth muscle fibers and are in contact with the epithelium of the mammary gland parenchyma, forming a basket-like covering of the alveoli and ducts. These cells are presumed to contract when the "let-down" of milk occurs.

In addition to the epithelial parenchyma and the myo-epithelial cells, the mammary gland is made up of a stroma of white fibrous connective tissue and yellow elastic connective tissue. Blood vessels, lymph vessels, and nerves ramify throughout the stroma in relation to the epithelial structures. Networks of capillaries surround the ducts and alveoli. The veins are valveless and form a rich network throughout the gland and within the wall of the teat. The vascular layer of the teat is called a corpus cavernosum because of its resemblance to the erectile tissue of the penis in the male. Lymphatic plexuses are found throughout the udder just deep to the skin and scattered throughout the parenchyma of the gland. Nerves appear to be largely sensory and vasomotor.

MAMMARY GLANDS OF SWINE

The normal number of teats in the domestic hog is seven pairs or fourteen teats, with the first pair just behind the junction of the sternum and ribs and the last pair in the inguinal region. The number may range from four pairs to nine pairs, and supernumerary teats are sometimes found between normal teats. Sows average 2.5 more teats than the number of pigs in their average litter. When litter size is eleven or more, sows with more teats produce slightly higher litter weights than sows with fewer teats.

Inverted teats (concave nipples) and mastitis are two of the most common conditions adversely affecting the mammary glands of sows.

Blood supply to the caudal mammary glands is by way of the external pudic artery, which passes forward and anastomoses with the *external thoracic artery* and possibly with the *internal thoracic artery*. The internal and external thoracic arteries supply the most cranial glands, and the middle group of glands may be supplied by any or all of the above mentioned arteries. The venous drainage is by veins that parallel the arteries and have the same names as the arteries.

The lymphatic vessels from all but the cranial one or two glands drain to the superficial inguinal lymph nodes. The lymphatic vessels from the cranial few glands may drain to the *cranial mediastinal lymph nodes*, the *caudal superficial cervical lymph nodes*, or both.

The teat of the sow contains two streak canals and two teat cisterns, one cranial to the other. Each teat cistern is continuous with a gland cistern. No hair is present on the teat, but hair is found at the base of the teat and on the gland.

Seedy cut bacon is due to pigmentation of mammary tissue, giving the appearance of small seeds in the bacon. Black seedy cut is due to invagination of pigmented epithelium at the time of mammary gland formation. It occurs only in dark-colored glands. Red seedy cut may occur in any color sow or gilt past puberty, as it is due to inflammation of mammary glands associated with the estrous cycle.

MAMMARY GLANDS OF SHEEP

The udder of the sheep differs from that of the cow in that each half of the udder of the sheep has only one teat, one streak canal, one teat cistern, and one gland cistern. One-half of the sheep udder resembles one-quarter of the cow udder. The teat of the sheep is sparsely covered with fine hair. Each half of the udder is located medially and cranially to the inguinal pocket (pouch) of the same side. Supernumerary teats in the ewe do not appear to have separate gland tissue, as is frequently found in the cow. Although attempts have been made to increase the number of teats in sheep by selective breeding, the additional teats have little effect on milk production.

The sphincter muscle around the streak canal is poorly developed, so closure is effected by elastic tissue in the end of the teat.

MAMMARY GLANDS OF THE HORSE

The mammary glands of the horse consist of one teat on each side attached to one-half of the udder. Each teat has two streak canals and two teat cisterns, each of which is continuous with a separate gland cistern and its system of ducts and alveoli. Turner (1939) reported that different colored dyes injected into the two glands never intermingle. This proves there is no communication between ducts or cisterns within the same half of the udder.

The udder and teats of the mare are covered with thin fine hair as well as with numerous sebaceous (oil) glands and sudoriferous (sweat) glands.

There is a difference of opinion as to the presence or absence of rudimentary teats in the stallion and gelding. They have been described in the skin forming the cranial part of the prepuce. Their presence here has also been denied. Apparently no adequate embryological study of this subject has been reported.

The streak canal, lined with dark-pigmented epithelium, is between 5 and 10 mm. in length. The junction of streak canal and teat cistern is marked by a distinctive rosette. In relation to the streak canal, the longitudinal smooth muscle fibers are better developed than in the cow, but the circular fibers are more poorly developed.

Ruminants have 1 duct per teat, the sow 2 to 3 ducts per teat, the mare 2 to 4 ducts per teat, the cat 4 to 7 ducts per teat, the bitch 8 to 20 ducts per teat, and the woman 15 to 24 ducts per teat.

CHAPTER 31

PHYSIOLOGY OF LACTATION

CONTROL OF MAMMARY GLAND DEVELOPMENT

EXTENSIVE development of the mammary gland is usually associated with puberty, the beginning of sexual maturity. It has been assumed that ovarian hormones of the estrous cycle are largely responsible for mammary growth, with *estrogen* stimulating growth of ducts and *progesterone* stimulating alveolar growth.

Experiments have shown modification of this pattern exists in some animals. In the spayed mouse, rat, and monkey, large quantities of progesterone alone will cause alveolar development and possibly duct development as well. In the spayed mouse, rat, rabbit, and cat, physiological (normal) levels of estrogen produced mainly duct growth. High levels of estrogen over a long period will cause alveolar development in these animals. In domestic ruminants and the guinea pig, estrogen alone will produce growth of ducts and alveoli, but the alveoli may be cystic, immature, or papillomatous (tumor-like) unless progesterone is also administered. The proper combination and amount of estrogen and progesterone in spayed female ruminants will produce mammary development and even milk production nearly equal to that produced by a normal pregnancy. In the spayed bitch and ferret, physiological

levels of estrogen cause little if any duct or alveolar development.

The anterior lobe of the *pituitary gland* is extremely important in controlling the development of the mammary gland. There is no question about anterior pituitary control of ovarian hormones, estrogen and progesterone, and their effect on the gland. In addition, the anterior pituitary may influence the mammary gland directly with prolactin and somatotrophin and indirectly by its control of the hormones of the thyroid gland and the adrenal cortex. Although experimental results and their interpretations are somewhat confusing, *prolactin*, *ACTH* (*Adreno-Cortico-Trophic Hormone*), *somatotrophin*, the placenta, and some adrenal corticoids are believed to stimulate mammary gland development. On the other hand, *thyroxine* and *cortisone* appear to inhibit mammary gland development.

The unproven possibility exists that nervous stimuli and even psychic stimuli may indirectly influence mammary gland development by way of the *hypothalamus* and *hypothalamico-pituitary* tracts.

LACTOGENESIS—THE INITIATION OF LACTATION

The balance of estrogen and progesterone maintained during pregnancy stimulates development of the mammary

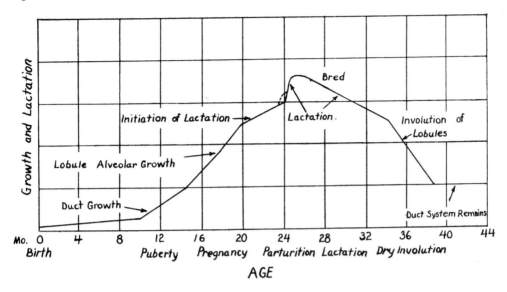

FIG. 31–1.—Graph of growth, lactation, and involution of the mammary gland of the cow. (Turner, *The Comparative Anatomy of the Mammary Glands*, courtesy of Columbia, Missouri, University Cooperative Book Store.)

gland but inhibits *lactogenesis*. The placenta no doubt plays a part in maintaining this balance. If the balance is upset by any cause such as parturition, ovarectomy, or removal of the pregnant uterus (resulting in involution of the corpus luteum), lactogenesis occurs. Lactation can be initiated experimentally with such diverse products as prolactin, estrogen, cortisone, and even the tranquilizers, chlorporomazine and reserpine. Estrogen and progesterone in some manner stimulate the anterior pituitary to secrete the complex of hormones responsible for lactogenesis.

GALACTOPOIESIS— MILK SECRETION

The pituitary gland is as essential for maintenance of lactation as it is for the initiation of lactation. However, whether all of the same hormones are involved in both functions has not been definitely established (Fig. 31–2). The exact role of prolactin has been debated for some time. Species variation as well as possible

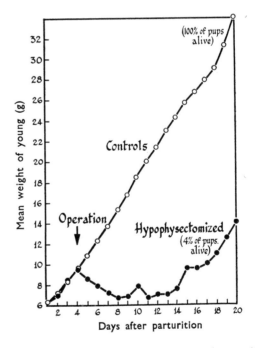

FIG. 31–2.—Effect of hypophysectomy (removal of pituitary gland) on lactation in the rat. (From unpublished experiments of A. T. Cowie.) (Folley, the *Physiology and Biochemistry of Lactation*, 1st English Ed., courtesy of Oliver and Boyd, 1956.)

contamination of extracts may account for some differences in reported results. *Intermedin* has been suggested as a possible contaminate that might affect lactation.

One theory holds that prolactin initiates lactation but is not essential to maintain it. This appears to be the case in the cow but may not be true in other species.

Adrenalectomy of rats causes partial inhibition, and adrenalectomy combined with ovariectomy causes a greater inhibition of lactation, as measured by litter weights. (See Fig. 31–3).

Thyroidectomy reduces milk production, but thyroxine will bring production back to normal in thyroidectomized ani-

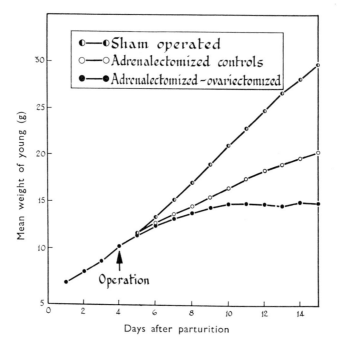

FIG. 31–3.—Comparison of the effects on lactation of adrenalectomy and of adrenalectomy + ovariectomy with sham operation. (A sham operation is similar to the other two operations but no tissue is removed after the glands are exposed.) (Results from flux, 1955.) (Folley, *The Physiology and Biochemistry of Lactation*, 1st English Ed., courtesy of Oliver and Boyd.)

Regardless of the exact role of prolactin, other anterior pituitary hormones such as ACTH, *thyrotrophin*, and possibly somatotrophin, appear to be involved in the maintenance of lactation.

Milk production can be decreased or in some cases stopped by removal of one or more of the following glands: pituitary gland, adrenal glands, ovaries, and thyroid gland. Even though the pituitary gland is necessary for lactation, injections of ACTH in cows appear to cause temporary decrease in milk production.

mals and will even increase milk production in normal animals.

Iodocasein, which also has thyroid activity, has been used for artificially stimulating increased milk production. However, it has a number of disadvantages, including an excess of iodine, a need for biological standardization, and a flavor that is unacceptable to some cows. *L-thyroxine* contains less iodine, can be assayed chemically, and increases milk production when given orally to ruminants.

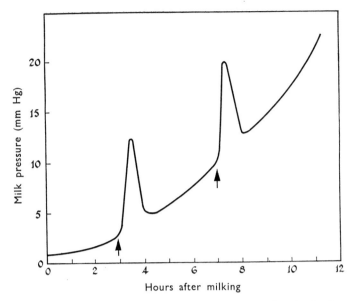

Fig. 31–4.—Milk pressure curve between one milking and the next (cow). Each arrow indicates the time the milking stimulus was applied but milk not withdrawn. (From Tgetgel.) (Folley, *The Physiology and Biochemistry of Lactation*, 1st English Ed., courtesy of Oliver and Boyd.)

MILK EJECTION
(MILK LET-DOWN)

Milking or *nursing* alone can empty only the cisterns and largest ducts of the udder. In fact, the resulting negative pressure will cause the ducts to collapse and prevent emptying the alveoli and smaller ducts. Thus, the dam must take an active although unconscious part in the milking process to force the milk from the alveoli into the cisterns. This is accomplished by active contraction of the *myo-epithelial cells* surrounding the alveoli and smaller ducts to produce *milk ejection* (*milk let-down*). These myo-epithelial cells contract when stimulated by *oxytocin*, a hormone found in the posterior lobe of the pituitary.

Milk let-down is a *systemic reflex* in which the afferent side consists of sensory nerves from the mammary glands and particularly the nipples or teats. These nerves carry impulses that reach the hypothalamus and initiate release of posterior pituitary hormones by way of the hypothalamico-pituitary tract. *Sucking* the teats by the young is the usual stimulus for the milk-let-down reflex. The response is slow compared with the usual neural reflex because of the time necessary for the hormone to travel from the posterior pituitary to the mammary gland by way of the blood stream. Whether milk is withdrawn from the teat or not, the milk ejection reflex produces a measurable increase in milk pressure within the cisterns of the udder (Fig. 31–4).

The fact that the *ejection reflex* is systemic in nature has been illustrated by experiments in which the abdominal mammary glands of rats were denervated to destroy the afferent side of the reflex. The young rats died if they were permitted to nurse only the abdominal mammary glands. However, if the thoracic glands were suckled, milk let-down occurred in all mammary glands, and the abdominal glands gave adequate amounts of milk for the young to survive.

If one half of an isolated udder (one surgically removed from a cow) is perfused with blood from a cow shortly after she receives a milking stimulus and the other half is perfused with blood from an unstimulated cow, the half receiving the blood from the stimulated cow will produce much more milk than the half receiving blood from an unstimulated cow.

tary removed) are able to produce normal litters. Electrical stimulation of the hypothalamus and of the *supra-optico-hypophysial tract* causes milk ejection, unless lesions are present in the tract. In animals with lesions in the tract between the hypothalamus and the posterior pituitary gland (supra-optico-hypophysial tract), suckling will not cause milk ejection.

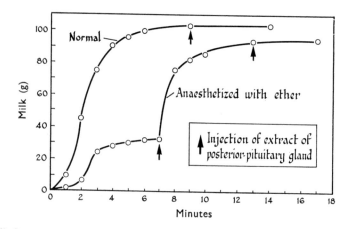

FIG. 31–5.—Milk flow curves for a bitch nursing puppies. (From Gains, 1915.) (Folley, *The Physiology and Biochemistry of Lactation*, 1st English Ed., courtesy of Oliver and Boyd.)

It has been known for many years that injecting an extract of the posterior pituitary will simulate the suckling reflex and cause milk let-down. Apparently oxytocin is the main factor responsible for this action. Immediately after completion of milking, an injection of posterior pituitary extract or oxytocin will release additional milk from the alveoli and small ducts that is richer in fat than the original milk. If the teats of a lactating cow are canulated (teat tubes inserted) an injection of oxytocin will cause milk to gush out in streams.

Ether anesthesia inhibits the suckling reflex in the bitch, but an injection of posterior pituitary extract will cause milk let-down in the anesthetized bitch. (See Fig. 31–5).

If oxytocin is given daily, *neurohypophysectomized* dams (with posterior pitui-

The suckling stimulus releases not only oxytocin but *ADH (anti-diuretic hormone)* as well from the posterior lobe of the pituitary gland. Both the oxytocic and vasopressor fractions from the posterior pituitary cause milk ejection, but the vasopressor fraction has only about 20 per cent as much activity as the oxytocic portion. The possibility exists that suckling reflex may cause not only milk ejection, but also release of hormones from the anterior lobe of the pituitary that are involved in lactation, including prolactin, somatotrophin, and others.

The milk-ejection reflex can be conditioned to stimuli associated with milking routine, such as feeding, barn noises, and washing the udder. It can also be inhibited by emotionally disturbing stimuli such as dogs barking, other loud noises, excess muscular activity, and pain. That the *sympathetic nervous system* may be responsible for this inhibition is suggested by the fact that *adrenaline* blocks the normal milk-ejection reflex as well as blocking experimental ejection caused by electrical stimulation of the hypothalamus. The site of action of adrenaline in this instance is believed to be in the mammary gland, although some authorities believe emotional stress interferes with the release of oxytocin from the posterior pituitary.

If failure to get an adequate stimulus for milk let-down, possibly due to inadequate preparation before milking, becomes habitual, the lactation period may be shortened because of excessive retention of milk in the udder.

COLOSTRUM

Colostrum, the first milk, contains lymphocytes, monocytes, histiocytes, and desquamated (sloughed) epithelial cells. Polymorphonuclear leukocytes are present only if inflammation of the udder is present. The *bodies of Deone*, also called *colostral corpuscles*, appear to be cells derived from histiocytes or monocytes. They form a type of *lipophage* (fat engulphing cell) of the reticulo-endothelial system. Because colostrum contains antibodies against diseases to which the dam has been exposed, it is extremely important for the newborn animals to drink the colostrum. In this way, the young animals obtain passive immunity until they can develop their own antibodies. Another special type of colostral secretion is the so-called *"witch's milk"* that newborn animals of both sexes sometimes secrete, presumably due to hormones from the dam stimulating mammary activity in the fetus just before birth.

NORMAL LACTATION

Normal lactation results from a combination of action of anterior pituitary hormones on the glandular cells of the mammary gland and action of the posterior pituitary hormones on the myoepithelial cells surrounding the alveoli and ducts. A secretory cycle within the alveolus has been described, which includes a resting phase of the cells, a secretory phase of the cells, and an excretory phase that may be *merocrine* at first and then at least partially *holocrine* in nature.

An alveolar cell in the resting phase appears empty; the nucleus is dark, the chromatin material is dispersed, and relatively few inclusions are present. During the *secretory phase*, the nucleus is displaced toward the tip of the cell and becomes more vesicular. Fat and protein materials accumulate in the tip of the cell, which is quite tall by this time.

The *excretory phase* is still subject to a great deal of controversy. The main question is whether the inclusions, particularly fats and proteins, can and do pass from the cells to the lumen of the alveolus without breaking the cell membrane. This type of excretion is called merocrine; however, if and when the cell membrane is broken and a part of the cell is also discharged into the lumen (decapitation), this type of excretion is called holocrine.

Turner (1952) suggests that during the interval between milkings when the intra-alveolar pressure is high, the secretory products may pass from the cell into the lumen through the intact membrane. The milk produced during this period is relatively dilute. Toward the end of milking, however, when the intramammary pressure is lower and the myoepithelial cells are actively contracting, the alveolar cells may rupture, and decapitation of the cells occurs. This could account for the higher fat and protein content of the last part of the milk extracted during a normal milking. Following a normal milking, an injection of oxytocin releases additional milk which is quite rich in fat and protein.

Studies of the mammary gland made with the electron microscope do not support the theory of excretion of cell contents by decapitation. These studies suggest that both fat and protein can be extruded from the cell without rupturing the cell membrane. The exact mode of release of these products is still in doubt.

SYNTHESIS OF MILK FATS —LIPOGENESIS

The *milk fats* (*glycerides*), particularly of ruminants, contain large numbers of short-chain fatty acids ranging from 4 to 12 carbon atoms each. These short-chain fatty acids are not generally found in *depot* (*storage*) *fats* of animals. Milk fat may be synthesized either by breaking down long-chain fatty acids found in the circulating blood or by synthesis from other substances.

Non-ruminants appear to use *glucose* more extensively than *acetate* (portion of a salt of acetic acid) in lipogenesis; however, ruminants use acetate much more than glucose. The organisms in the rumen break down polysaccharides to volatile fatty acids, including large amounts of acetic acid. These volatile *fatty acids* are absorbed into the blood stream to form an important metabolite in the animal body and are available for synthesis of milk fat.

The difference between ruminants and non-ruminants in substrate (active substance) used for fat production has been demonstrated by experiments using udder slices, udder homogenates, and glucose with labeled radioactive carbon.

In the ruminant it is probable that short-chain fatty acids, the length of palmitic acid and shorter, are formed from small molecules such as acetates. The long-chain fatty acids (oleic, stearic, and longer) probably are formed from blood glycerids. In the rabbit, most of the glycerol fraction of milk fat is formed from glucose, as shown by experiments with glucose containing labeled carbon.

HORMONAL CONTROL OF LIPOGENESIS

In the non-ruminant, *insulin* promotes the formation of milk fat from carbohydrates, and in the rat mammary tissue insulin has been shown to stimulate lipogenesis from glucose and acetate *Cortisone, corticosterone*, and *deoxycorticosterone* tend to inhibit the stimulating effect of insulin and may inhibit lipogenesis itself.

Neither insulin nor cortisone appears to have much effect on lipogenesis in the ruminant mammary gland.

The action of insulin may be related to the breakdown of glucose rather than the synthesis of fat, a situation which would account for the difference in species action, since non-ruminants utilize glucose freely in lipogenesis and ruminants do not.

LACTOSE—MILK SUGAR

Lactose, a disaccharide (glucose 4-B-galactoside), normally is found only in the mammary gland or in the milk, unless some lactose is absorbed into the blood stream after milking is discontinued.

Presumably *glucose* is the major substance used by the mammary gland to form lactose, since the venous blood leaving the udder contains less glucose than the arterial blood entering it. Lowering blood sugar tends to decrease milk lactose, but *hyperglycemia* (increased glucose in blood) increases lactose level in milk. Lactose could be formed from lactic acid, pyruvate, or hexoses in the blood. Amino acids could also be used, but they probably are all needed for synthesis of milk protein. Experimentally, mammary gland tissue homogenates (blended or ground tissue) have produced lactose with glucose as the only substrate.

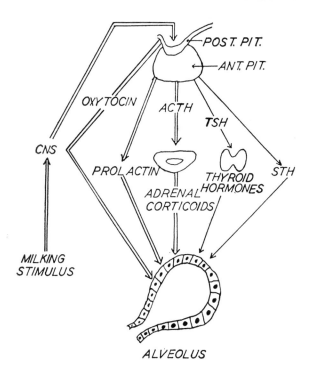

Fig. 31–6.—Nervous and hormonal factors believed to maintain lactation after parturition. The milking stimulus is believed to induce the release primarily of oxytocin, prolactin, ACTH, and adrenal corticoids. Other hormones favorable to lactation may also be released by the milking stimulus. STH (somatotrophic or growth hormone) and thyroid hormones exert an important influence on the rate of milk production in some species. CNS refers to central nervous system. (Cole and Cups, *Reproduction in Domestic Animals*, courtesy of Academic Press.)

In the laboratory, transformation of galactose to glucose is relatively easy, but making galactose from glucose is quite difficult. The enzymes necessary for changing galactose to glucose are present in the udder and perhaps function in the reverse direction during life. Another possibility is that the galactose portion of lactose might be obtained from the blood rather than being synthesized from glucose in the udder.

MILK PROTEIN SYNTHESIS

The chief protein of milk is *casein*, a phosphoprotein that is found only in milk. Small amounts of whey proteins, mostly *lactoalbumin* and *lactoglobulin*, are also present in milk.

Milk proteins may be synthesized by uniting amino acids, by degradation of blood plasma proteins, by rearrangement of peptide chains in plasma proteins, or by a combination of all three methods. Blood passing through the udder of a lactating cow decreases in amino acid content, but the quantity of amino acids taken up does not appear sufficient to account for the formation of total milk protein.

The udder appears to take up specific amino acids in approximately the same proportion as they exist in casein. All of the casein may be formed from amino acids; the whey proteins may be derived at least in part from peptide portions of plasma proteins, and some immune globulins may pass directly from the blood into the milk. The phosphorus of casein probably is derived from inorganic phosphates of the blood.

Cells in the virgin mammary gland contain little fat and no protein granules. During pregnancy the internal structures of the cell, such as the Golgi apparatus, develop, and fats begin to form, but protein is not secreted until lactation starts. As lactation progresses, there is a tendency for a gradual decrease in number of active alveoli, involution (decrease in size) of epithelial tissue, loss of secretory activity, and an increase of connective tissue stroma.

The normal decrease in lactation probably is due to hormonal changes that may result from changes in neuro-hormonal stimuli associated with suckling. Addition of anterior pituitary hormones or thyroid hormones will lengthen the lactation period. Lactation in rats can be extended by replacing older litters with younger litters and by the use of oxytocin or reserpine (a tranquilizer).

When milking is stopped abruptly, a number of changes in the udder occur. At the end of 24 hours, the alveoli become distended to a maximum, and the capillaries are full of blood. Between 36 and 48 hours, there is a decrease in the number of patent (open) capillaries, and the alveoli do not respond to intravenous oxytocin.

Premature *weaning* causes earlier involution of the alveoli, retention of secretory products, and infiltration with lymphocytes. Some alveoli may distend and rupture and others become smaller as the contents are absorbed and the lumens become obliterated. When involution is complete the lobules consist mainly of ducts within a vascular loose connective tissue. However, the gland never regresses to the condition it is in before the first pregnancy.

CHAPTER 32

ENDOCRINOLOGY

GENERAL

THE subject of *endocrinology* is becoming more difficult to define in a meaningful way. The concept has been accepted for many years that an endocrine gland produces a chemical substance (*hormone*) that is carried by the circulation to a target organ at some considerable distance from the original endocrine gland. As an example of some difficulty of classification under this definition, the adrenal medulla produces epinephrine, which is carried by the blood to distant target organs. Sympathetic nerves, however, produce a similar substance, norepinephrine, that acts in the immediate vicinity of the nerve ending. It is difficult to classify one substance as a hormone and not the other, because they have so many similarities, and yet one fits the definition and the other does not. On the other hand, if the definition is broadened to include all chemically integrative products, many substances such as carbon dioxide, that are not usually considered to be hormones would fit the definition. No doubt general concepts of endocrine function will change as studies move from a strictly clinical approach with the entire animal to cellular and subcellular studies.

Historically, proof of the presence of a hormone has consisted of experimental removal of the gland believed to produce the hormone in question. If this operation is always followed by the same symptoms and if these symptoms can be relieved by appropriate extracts of the gland, a hormone is presumed to be proven as a product of the specified gland. Although this technique produces spectacular results that can be repeated readily, it leaves many questions unanswered about the mode of hormone action and about hormone relationships. Hormones and their actions are also studied by treatment with known hormones in diseases of endocrine glands and by the use of radioactive isotopes as tracers in hormone studies.

Endocrine glands usually are slower and more sustained in their action than the nervous system, although autonomic nerves tend to act over a longer period of time than peripheral nerves. Some reflexes involve nerves on the afferent limb and hormones on the efferent side of the reflex arc.

Various "neuroendocrine" reflexes, such as induced ovulation following coitus in the rabbit, the suckling stimulus and milk let-down, and the effect of light on seasonally breeding species are examples of the combination of nerve action and hormone action. Glands usually considered to be endocrines include the pituitary, thyroid, parathyroid, pancreas, adrenal, and the gonads (ovaries and testes). The pineal gland and thymus are sometimes also included.

The glands of internal secretion, or the endocrines, comprise a system of ductless glands which dramatically influence various vital functions of the animal from before birth until death. The events leading up to and controlling conception, gestation and parturition are endocrine influenced, as are digestion, metabolism, growth, puberty, aging, and many other physiologic functions. *Homeostasis* is largely under the control of the secretions of these endocrine organs, the hormones. These endocrine products are secreted without benefit of a duct, directly into the vascular system, where they circulate and can profoundly influence various fundamental mechanisms. They may be considered biocatalysts in function, and the sharp distinction sometimes made between hormones and enzymes largely disappears when their mechanisms of action are studied at the cellular level.

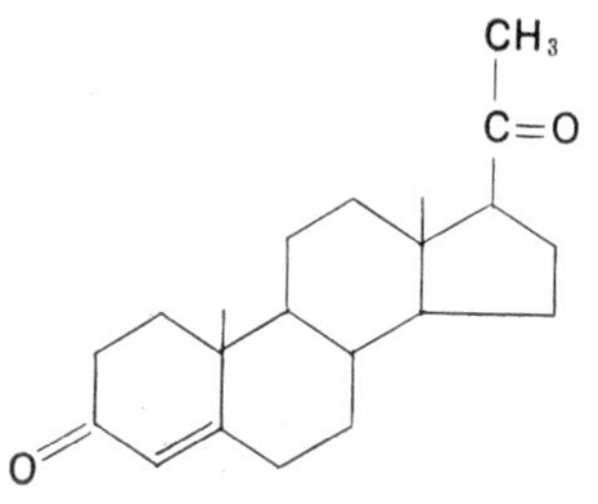

Hormones can be classified according to their chemical structure or nature of action. Chemically they are divided into three groups: the proteins or *polypeptides*, the *steroids*, and the *phenols*. The major steroid-producing organs are the gonads, the adrenal cortex, and certain fetal membranes. Phenolic hormones originate in either the adrenal medulla or thyroid, whereas the pituitary, parathyroid, pancreas, fetal membranes, and the endometrium are capable of elaborating peptides.

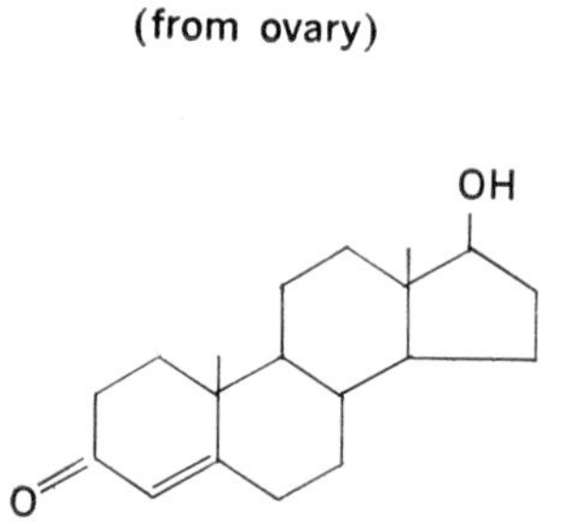

Hormones must have an exact structural arrangement to exert their actions. Even small changes in structure or chemical composition result in vastly different hormonal activity or possibly no activity at all.

Some hormones affect all body tissues, but others act on one organ or gland in particular. In this latter case the organ primarily affected is known as the "*target organ*," and the hormone exerting this rather specialized influence is referred to as a "trophic hormone." The major sites of trophic-hormone production are the anterior pituitary gland and certain fetal membranes, whereas the chief target organs of the body are the gonads, the thyroid, and the adrenal cortices. Why one type of cell responds to a specific hormone and some other cell type does not is unknown, but the reason probably is related to activity of specific enzyme systems and may be associated with the binding of some hormones to certain proteins.

Tables and diagrams designed to illustrate hormone activity are likely to oversimplify the many factors involved in the action of a given hormone. Amount of the hormone circulating, the interrelationship with other hormones, and the receptivity of target tissues all influence hormone activity. Some hormones increase the activity of other hormones. This is called *potentiation* or *synergistic action*. The opposite effect is sometimes seen in which one hormone inhibits the action of another hormone.

Fig. 32–1.—Some naturally occurring steroid hormones.

One other basic consideration is the interaction between different endocrine glands, which is best seen in the interplay between a trophic hormone and its target gland. *Trophic hormones* are generally stimulating in nature, causing the target organ to elaborate and release increased amounts of its own hormone. This target-gland hormone, as well as acting on the body cells in general, also acts at the site of trophic hormone production to inhibit further production of the trophin—thus a delicate balance can be maintained. Increased trophin production causes increased release of some other hormone which reciprocally inhibits further trophin production. Conversely, a decreased circulating level of some hormone may release the gland producing the trophic hormone from its inhibition, and trophic hormone is produced, which, in turn, elevates the blood level of the hormone which initially was low by stimulating its parent gland. (This mechanism is called "feedback.")

With these fundamental concepts in mind, we may proceed to a discussion of the various endocrine organs.

THE PITUITARY GLAND

The *pituitary gland* (*hypophysis cerebri*) is located at the base of the brain in the *sella turcica* (*Turkish saddle*), a depression in the sphenoid bone on the floor of the cranial cavity. The pituitary gland consists of an anterior lobe, an intermediate lobe, and a posterior lobe. The anterior lobe and intermediate lobe are from *Rathke's Pocket*, a structure derived from the mucous membrane of the embryonic pharynx. This accounts for the epithelial structure of these lobes. The posterior lobe (*pars nervosa*) originates from the embryonic brain and in the adult is still connected to the brain by means of the *pituitary stalk*. The infundibulum of the stalk attaches to the *tuber cinereum*, a cone-shaped projection from the brain located at the base of the brain between the

optic chiasm (crossing of the optic nerves) and the *mammillary body*.

The *anterior lobe* of the *pituitary* has a projection called the *pars tuberalis* that extends a variable distance along the front of the pituitary stalk toward the brain. Microscopically, the anterior lobe consists of cords of epithelial cells and

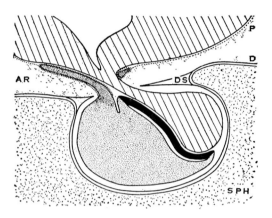

Fig. 32–2.—Diagrammatic sagittal section of pituitary, illustrating relation to meninges. Brain floor and pars nervosa are lined; pars distalis, lightly stippled; pars tuberalis, closely stippled; pars intermedia, solid black. *AR*, Arachnoid spaces; *D*, dura; *DS*, diaphragma sellae; *P*, pia mater; *SPH*, sphenoid bone. (Atwell, Am J. Anat.)

connective tissue, separated by blood sinusoids. The cells toward the center of the cords show little affinity for stains, so they are called *chromophobes*. The cells near the periphery of the cords stain readily so they are called *chromophils*. Chromophils that contain acidophilic cytoplasmic granules are called *acidophils* (or *alpha cells*), and chromophils that contain basophilic cytoplasmic granules are called *basophils* (or *beta cells*). There has been much speculation as to which type of cells produce which hormones, but this subject needs much more clarification before definite conclusions can be drawn.

The pars tuberalis microscopically differs considerably from the rest of the anterior lobe, as does the intermediate lobe. Functions of the pars tuberalis and the intermediate lobe have not been established in mammals.

The posterior lobe of the pituitary gland consists largely of special neuroglial cells (called *pituicytes*) and nerve fibers derived from nerve cells in *hypothalamic nuclei*, particularly the *supraoptic* and *paraventricular nuclei*. For many years it was believed that the pituicytes produced the posterior lobe hormones, but it has now been established that the hormones are produced by the nerve cells in the hypothalamic nuclei and then pass down the nerve fibers to the posterior lobe. This process is called *neurosecretion*.

The few nerves that enter the anterior lobe of the pituitary gland probably control vessel size rather than directly causing glandular secretion. Actual control of secretion is believed to be by way of veins that carry blood from the pituitary stalk and possibly the median eminence of the brain to the anterior lobe of the pituitary gland. These veins break up into capillaries in the substance of the anterior lobe, forming the *hypothalamicohypophyseal portal system*. This route of control from the hypothalamus is well accepted, but most details about the mechanism of anterior pituitary control are yet to be worked out. All parts of the pituitary gland receive arterial blood from adjacent arteries (the *circle of Willis* in most animals).

Anterior Lobe Hormones

Hormones definitely known to be produced by the *anterior lobe* of the pituitary gland include: STH (somatotropin, or growth hormone), ACTH (adrenocorticotrophin or corticotrophin), TSH (thyrotropin), FSH (follicle-stimulating hormone), LH (luteinizing hormone or interstitial-cell-stimulating hormone or ICSH), and LTH (luteotrophic hormone, luteotrophin, or prolactin). These hormones are all *peptides*, and TSH, FSH, and LH also contain carbohydrate, making them *muco-proteins*.

Most attempts to correlate cell types within the pituitary gland with specific hormones are related to the changes in histological appearance of the cells in various physiological and pathological states. The acidophils are believed to be concerned with secretion of STH and the basophils are believed to produce FSH, LH, and possibly TSH. Agreement is lacking as to the source of ACTH, but certain basophils have been suspected of producing ACTH.

STH (*somatotrophin*, or *growth hormone*) probably stimulates growth of all body cells but is particularly effective with bone and muscle tissue. The action of STH is most noticeable when either an excess or deficiency of the hormone exists. An excess of STH in the immature animal results in overall excess growth, including longer limbs, that produces a giant individual. In the mature animal, after the epiphyses have closed, the extremities enlarge in diameter but not in length, and other areas and tissues enlarge under the influence of excess STH, producing a condition called *acromegaly*.

Deficiency of STH is seen typically in hypophysectomized (pituitary gland removed) young animals. These animals are dwarfs and, of course, lack not only STH but all other pituitary hormones as well. A lack of STH in the adult usually is associated with undersecretion of all anterior-lobe hormones, a condition called *panhypopituitarism*, or *Simmonds' disease*.

STH has an important effect in encouraging protein production and protein retention by the body. This is known as the *protein anabolic effect*. STH increases the severity of *diabetes mellitus* and causes a decrease in body fat.

As the name implies *ACTH* (*adrenocorticotrophic hormone* or *corticotrophin*) has its greatest effect in stimulating the adrenal cortex (but not the adrenal medulla). The zona fasciculata and zona reticulrais, which produce the glucocorticoids, appear to be much more sensitive to ACTH than the zona glomerulosa, which produces mineral corticoids. The primary effects of ACTH are hypertrophy of cortical tissue, increased production of cortical hormones, and a decrease of *ascorbic acid* (*vitamin C*) in the cortex. ACTH activity of a substance can be measured by determining the amount of ascorbic acid depleted from the adrenal cortex in appropriate experimental animals. Actions of the hormones of the adrenal cortex are discussed with the adrenal gland on p. 426. The interrelationship between the pituitary gland and the adrenal cortex is important in maintaining homeostasis of the animal body. Direct action of ACTH, other than its action on the adrenal cortex, is difficult to determine, but it appears to resemble that of STH in many respects. ACTH activity may be essentially the same for all tissues, but the adrenal cortex is more sensitive to the action of ACTH than other tissues.

The scarcity of nerve endings in the anterior lobe of the pituitary gland leads to the conclusion that control of the anterior lobe must be by way of substances carried to the gland by the blood, either by the arterial supply or by the hypophysial portal system or both. A usual feedback mechanism in which a decrease in circulating adrenal cortical hormones calls forth an increase in ACTH and an increase in adrenal cortical hormones inhibits release of ACTH appears to function as a homeostatic mechanism in relatively quiet situations. In conditions of stress, however, the release of ACTH is too rapid to be explained as a simple feedback phenomenon, and afferent nerve impulses to the hypothalamus with the subsequent release of controlling substances by way of the hypophysial portal circulation are probably responsible for pituitary control. *CRF*, a *corticotrophin-release factor*, has been postulated as the substance responsible for ACTH release from the anterior lobe of the pituitary gland. There is no general agreement as to the exact nature of CRF nor as to its exact origin. Epinephrine, norepinephrine, histamine, and the posterior lobe hormones (vasopressin and oxytocin) have all been suggested as playing a role either directly or indirectly in control of ACTH release.

TSH (*thyroid-stimulating hormone* or *thyrotrophin*) has its primary action on the thyroid gland proper. Thyroid epithelial cells undergo hypertrophy and hyperplasia and increased production and release of thyroid hormone under the influence of TSH. Effects of increased or decreased TSH in the body are manifested only by the changes seen with the concurrent increase or decrease in production of thyroid hormone. As with control of ACTH, the feedback mechanism from the target organ seems to be the main method of control of STH secretion.

Pituitary gonadotropins (*gonad-stimulating hormones*) include FSH (follicle-stimulating hormone), LH (luteinizing hormone), and LTH (luteotrophic hormone, luteotrophin, or prolactin).

FSH (*follicle-stimulating hormone*), as the name suggests, causes follicles in the ovary to develop and enlarge, with the resultant elaboration of *estrogen* from the follicle. As the level of circulating estrogen increases, production of FSH is inhibited, as seen in other feedback mechanisms. As FSH production decreases, LH production increases, with the result that the follicle matures and ovulates. FSH is believed to stimulate gametogenesis in the *testicle* of the male, but this function has not been conclusively proven.

LH (*luteinizing hormone*) production increases as FSH decreases. This increase in LH is correlated with maturation of the *ovum*, *ovulation*, and *formation* of the *corpus luteum*. The corpus luteum produces the hormone *progesterone*, which not only inhibits production of more LH, but also prevents follicle growth and ovulation, thus preventing estrus during the life of the corpus luteum. In animals that ovulate only following coitus, the secretion of LH is stimulated by way of the neuro-endocrine reflex of the *hypothalamus*. Because of the action of LH in stimulating the interstitial cells (*cells of Leydig*) in the testicle, LH is also called *ICSH* (*interstitial-cell-stimulating hormone*). The interstitial cells of the testicle produce *testosterone*, the male sex hormone.

LTH (*prolactin, luteotrophic hormone,* or *luteotrophin*) is associated with the initiation and maintenance of milk secretion in all mammals. The release of LTH in the mammal is reflexly stimulated by suckling (nursing). In the rat, mouse, and sheep, LTH has been shown to help maintain the corpus luteum of pregnancy. This action has not been proven in other mammals.

Intermediate Lobe Hormone

The intermediate lobe of the pituitary gland produces *MSH* (*melanocyte-stimulating hormone,* or *intermedin*). This hormone has been known for many years to be associated with control of pigment cells in lower forms of animals, including fish, amphibians, and reptiles. The administration of MSH causes darkening of the skin in these animals and also in man. Darkening of human skin during pregnancy and in *Addison's disease* (adrenal deficiency) may be caused by MSH or possibly by ACTH. Knowledge is incomplete as to the activity of MSH in most mammals, and much work is needed before its function can be understood.

Posterior Lobe Hormones

The actual source of posterior pituitary gland hormones is from the nerve cells of the hypothalamus. From here the hormones are carried to the posterior lobe by way of the nerve fibers that pass from the hypothalamus to the posterior lobe of the pituitary, pars nervosa, where they are stored until released. The posterior lobe hormones are ADH (antidiuretic hormone, also termed vasopressin) and oxytocin.

ADH (*antidiuretic hormone*) has an important function in control of water loss from the kidney by facilitating reabsorption of water from the distal portions of the nephron. Lack of ADH produces a disease called *diabetes insipidus* that is characterized by excess loss of fluid, coupled with retention of sodium. In the normal animal, release of ADH is stimulated by increased osmotic pressure of the blood reaching the hypothalamus. Conditions requiring conservation of water that stimulate release of ADH include dehydration and hemoconcentration. Low osmotic pressure of the blood, as caused by drinking hypotonic fluids, inhibits the release of ADH and permits diuresis to occur. This loss of fluid in turn restores normal osmotic pressure of the blood. As its synonym "*vasopressin*" implies, ADH also elevates the general blood pressure, but this action has not been proven to be of physiological importance.

Oxytocin, the other posterior pituitary hormone, acts on the *myometrium* (uterine muscle) and on myoepithelial cells in the mammary gland. During parturition oxytocin causes contraction of the uterus and in this manner aids expulsion of the fetus. Following coitus, oxytocin is believed to stimulate uterine contraction in a manner that aids transport of sperm to the oviducts.

Nursing causes reflex release of oxytocin, which stimulates the myo-epithelial cells surrounding alveoli of the mammary gland to contract. This process, called "milk let-down," forces milk out of the alveoli into the ducts of the mammary gland.

ADRENAL GLAND HORMONES

The *adrenal glands* (also called *suprarenal glands* from their position in man) are located close to the kidneys. Shape, size, and exact location varies from one species to another. Each adrenal gland consists to an outer (peripheral) zone (the cortex) and an inner zone (the medulla), with the entire gland surrounded by a connective-tissue capsule. The parenchymal cells of both the cortex and medulla are arranged in clumps that are related to blood vessels. Microscopically, the cortex is arbitrarily divided into three layers named, from superficial to deep, the zona glomerulosa, zona fasciculata, and zona reticularis. The *zona glomerulosa*, just deep to the capsule, contains slightly basophilic columnar cells that contain lipoid droplets. Cells of the *zona fasciculata*, the thickest layer, are irregular in shape and are arranged in relatively straight cords which run at right angles to the surface, interspersed with straight capillaries. The cytoplasm of these cells is slightly acidophilic and contains more lipoid inclusions than the superficial layers of cells (zona glomerulosa). The thin *zona reticularis* contains irregularly shaped cells arranged in cords that run in various directions, separated by irregular sinusoids. There has been little success in relating microscopic appearance of these cells to differences in the many hormones produced by the adrenal cortex.

The adrenal medulla is derived from the same type of embryonic cells that sympathetic ganglia cells are derived from. The cells range from ovoid to columnar and in properly prepared sections appear to be oriented toward veins or capillaries. Sympathetic preganglionic nerve fibers enter the adrenal medulla and stimulate the cells to release *epinephrine* (also called *adrenaline*) and norepinephrine.

The blood supply to the adrenal gland is quite variable, but, in general, a number of small arteries enter the capsule. These arteries are derived from the aorta directly or from branches of the aorta, including the *renal arteries*, *intercostal*

arteries, and *lumbar arteries*. Some branches of the adrenal arteries supply the capsule, some supply the cortex, and some supply the medulla directly. The *medullary vein* drains both the cortex and medulla.

A large number of steroid compounds have been found in the adrenal cortex. These include adrenal cortical hormones with glycogenic activity (*glucocorticoids*), adrenal cortical hormones with electrolytic activity (*mineralocorticoids*), and sex hormones including *androgens*, estrogens, and progesterone-like compounds. A number of other steroids of unknown

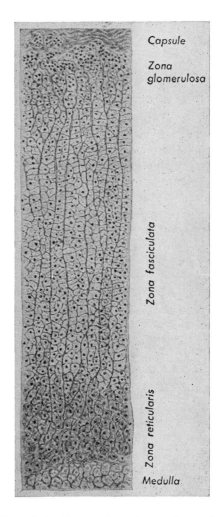

Fig. 32–3.—Section through the adrenal gland. (Copenhaver, *Bailey's Textbook of Histology*, courtesy Williams & Wilkins Co.)

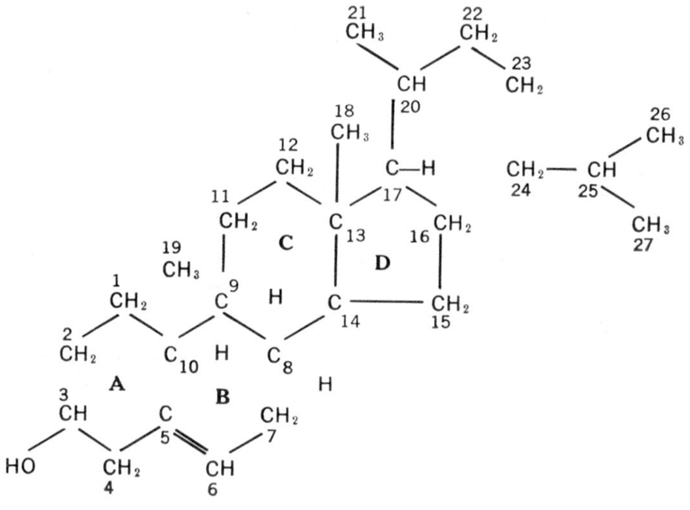

Cholesterol

Fig. 32–4.—The structure of cholesterol to show the conventional system of numbering the carbon atoms and designating the rings.

function that may be used in building hormones or may be break-down products of hormones, or both, are also found in the adrenal cortex. Chemical naming of steroid hormones is rather complicated, but they all bear some resemblance to *cholesterol*, with various functional groups added or substituted at specific locations on the structural formula. Figure 32–4 shows the letter designation of rings and the numbering scheme of carbon atoms in a typical steroid (cholesterol). Presence or absence of oxygen or the hydroxyl group (OH) at the 11-carbon position seems to be an important factor in the biological activity of adrenal cortical hormones (corticoids).

Corticoids without oxygen at the 11-carbon position appear to be much more active in control of electrolytes and water than in carbohydrate and protein metabolism. These mineral corticoids include *DOC* (*11-deoxycorticosterone*) and *17a-hydroxy-11-deoxycorticosterone*. Although *aldosterone* has oxygen at the 11-carbon position, it also is very effective in control of electrolytes.

Steroids with either a hydroxyl (OH) or ketone (C=O) group at the 11 position tend to be effective in metabolism of carbohydrate and protein but have little effect on water or on electrolytes. Active steroids in this group include *11-dehydrocorticosterone*, *corticosterone*, *cortisone*, and *cortisol*.

In addition to the preceding natural steroids, a number of modifications of some of them have been artificially prepared in the laboratory. Some of these artificial steroids have entirely different actions than the parent compound. For example, the addition of *fluorine* greatly increases the biological activity of some steroids.

Adrenalectomy (removal of the adrenal glands) of experimental animals gives a good concept of the functions of the adrenal cortical hormones by showing what occurs when they are absent. If no adrenal cortical tissue is left and no treatment is given, adrenalectomized animals usually will not live more than two weeks. Young animals stop growing, and there is a reduction in blood sugar, blood pressure, and body temperature. The kidneys cannot function properly, and the animal lacks resistance to stresses of all kinds including extreme temperatures, lack of food, too much exercise, infections, and injuries. The thymus and lymph nodes may become enlarged, *gluconeogenesis* is inhibited, sodium and chloride are lost, and potassium is retained. These disturbances, also seen in Addison's disease, can be corrected by the administration of adrenal cortical hormones. The addition of salt to the diet without hormone therapy corrects some of the symptoms of adrenalectomy but does not correct the basic cause of the difficulty. The renal tubules are unable to reabsorb sodium, chloride, and water from the glomerular filtrate and cannot excrete potassium into the filtrate if cortical insufficiency is present.

Aldosterone, the most effective mineralocorticoid, and deoxycorticosterone are more useful for aiding sodium retention and potassium excretion than are the 11-oxygenated steroids. Impairment of carbohydrate metabolism in adrenalectomized animals includes low blood sugar, decreased glucose absorption, depletion of liver glycogen, and failure of gluconeogenesis. At the same time glucose oxidation is increased, and conversion of carbohydrate to fat is also increased.

The 11-oxygenated corticoids have a slight action on electrolytes and water but are particularly effective in correcting carbohydrate metabolic upsets due to adrenalectomy. They also decrease *eosinophils* and *lymphocytes* in circulating blood. Effects of various stresses are reduced, in-

flammation is decreased, and time of wound healing is increased under the influence of oxygenated corticoids.

ACTH is the chief factor in adrenal corticoid production, and the pituitary ordinarily responds to lowered level of circulating adrenal cortical hormones with an increase in ACTH. Additional ACTH in both the hypophysectomized animal and in the normal animal causes an increase in cortical steroids, particularly 11-oxycorticosteroids, in the venous blood from the adrenal gland. ACTH seems to have less influence on production of aldosterone than some other factors do, including sodium-potassium ratio in the blood.

The pathological conditions seen in lack of adrenal cortical secretion have been described on p. 428. Excess secretion by the adrenal cortex may occur in cases of adrenal tumors or in response to more ACTH than normal. In both instances the resulting signs and symptoms are primarily the result of large amounts of androgens (male sex hormones) produced by the adrenal cortex, with the consequent masculinization of the animal regardless of sex. The adrenal gland seems to be limited in the amount of corticoids it can produce regardless of the amount of ACTH present, but it is not limited in the amount of androgens it can produce.

Hormones of the Adrenal Medulla

The adrenal medulla produces two hormones, epinephrine and *norepinephrine*. Epinephrine contains a methyl (CH_3)

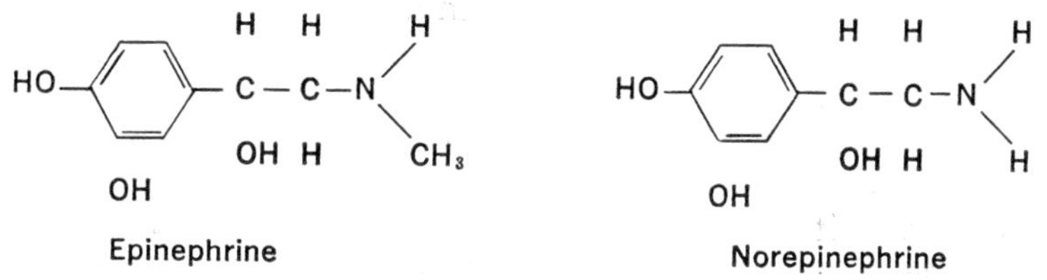

FIG. 32–5.—Two hormones of the adrenal medulla.

group not found in norepinephrine. Higher proportions of norepinephrine in the adrenal medulla are found in aggressive animals, such as members of the cat family, than in the quieter animals, including the rabbit and guinea pig. In man, the adult adrenals secrete about 10 times as much epinephrine as norepinephrine. Acetylcholine released by the preganglionic sympathetic fibers that enter the adrenal medulla provides the normal stimulus for release of medullary hormones. The exact mechanism of differential release of the two hormones is not completely known, although histochemical studies have attempted to correlate a different cell type in the adrenal medulla with each of the hormones. It is presumed that each cell type has its own independent nerve supply to account for differences in secretory activity of the adrenal medulla under different conditions or different stimuli. In man, aggressive activity seems to be associated with increased norepinephrine, but passive emotional tension is associated with increased epinephrine.

Postganglionic sympathetic nerve endings also elaborate both norepinephrine and epinephrine. Norepinephrine appears to be the transmitter substance from sympathetic nerves to visceral structures during ordinary activity. It can maintain tone of the vascular system (smooth muscle in vessel walls) even in the absence of the adrenal medulla, and probably is an important factor in maintenance of blood pressure. Adjustments to stress situations (the fight or flight mechanism) seems to be more dependent on epinephrine than on norepinephrine, particularly in relation to metabolism.

Epinephrine counteracts the depressing action of insulin on blood-sugar level by mobilizing glycogen from both the liver and from muscles, thus raising the glucose level in the blood. It also causes the anterior lobe of the pituitary to secrete ACTH, which in turn stimulates produc-

tion of adrenal cortical hormones that encourage glyconeogenesis (formation of new glucose from proteins). Epinephrine may also help raise the blood-sugar level in some unknown way by decreasing the utilization of glucose by the tissues.

Increased thyroid secretion increases the sensitivity of the body to epinephrine, and decreased thyroid secretion makes the body less sensitive to epinephrine. This latter effect may be due to higher levels of *amine oxidase*, an enzyme capable of inactivating epinephrine and norepinephrine.

Under laboratory conditions, where stress can be held to a minimum, animals survive quite well without the adrenal medulla. However, animals exposed to stresses of ordinary living cannot adapt to the environment if deprived of both adrenal medullae.

THYROID GLAND HORMONES

The thyroid gland consists of two lobes located near the thyroid cartilage of the larynx. One lobe is found on each side of the larynx, and an isthmus may or may not connect the two lobes, depending on the species. A connective-tissue capsule covers the gland and sends into the substance of the thyroid, septa which give support and conduct vessels to the epithelial cells. Microscopically, the thyroid gland consists of follicles filled with material called *colloid* that is believed to be a protein-iodine complex called *thyroglobulin*. Height of the epithelial cells forming the follicular walls varies from low cuboidal to high columnar, depending on the secretory activity of the thyroid gland.

The thyroid gland has been recognized as an endocrine gland for many years, and a great deal has been learned about the functioning of the gland, but the chemistry of the active hormone is still unsettled. There is evidence that both *thyroxine (tetraiodothyronine)* and *tri-*

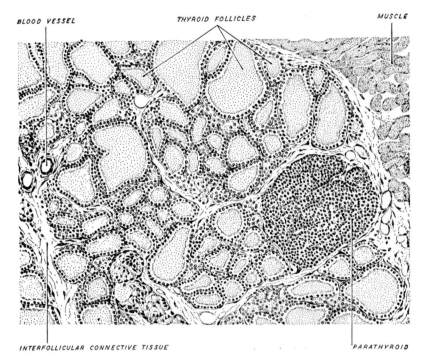

FIG. 32–6.—A section of the thyroid and parathyroid glands of the rat as seen under low power of the microscope. (Turner, *General Endocrinology*, courtesy of W. B. Saunders Company.)

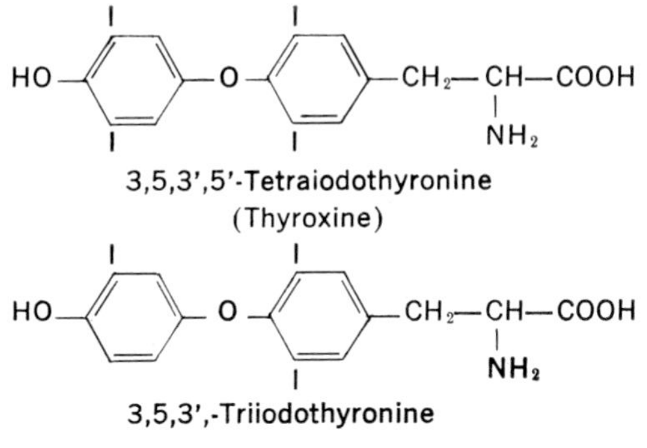

3,5,3',5'-Tetraiodothyronine
(Thyroxine)

3,5,3',-Triiodothyronine

FIG. 32–7.—Iodinated amino acids of the thyroid gland.

iodothyronine are active biologically. A large number of iodinated amino acids in addition to the two mentioned can be hydrolyzed from thyroglobulin, a large protein molecule believed to be the storage form of the thyroid hormone in the colloid of the follicles.

The thyroid hormone, regardless of its structure, requires iodine as an essential part of the molecule in order to be biologically active. It influences cellular processes throughout the body rather than having a specific target organ. The calorigenic (heat producing) activity of the thyroid hormone accounts for about one-half of the basal metabolic rate of the normal animal. Exposure to cold causes release of thyroid hormone and consequent increase in metabolism. This response is too rapid to be a usual feedback mechanism, so a nervous reflex stimulated by cold is believed to be involved. Prolonged exposure to cold is followed by hyperplasia of the thyroid gland.

Emotional and physical stresses tend to inhibit secretion by the thyroid gland. This is also so rapid that a nervous reflex probably is involved in some way. Thyroid hormone is necessary for normal growth and tissue differentiation. Lack of thyroid hormone (*hypothyroidism*) in the young animal causes a dwarf condition called *cretinism*. Deficiency of thyroid hormone affects most, if not all, systems of the body and interferes with metabolism of carbohydrates, fats, proteins, and electrolytes. *Hypothyroidism* in the adult results in lowered metabolism, lethargy, loss of hair, and a tendency to gain weight; it also may produce *myxedema*, a condition characterized by retention of sodium and chloride and water, with a reduced blood volume.

Hyperthyroidism (excess thyroid hormone) is associated with increased metabolic rate, loss of weight with a normal or increased appetite, irritability, and nervousness. In man, *exophthalmos* (protrusion of the eyeball) may be seen in hyperthyroidism.

Control of thyroid hormone secretion appears to depend largely on TSH (thyroid-stimulating hormone) from the anterior lobe of the pituitary gland. It functions by means of the typical feedback mechanism, in which a low level of circulating thyroid hormone stimulates release of TSH, and a high level of circulating thyroid hormone inhibits release of TSH, thereby indirectly increasing or decreasing thyroid hormone production by the thyroid gland. In some situations, changes in level of thyroid hormone production are too quick to be explained by the normal feedback response and must be mediated in some way by the nervous system, probably by way of the hypothalamus and the pituitary.

The thyroid gland is able to concentrate iodine to levels over 20 times that in the circulating blood. Most iodine in the blood is in the inorganic form, but nearly all iodine in the thyroid gland is in combination with organic compounds, mostly amino acids.

An insufficient amount of circulating thyroid hormone from any cause, leads to an increased output of TSH from the anterior pituitary. If the thyroid gland cannot respond by increasing elaboration of thyroid hormone, it hypertrophies (increases in size). An appreciable enlarge-

ment of the thyroid gland is termed *goiter*. A deficiency of iodine in the diet over an extended period of time has been a common cause of goiter. The use of iodized salt by man has essentially eliminated this type of goiter in the United States.

In addition to iodine deficiency, certain drugs called *goitrogens* or antithyroid compounds also produce goiters by blocking formation of the thyroid hormone. This may be done by preventing iodination of tyrosine, an amino acid component of the thyroid hormone. *Sulfonamides* and related drugs act as goitrogens if administered over long periods of time.

PARATHYROID GLAND HORMONE

The *parathyroid glands* are small nodules located within or near the thyroid gland. Commonly there are two parathyroid glands on each side, but the exact number and location varies with the species. Accessory parathyroid glands may be found at a considerable distance from the usual glands. These accessory glands may cause inconstant results in experiments involving removal of the parathyroid glands.

Parenchyma of the parathyroid glands consists of clumps and cords of epithelial cells interspersed with capillaries. Two types of cells are described, chief cells and oxyphil cells. *Chief cells* are small cells with dark-staining nuclei and either granular or clear cytoplasm. The closeness of the nuclei to each other gives the tissue a dark appearance. *Oxyphil cells* are not present in some animals and are not found in man until after ten years of age. The cytoplasm of oxyphil cells is acid-staining. Relationship between cell appearance and secretory activity has not been well established.

The parathyroid glands were difficult to differentiate from the thyroid gland because of their close anatomical relationship, and function of the parathyroid was believed to be a function of the thyroid gland. Although the parathyroids are known to be a separate entity from the thyroids, and active extracts of the gland have been prepared in relatively pure form, the exact structure of the hormone and its mechanism of action need more study.

Removal of the parathyroids is particularly damaging to carnivorous animals, because their diet is relatively high in phosphorus and low in calcium, and *PTH* (*parathyroid hormone*) is the major factor controlling the level of blood calcium. Parathyroidectomy results in low ionic calcium in the blood and urine, with concurrent increase in phosphorus in the blood but reduced phosphorus in the urine. Blood calcium drops from a normal of about 10 mg. per 100 cc. to as low as 5 mg. per 100 cc. Low ionic calcium blood levels affect the neuromuscular system leading, in increasing severity, from twitchings to tremors and spasms of the muscles and finally to convulsions. *Tetany* (sustained muscular contraction) from parathyroidectomy leads to increased body temperature, rapid breathing, and alkalosis of the blood. The alkaline condition of the blood in turn further inhibits ionization of calcium, thus leading to more convulsions and finally death. Forced exercises or increased body temperature makes the condition even more acute.

An excess of PTH causes an increased mobilization of calcium that may reach as high as 20 mg. per 100 cc. of serum. There is also increased excretion of calcium and phosphorus in the urine, with accompanying diuresis (increased urinary output). Continued withdrawal of calcium from the skeleton causes it to become softened and weak and subject to deformities, resulting in a condition called *osteitis fibrosa*, or *von Recklinghausen's disease*. The high blood serum calcium predisposes to the formation of calcium deposits in various soft tissues of the body, including the kidneys, lungs, heart, stomach, intestines, and blood vessels. *Hypercalcemia* decreases excitability of nerves and increases coagulation of the blood.

The main functions of PTH are mobilization of calcium from the skeleton, promotion of absorption of calcium and phosphorus from the digestive tract, and causing the kidneys to excrete phosphorus. The exact mechanism of PTH action is still being studied very extensively. A possible action of PTH is the local release of citrate, which in turn demineralizes bone in the specific area. The entire subject of bone metabolism is quite complex and is currently being investigated extensively.

Normal control of secretion by the parathyroids depends largely on the level of serum calcium and is independent of the pituitary gland. A high level of serum calcium inhibits PTH production, and a low level of serum calcium stimulates release of PTH.

HORMONES OF THE PANCREAS

The *islets of Langerhans* are clumps of pale-staining cells (H & E stain) scattered among the alveoli and ducts of the *pancreas*. Cells of the islets, the endocrine portion of the pancreas, are arranged in irregular cords separated by capillaries. Special stains are used to demonstrate the three types of epithelial cells described in the islets of Langerhans. These are the *A* or *alpha cells*, *B* or *beta cells*, and *D cells*. The B cells are usually the most common and have been shown to produce the hormone *insulin*, which is necessary to prevent *diabetes mellitus*. A cells are presumed to form a hormone, *glucagon*, that is antagonistic to insulin. Significance of the D cell is unknown.

Removal of the pancreas simulates diabetes mellitus, a disease caused by lack of insulin or inability to utilize insulin. The most obvious effect of insulin shortage is a sharp rise in blood sugar (hyperglycemia) that soon passes the renal threshold (about 160 to 180 mg. per 100 cc.), and glucose spills over into the urine (glycosuria). Without insulin there is a much reduced ability to metabolize glucose to carbon dioxide and water or synthesize fat from glucose. Glycogen stores of the liver and muscles are low, and resynthesis is slow if it occurs at all in the absence of insulin. Since the large amount of glucose in the blood cannot be utilized effectively by the tissues, both fat and protein serve as energy sources in the diabetic animal, resulting in wasting away of body tissues. The blood contains greater amounts of fat and products of incomplete metabolism of fats and proteins, particularly ketone bodies including aceto-acetic acid, acetone, and B-hydroxybutyric acid. The presence of ketones in the blood is called *ketonemia*; when ketones spill over into the urine, *ketonuria* exists.

In the pancreatectomized animal, nearly all of the diabetic tendency can be corrected by the administration of insulin, and the animal can be kept alive in relatively good health if the diet is suitable.

Insulin corrects the hyperglycemia and glycosuria and increases utilization of glucose by the tissues. It also aids conversion of glucose to fat, stimulates protein synthesis, reduces ketone formation, and increases storage of glycogen by the liver and muscles.

The action of insulin is not entirely understood, but there is evidence that it aids in the transfer of glucose across cell membranes and that it also facilitates carbohydrate metabolism in the liver. A complex relationship exists between insulin, the thyroid, the adrenal cortex, and the anterior pituitary. Hyperthyroidism may increase the severity of diabetes, but removal of the adrenal glands relieves many of the symptoms of diabetes. The anterior pituitary may have a direct or in-direct effect in increasing the severity of diabetes. If both the pancreas and pituitary gland are removed, the animal (called a *Houssay animal*) is more resistant to disease and will survive longer than one with only the pancreas removed. However, the Houssay animal has difficulty controlling blood-sugar level. A diabetic state may result from any interference with the action of insulin, as well as from its complete absence.

Control of insulin production appears to depend entirely on blood-sugar level. An increase in blood sugar stimulates release of insulin. The insulin in turn decreases the blood-sugar, and the resulting low level of blood-sugar inhibits further insulin formation.

Glucagon is a substance that has been isolated from the pancreas and is presumed to be produced by the Alpha cells of the islets of Langerhans. Glucagon elevates the blood-sugar level by stimulating *glycogenolysis* (formation of glucose from glycogen) in the liver. The relation of glucagon to insulin is not clear, although they appear to be somewhat antagonistic in action. The mechanism of action of glucagon as a hormone is not completely resolved, and no indispensable function of this hormone has been discovered.

THE PINEAL BODY

The *pineal body* (*epiphysis cerebri*) is usually included as an endocrine gland, although its function is not known, and no definite hormone has been isolated from the gland. It is a remnant of a median eye of some extinct amphibians and reptiles. The pineal body is located above the thalamus and is attached to the roof of the third ventricle. Parenchymal cells, neuroglial cells, and nerve fibers are found in the substance of the pineal body, but no secretory activity has been definitely established. There is some evidence that the pineal body tends to inhibit development of gonads in the male.

THE THYMUS GLAND

The *thymus gland* is the true sweetbread, although the pancreas is sometimes classed as a sweetbread. The thymus is a lymphoid organ found on both sides of the trachea within the cranial mediastinal space and along the neck for a variable distance, depending on the age and species of animal. Normally the gland begins to disappear shortly after puberty, but castration or adrenalectomy may postpone or slow involution of the gland.

During early development of the thymus it resembles an endocrine gland, because of the arrangement of parenchymal cells in cords. However, production of a hormone has not been proven. As development progresses, the parenchymal cells are crowded by cells that appear to be identical to small lymphocytes, but are sometimes called *thymocytes*. Odd groups of degenerating cells called *thymic corpuscles* (*Hassal's corpuscles*) are scattered throughout the substance of the thymus.

The ovaries are described in Chapter 23, p. 324, and the testes in Chapter 26, p. 361.

OTHER HORMONES OR HORMONE-LIKE SUBSTANCES

Turner (1960) discusses a group of substances produced by the body that have hormone-like action but may not fit exactly the classical concept of a hormone.

The so-called gastrointestinal hormones include secretin, pancreozymin, cholecystokinin, gastrin, enterogastrone, and urogastrone.

Secretin was the first substance called a hormone. It is released into the blood by cells of the *duodenum* in response to the presence of *chyme* from the stomach. The chief site of action of secretin is the exogenous portion of the pancreas, which is stimulated to produce pancreatic juice. The exact cells of origin of secretin and the mechanism of its action are unknown, leaving its classification as a hormone somewhat unsettled.

Pancreozymin is believed to be a substance from the duodenum that causes an increase in enzymatic content of pancreatic juice.

Cholecystokinin, also produced by the duodenum in response to the presence of certain substances (including fats and fatty acids), causes the gallbladder to contract. This contraction occurs also in a denervated gallbladder or in one that has been transplanted to another site.

Gastrin, which may be identical with histamine, is presumed to be produced by the stomach and, in turn, stimulates secretion of hydrochloric acid by the stomach.

Enterogastrone is believed to inhibit activity of the stomach when fat is present in the duodenum.

Urogastrone is another substance that inhibits the stomach. It is found in urine, but not in urine of hypophysectomized dogs, suggesting a relationship to the pituitary gland.

In addition to the above gastric hormones, the kidney produces a substance, *renin*, that in some manner increases blood pressure. Damage to the kidney, particularly lowered blood supply, causes release of renin. Renin may be an enzyme that acts on some other substance to produce the chemical responsible for increased blood pressure by causing constriction of arterioles.

A factor called *erythropoietin* is believed to stimulate formation of red blood cells. Little is known about this substance, but the kidney is postulated as its source.

A number of substances are involved in the inflammatory reaction in which tissues respond in a predictable manner to injury. These substances that escape from injured cells appear to be inhibited by hormones from the adrenal cortex.

TABLE 32–1.—ENDOCRINE GLANDS

Gland	Hormone(s)	Principal Actions
Thyroid	Thyroxin	Accelerates metabolic rate
Parathyroids	Parathormone	Regulates metabolism of calcium and phosphorous
Adrenals		
Cortex	Glucocorticoids	Stimulate conversion of proteins to carbohydrates for energy (gluconeogenesis)
	Mineralocorticoids	Regulate Na-K metabolism
		Control electrolytes and water
Medulla	Epinephrine and Norepinephrine	Same action as sympathetic nervous system, preparation for emergency, mobilization of energy
Pituitary Gland (Hypophysis)		
Anterior lobe	Somatotrophin (STH)	Stimulates growth
	Thyrotrophin (TSH)	Stimultaes thyroid gland
	Adrenocorticotrophin (ACTH)	Stimulates adrenal cortex
	Gonadotrophins:	
	Follicle stimulating (FSH)	Stimulates ovarian follicle development in female and spermatogenesis in male
	Lutenizing (LH) or (ICSH)	Stimulates luteinization in female, and interstitial cell secretion in male
	Luteotrophin (LTH, lactogenic, prolactin)	Maintains corpora lutea and stimulates lactation
Intermediate lobe	Intermedin (MSH)	Regulates pigment cells in lower vertebrates Function in domestic animals uncertain
Posterior lobe	Oxytocin	Stimulates uterine contraction and causes milk let-down
	Antidiuretic hormone (ADH or Vasopressin)	Inhibits diuresis and stimulates contraction of smooth muscle of arterioles
Islets of Langerhans of Pancreas	Insulin	Regulates carbohydrate metabolism
	Glucagon	Increases blood-sugar: anti-insulin
Ovaries		
Follicles	Estrogen	Regulates female secondary sexual characters and sexual behavior
Corpus luteum	Progesterone	Prepares for pregnancy and lactation
Testes	Androgen (Testosterone)	Regulates male secondary sexual characters and sexual behavior
Placenta	Estrogen	Maintains normal pregnancy
	Progesterone	Maintains normal pregnancy
	Gonadotrophin (chorionic)	Maintains normal pregnancy
Duodenal mucosa	Secretin	Stimulates flow of pancreatic juice
	Cholecystokinin	Stimulates contraction of gall bladder
	Enterogastrone	Inhibits gastric secretion and motility
	Pancreozymin	Increases enzymes in pancreatic juice
Stomach mucosa	Gastrin	Stimulates secretion of gastric juice

(Modified from Finerty and Cowdry, *A Textbook of Histology*, 5th ed., Lea & Febiger.)

APPENDIX TABLE OF THE ORGANS

TONGUE

	Horse	Cow	Sheep	Pig	Dog	Cat
Apex	Spatula shaped	Pointed	Slightly pointed	Thin and pointed	Wide, round, and thin	Wide, round, and thin
Shape	Long and relatively even width	Root and body wider than horse	Narrower in middle of body, root and apex same width	Long and narrow	Narrow root and body with wider apex	Short and wide body and root
Color	Pinkish	Variable pigmentation	Variable pigmentation	Pinkish	Bright red	Pink
Papillae	2 or 3 vallate on dorsum caudally. Foliate near anterior pillars of soft palate	8 to 17 vallate in caudo-lateral region. No foliate. Large papillae on prominence which increase in size towards root. Long horny papillae on apex, pointing caudally	14 to 16 vallate in caudo-lateral region. No foliate. Papillae on prominence more conical and relatively larger than cow.	2 or 3 vallate as in horse. Large conical papillae on root with free end directed caudally. Foliate	4 vallate (2 each side) near median sulcus. 2 foliate laterally near root	Horny papillae on apex pointing caudally. 2 foliated each 1 to 2 cm long
Specific characters	Relatively smooth, but thick and dense on the dorsum	Prominence on caudal part of dorsum with well-defined transverse depression in front of this elevation	As cow but not as well marked	2 frenulae	Definite median sulcus	No median sulcus

28

* Reprinted from *The Anatomy of the Sheep*, 2nd edition, by N. D. S. May and by permission of the University of Queensland Press, St. Lucia, Queensland, Australia.

STOMACH

	Horse	Cow	Sheep	Pig	Dog	Cat
Capacity	1.5 to 3 gal. (7 to 14 liters)	3 to 17 gal. (13 to 77 liters), Blamire. 20 to 48 gal. (90 to 218 liters), Sisson	2.5 gal. (11.3 liters)	1.25 to 1.5 gal. (5.5 to 7 liters)	5 pints to 1.75 gal. (3 to 8 liters)	0.5 pints (0.3 liters)
Shape	J-shaped. Left extremity enlarged	Complex with four parts. In order of capacity: Rumen, 80% Omasum, 7 to 8% Abomasum, 7 to 8% Reticulum, 5%	Complex as cow. Capacity: Rumen, 78% Abomasum, 12.5% Reticulum, 6.5% Omasum, 3.0%	Somewhat J-shaped, with diverticulum ventriculi to left of the esophageal opening	Irregularly piriform, and V-shaped. Shape varies with fullness. Stomach is sharply curved when empty with the contraction mainly affecting the fundus. When full has three distinct regions. Fundus fills rapidly and ingesta moves through cavity relatively fast	Irregularly piriform and a more uneven V-shape. Fundus longer than pyloric region
Position	Mainly to left of median plane in the epigastrium and dorsal to the coils of the large colon. On the external surface of the body, the outline extends from the 9th to the 14th rib in an oblique manner	Occupies most of the left half of the abdominal cavity extending over the median plane ventrally	As cow. but right face of ventral sac of rumen often against right abdominal wall	Mainly to left of median plane with long axis in a transverse direction. Reaches floor of abdominal cavity between xiphoid cartilage and umbilicus	Position variable with fullness. When empty, stomach is separated from abdominal floor by liver and intestines. When full, it migrates caudally and reaches floor near umbilicus	Like dog, but movements are not as great

STOMACH (*Continued*)

	Horse	Cow	Sheep	Pig	Dog	Cat
External characters	Large area of external surface devoid of serous covering. Relatively small stomach situated dorsally	Dorsal posterior blind sac extends more caudally than ventral sac	Left longitudinal groove extends dorsally and does not join posterior transverse groove. Right longitudinal groove in two parts. Dorsal part occupied by vessels; ventral part corresponds to internal longitudinal pillar. Ventral posterior blind sac extends more caudally than the dorsal sac	Blind diverticulum ventriculi directed caudally. Relatively large stomach	Extensive fundus. Stomach has relatively sharp inflection	Inflection more pronounced than dog. Constriction between fundus and pylorus less marked
Internal characters	Marked division by margo plicatus into white non-glandular esophageal part and darker and softer glandular part. The glandular part is formed of: (i) cardiac area, (ii) fundus, and (iii) pyloric region	Rumen—papillated but papillae absent on dorsal wall and on edges of pillars. More numerous in posterior blind sacs	Rumen completely papillated. Smaller on ridges. Reticulum—serrated edges to cells Omasum—40 leaves Abomasum—as cow Reticular groove 10 to 12.5 cm.	Four regions: Esophageal—small folds Cardiac—pale grey Fundus—thick and red brown Pyloric—thinner and paler than fundus	Fundus—thick and red brown Pyloric—thinner and lighter Folds relatively even in height and extending almost length of organ	As dog, but folds begin midway along fundus and are more marked in the pyloric region.

SMALL INTESTINES

	Horse	Cow	Sheep	Pig	Dog	Cat
Size	60 to 100 ft. (19.0 to 30.0 m.) long, 3 to 4 in. (7 to 10 cm.) diameter	90 to 150 ft. (27 to 49 m.) long, 2 in. (5 cm.) diameter	60 to 110 ft. (18 to 35 m.) long, 1 in. (2.5 cm.) diameter	50 to 65 ft. (15 to 21 m.) long, 1.5 in. (4 cm.) diameter	6 to 16 ft. (2 to 4.8 m.) long, 1 in. (2.5 cm.) diameter	3 to 4 ft. (0.9 to 1.2 m.) long, 1 in. (2.5 cm.) diameter
Duodenum	3 to 5 ft. (1 to 1.5 m.) long	3 to 4 ft. (1 to 1.2 m.) long	2 to 3 ft. (0.6 to 0.9 m.) long	2 to 3 ft. (0.6 to 0.9 m.) long	About 1 to 2 ft. (0.2 to 0.6 m.) long	About 4 in. (0.12 m.) long
Position	Chiefly in dorsal part of left half of abdominal cavity with duodenum mainly in right costal region. Coils reach the abdominal floor and pelvic cavity	In the right half of abdominal cavity with a few coils caudal and ventral to the rumen. Ventral to large intestine. Duodenum is often highest part of alimentary tube in right flank	As cow	Mesenteric part above colon and to right of cecum. Against dorsal right flank and caudal abdominal floor. Duodenum in similar position to the cow	When stomach empty, intestines lie ventrally and caudally but are forced more caudally when stomach full	Similar to dog but proportionately longer with less movement
Omentum	Greater omentum is not visible ventrally but lies between stomach and large colon. Lace-like.	Greater omentum covers intestinal mass ventrally. Stronger in texture than horse, with fatty deposit. Lymph nodes in mesentery lie between small and large intestines	Greater omentum as cow but fat firmer and whiter. Small and large intestines lie adjacent, with lymph nodes in the mesentery on the attached side of the large intestine	Covered by fatty greater omentum as in cow	Lace-like omentum but not as thin as horse	As dog

LARGE INTESTINES

	Horse	Cow	Sheep	Pig	Dog	Cat
Size	(a) Large colon: 10 to 12 ft. (3 to 3.5 m.) long, 10 in. (25 cm.) diameter, (average) (b) Small colon: 10 to 12 ft. (3 to 3.5 m.) long, 3 in. (7.5 cm.) diameter	35 ft. (10.5 m.) long, 3 in. (7.5 cm.) average diameter	15 ft. (4.5 m.) long, 2 in. (5 cm.) average diameter	10 to 15 ft. (3 to 4.5 m.) long, 2 in. (5 cm.) average diameter	2 ft. (0.6 m.) long, 1 in. (2.5 cm.) diameter. Size varies with breed	As dog but proportionately smaller in length. 1.0 to 1.5 ft. (0.3 to 0.45 m.) long
Specific characters	Sacculated with longitudinal bands. Vary in number from 1 to 4 on large colon, to 2 on small colon	Tubular, no bands or sacculations. Part is coiled in two directions (ansa spiralis). No differentiation into large and small colon	As cow	Coiled like cow Cecum 3 bands and 3 sacculations. First part of colon 2 bands and 2 sacculations extending to coils. Remainder has no bands	Short and like shepherd's crook. In 3 parts: (i) ascending, (ii) transverse, and (iii) descending. No bends	As dog
Position	Large colon: Mainly in ventral abdominal cavity as dorsal and ventral coils. Extends from sternum to pelvic brim. Origin and termination situated dorsally caudal to stomach. Small colon: Lies dorsal to large colon and mingled with small intestines	In dorsal abdominal cavity, to right of median plane with small intestines. Coiled part in lower right flank	As cow	On each side of median plane, mainly to the left caudal to the stomach. Coiled part in ventral part of abdominal cavity, dorsal to umbilicus	Short ascending part lies along right flank, with long descending part on left of median plane extending to the pelvic cavity	As dog

CECUM

	Horse	Cow	Sheep	Pig	Dog	Cat
Capacity	4 to 5 gal. (18 to 22 liters)	1 to 1.25 gal. (4.5 to 5.5 liters)	1 quart (1 liter)	3 pints to 1 gal. (1.5 to 4.5 liters)	Less than 0.5 pint (0.25 liters)	About 2 oz. (60 cc.)
Size	4 ft. long, 8 to 10 in. diameter (1.25 m. × 20 to 25 cm.)	30 in. long, 5 in. diameter (75 × 12 cm.)	10 in. long, 2 in. diameter (25 × 5 cm.)	8 to 12 in. long, 3 to 4 in. diameter (20 to 30 cm. × 7.5 to 10 cm.)	5 to 6 in. long, 1 to 1.5 in. diameter (12 to 15 cm. × 2.5 to 4 cm.)	1 to 2 in. long, 0.75 in. diameter (2.5 to 5 cm. × 2 cm.)
Shape	Comma-shaped. Sacculated with four longitudinal bands. Two extremities, one rounded (base), other pointed (apex)	Tubular with rounded free extremity	As cow	Tubular and sacculated with three longitudinal bands. Extremity rounded	Tubular and coiled	Tubular or conical and slightly curved
Position	Base extends from 15th rib to tuber coxae on right of median plane. Longitudinal axis extends ventrally over right flank to xiphoid region generally. Cranial border lies parallel with and 5 to 6 in. (12.5 to 15 cm.) ventral to costal arch	Extends along right flank from near the ventral end of the last rib to the pelvic inlet	As cow	A vertical position in the left or right flank, reaching the abdominal floor between the umbilicus and the pubis	On the right, midway between flank and median plane, dorsal to the umbilical region	As dog
Openings	The ileum and large colon enter at lesser curvature of the base. Openings are 2 in. (5 cm.) apart	Colon and cecum continuous. Ileum joins obliquely	As cow	As cow	Ileum and colon continuous and cecum joins obliquely	As cow

LIVER

	Horse	Cow	Sheep	Pig	Dog	Cat
Weight	10 to 12 lb. (about 5 kg.) 0.8 to 1.5% body weight	10 to 12 lb. (about 5 kg.) about 1.2% body weight	20 to 25 oz. (about 700 g.) about 1.5% body weight	4 lb. (1 to 2 kg.) about 1.7% body weight	4 oz. to 3 lb. (120 g. to 1.4 kg.) 1.5 to 5.9% body weight	2 to 4 oz. (60 to 120 g.) 2.5% body weight
Shape	Oblique and irregular ellipse	Irregularly rectangular with rounded corners	Rectangular	Irregular	As pig	As pig
Characters	Three lobes: right, lateral, left lateral, and central lobes. Right lateral more extensive in foal, left lateral in old animal. Caudate process	Two lobes (dorsal and ventral). Caudate process	As cow. Occasionally papillary process	Four lobes: (i) right lateral, (ii) left lateral, (iii) right central, (iv) left central. Caudate process. Large amount of interlobular tissue producing mottled appearance	Four lobes with caudate and papillary processes. Often caudate process called a lobe. Left lateral lobe largest and left central smallest. Papillary process large	As dog, but right central lobe largest and right lateral smallest
Relationship to right kidney	Renal impression	As horse	As horse	No renal impression	As horse	As horse
Umbilical fissure	Small and shallow on central lobe	Shallow depression on right border between dorsal and ventral lobes	Deep depression in right border and almost completely divides organ into dorsal and ventral lobes	Between right and left central lobes	As pig	As pig
Esophageal notch	Deep	Deep, but not as much as horse	Shallow	Deep and wide	As pig	As pig
Gallbladder	Absent	Pear-shaped, 4 to 6 in. (10 to 15 cm.) long	Tubular and narrow, 4 in. (10 cm.) long	Pear-shaped. Lies between central lobes. Partly visible	Pear-shaped and hidden in depression in right central lobe. Does not reach ventral border	Tubular and bent. Visible on right central lobe. Cystic duct sinuous

(443)

LIVER (*Continued*)

	Horse	Cow	Sheep	Pig	Dog	Cat
Bile duct	Enters duodenum beside pancreatic duct in diverticulum 5 to 6 in. (12 to 15 cm.) from pylorus	Enters duodenum 2 ft. (60 cm.) from pylorus	Enters duodenum with pancreatic duct about 12 in. (30 cm.) from pylorus	Opens on papilla 2 in. (5 cm.) from pylorus	Enters duodenum 3 in. (7.5 cm.) from pylorus	Enters duodenum 1 to 1.5 in. (2.5 to 4 cm.) from pylorus
Posterior vena cava	Only small amount embedded along dorsal border	Partially embedded	As cow	Almost entirely embedded	Deeply embedded	As dog
Color	Red brown to purple. Friable	Red brown. Friable	Red brown. Occasionally specimen black. Friable	Red brown. Lobulated and not friable	Dark red. Not friable	Deep red but not as dark as dog. Not friable
Ligaments	1. Coronary 2. Falciform 3. Round 4. Right lateral 5. Left lateral 6. Caudate	1. Coronary 2. Falciform (may be present) 3. Round (in young) 4. Right lateral 5. Caudate	As cow	1. Coronary 2. Falciform (may be present) 3. Round (in young)	1. Coronary 2. Falciform (small in young) 3. Round 4. Right lateral 5. Left lateral 6. Caudate	As dog

PANCREAS

	Horse	Cow	Sheep	Pig	Dog	Cat
Weight	12 oz. (350 g.) 0.06% body weight	12 oz. (350 g.) 0.06% body weight	3 to 5 oz. (100 to 150 g.)	1 to 2 oz. (25 to 60 g.)	0.5 to 3.5 oz. (15 to 100 g.) 0.13 to 0.35% body weight	0.5 to 1.5 oz. (15 to 45 g.)
Shape	Irregularly triangular	Irregularly quadrilateral	Irregularly triangular	Triradiate	V-shaped	V-shaped
Position	Ventral to the 16th, 17th, and 18th thoracic vertebrae	Almost entirely to right of median plane, ventral to 1st, 2nd, and 3rd lumbar transverse processes	As cow, but ventral to the upper part of last rib and 1st lumbar transverse process	Across the dorsal wall of the abdomen ventral to the 1st, 2nd, and 3rd lumbar vertebrae	Right arm dorsal to first part of duodenum, ending a short distance caudal to the kidney and the left branch between stomach and colon, ending at the left kidney	As dog
Ducts	Two ducts: (a) Pancreatic duct enters beside the bile duct (b) Accessory pancreatic duct enters the duodenum on the opposite side to the other duct	One duct opening 12 in. (30 cm.) caudal to the bile duct	One duct opening in common with the bile duct—ductus choledochus communis	One duct opening near the bile duct—4 to 5 in. (10 to 12 cm.) from pylorus	Two ducts: (a) Opens close to bile duct or may open in company with bile duct. (b) Opens 1 to 2 in. (2.5 to 5 cm.) caudal to other duct	One duct opening near bile duct

SPLEEN

	Horse	Cow	Sheep	Pig	Dog	Cat
Weight	35 to 40 oz. (1000 to 1200 g.), 0.16% body weight	32 oz. (700 to 1100 g.) 0.17% body weight	3 to 4 oz. (90 to 120 g.), 0.17% body weight All extremely variable	10 to 15 oz. (280 to 425 g.), 0.12% body weight	0.5 to 5 oz. (15 to 150 g.) (Bressou—2 g. per kg.), 0.2% body weight	5 to 10 g. 0.3% body weight
Size	About 20 in. (50 cm.) long and 8 to 10 in. (23 cm.) wide	20 in. (50 cm.) long and 6 in. (15 cm.) wide	5 to 6 in. (13 cm.) by 3 to 4 in. (8.5 cm.) All measurements are extremely variable	12 to 25 in. (30 to 65 cm.) by 2 to 4 in. (5 to 10 cm.)	7 to 10 in. (18 to 25 cm.) long	About 3 in. (7 cm.) long
Shape	Comma or tri-angular shaped	Elongate and elliptical with ends rounded and thin	Approximately triangular with angles rounded	Strap-like and slightly curved	Falciform (sickle-shaped), long, narrow, and widest ventrally	Generally like dog, less falciform
Color	Dark bluish red	Mulberry	Bluish red	Dark red	Red	Red
Hilus	Longitudinal on visceral surface	On dorsal third of visceral surface near cranial border	As cow	Longitudinal ridge on visceral surface	As pig	As pig

KIDNEYS

	Horse	Cow	Sheep	Pig	Dog	Cat
Weight	Right—23 to 24 oz. (about 700 g.) Left—22 to 23 oz. (about 680 g.)	Right—20 to 25 oz. (about 700 g.) Left—about 1 oz. (30 g.) heavier than right	3 to 5 oz. (about 90 to 150 g.)	7 to 9 oz. (about 235 g.)	2 oz. (57 g.) (varies with breed)	0.25 to 0.5 oz. (about 7 to 15 g.)
Size	Right—6 × 6 × 2 in. (15×15×5 cm) Left—7 × 4 to 5 × 2 in. (17.5 × 10 to 12.5 × 5 cm.)	8 to 9 × 4 to 5 × 2.5 in. (20 to 22.5 × 10 to 12.5 × 6.25 cm.)	3 × 2 × 1 in. (7.5 × 5 × 2.5 cm.)	5 × 2.5 × 1 in. (12.5 × 6.25 × 2.5 cm.)	2 × 1 × 1 in. (5 × 2.5 × 2.5 cm.)	1 × 0.75 in. (2.5 × 1.8 cm.)
Shape	Right—like heart of playing card Left—bean-shaped	Lobulated Right—elliptical with cranial end larger and rounder Left—twisted and pear-shaped with smaller cranial end	Bean-shaped and smooth	Bean-shaped, flattened, and smooth	Bean-shaped, and relatively large. Darker in color and not as regularly bean-shaped as the sheep	Irregularly globular with 3 or 4 superficial veins converging to hilus and producing wrinkled appearance. Paler than dog (yellowish red). Otherwise as dog
Position	Right—ventral to the upper part of 17th and 18th ribs and 1st lumbar transverse process Left—nearer median plane ventral to 18th rib and 1st and 2nd lumbar transverse process	Right—ventral to last rib and first two or three lumbar transverse processes Left—right of median plane ventral to 3rd to 5th lumbar vertebrae	Right—ventral to first three lumbar transverse processes Left—right of median plane ventral to 3rd to 5th lumbar vertebrae	Symmetrical, ventral to the first four lumbar transverse processes. No contact with the liver	Right—ventral to first three lumbar transverse processes Left—ventral to the 2nd, 3rd, and 4th lumbar transverse processes (very variable position)	Right as dog. Left as dog, but has less variation in position

	Horse	Cow	Sheep	Pig	Dog	Cat
External appearance	Relatively high compared with length. Very oblique rostral opening	Width, length, and height almost equal	As cow but on smaller scale	Greater length than width or height. Opening more horizontal than cow. Looseness and flexibility of entire structure when compared with other larynges. No articulation with hyoid bone	Like cow in relative dimension but opening is more horizontally placed	As dog
Arytenoid cartilage	Apex of opening formed by union of corniculate cartilages dorsally is narrow and sharp. Inverted V-shape	Apex of union rounded with cartilages more parallel. Edges of cartilages are everted	Apices of cartilages meet more obtusely than cow and thus ventral edges are wider apart. Edges slightly everted	Apices divided and produce an appearance of a second and smaller pair of cartilages between the larger corniculate cartilages	Thickened and rounded folds extending transversely from the lateral borders of the epiglottis. Folds are separated in the median plane by a cleft. Cleft also separates corniculate cartilages more caudally. Opening to larynx is triangular with base caudo-dorsal and the cleft is median in the dorsal border	Corniculate cartilages very small lying parallel with each other. Borders of cartilages approximated in midline. Aryepiglottic fold does not pass directly between cartilages but forms deep recess on each side
Epiglottic cartilage	Elongate and oval with sharp apex and border rounded and irregular	Oval to round. Border thickened, rounded, and regular	More triangular than cow. Border thinner and irregular. Apex pointed and thin	Rounder than cow and larger in comparison. Slight apex present with thinner border than cow. More scoop-like than cow	Regularly triangular, with thickened and rounded border. Apex pointed and thick	Leaf-shaped with pointed and thin apex. Width relatively regular and lateral border thick and round

LARYNX (*Continued*)

	Horse	Cow	Sheep	Pig	Dog	Cat
Thyroid cartilage	Thyroid notch with slight laryngeal prominence rostrally. Articulates with hyoid bone	No notch, and thyroid prominence is caudal. Articulates as horse	As cow. Articulates as horse	No notch or prominence. No articulation with hyoid bone	Small notch. Articulates as horse	Small notch. Articulates as horse
Internal characters	Lateral ventricle leading to saccule between ventricular and vocal folds and muscles. Saccule directed caudally and dorsally. Middle ventricle present	No defined middle or lateral ventricles or saccule. Thyro-arytenoid muscle	As cow	Narrow ventricle opens to saccule between the divisions of the vocal ligament. Saccule directed rostrally. Thyro-arytenoid muscle is undivided. Middle ventricle present	Wide ventricle opens to saccule through vocal fold. Saccule directed dorsally and caudally. Thyro-arytenoid muscle is divided and part attached to epiglottic cartilage	Two ventricles on each side represented by depressions, of which the rostral is the larger. Smaller caudal depression represents ventricle of the dog and occurs between the two parts of the vocal ligament. More rostral depression lies immediately caudal to the lateral parts of the epiglottis.
Vocal fold	Vocal fold oblique, with dorsal end more caudal	Vocal fold almost vertical	As cow	Vocal fold oblique, with dorsal end cranial	Vocal fold oblique, with dorsal end slightly caudal	As dog

LUNGS

	Horse	Cow	Sheep	Pig	Dog	Cat
Size	Average weight 13 lb. (6 kg.)	Average weight 7.5 lb. (3.5 kg.). Right lung 1.5 times left lung	Weight 8 to 10 oz. (250 to 300 g.) As cow	Weight 2 lb. (about 1 kg.)		
Lobes	Not divided into lobes	Left lung—3 lobes Right lung—4 or 5 lobes Right apical lobe reaches left costal wall	As cow	Left lung—2 or 3 lobes; Right lung—4 lobes	Left lung—3 lobes; Right lung—4 lobes	As dog Apical lobes more triangular
Fissures	Absent	Extend two-thirds to dorsal border. Variable fissure between right apical lobes	As cow	Generally as cow but fissure between right apical lobes generally absent	Fissures extend over dorsal border to root	As dog
Cardiac notch	Larger on left side 2nd intercostal space to 6th rib	Extends to 4th intercostal space on left side and, on right, pericardium may be completely covered.	Left side as cow Right side: notch triangular opposite ventral parts of 4th and 5th ribs	Notches triangular and small with left larger	Notch larger on right side, triangular and from 4th to 6th ribs. On left side, shallow and well defined	As dog
Bronchi	Main bronchus divides internally. No apical bronchus	As horse. Apical bronchus on right side	As cow	As cow	Main bronchus divides outside lung. No apical bronchus	As dog
Dorsal border	Narrow	As horse	As horse	As horse	Wide and rounded	As dog
Lobulation	Indistinct	Very distinct with large lobules	Very distinct with small lobules	As cow	Indistinct	As dog

TESTIS AND EPIDIDYMIS

	Horse	Bull	Sheep	Pig	Dog	Cat
Weight of testis	6 to 10 oz. (200 to 300 g.)	7 to 10 oz. (250 to 300 g.)	6 to 10 oz. (200 to 300 g.)	5 oz. (150 g.)	0.05 to 0.75% body weight	
Shape	Oval	Elongate oval	As bull	Elliptical	Round to oval	More rounded than dog
Superficial vascular pattern on testis	Small vessels extending from free border towards body of epididymis	Very large and tortuous vessels extending from tail towards head	Vessels of different sizes extending from epididymal border. Tunica vaginalis and tunica albuginea are thicker than in cow and superficial vessels are not so visible through tunics	Many small vessels extending from free border towards body of epididymis	Single vessel and branches extending from tail towards head of testis	Less extensive system than dog but extending in a similar direction
Parenchyma	Reddish gray	Yellow to creamy orange	Creamy white	Grayish to dark red	Reddish	Reddish
Epididymis	Head and body associated with attached border of testis. Tail forms only slight prominence caudally	Epididymis extends one-third distance down cranial border, forming wide V-shape. Tail rounded and molded to distal extremity of testis	Epididymis extends one-half distance down cranial border, forming narrow V-shape. Tail rounded with defined neck. Tail more pronounced than in bull. Readily palpated in live animal	Head and body like horse. Tail caudal prominent, forming blunt conical projection	Head and body like horse. Tail slightly prominent	Epididymis along attached border only. Tail not prominent

OVARIES

	Horse	Cow	Sheep	Pig	Dog	Cat
Shape, size, and weight	Bean-shaped. 3 × 1 × 1.5 in. (7.5 × 2.5 × 3.75 cm.). About 2.5 to 3 oz. (70 to 90 g.)	Oval. 1.5 × 1 × 0.5 in. (3.75 × 2.5 × 1.25 cm.). About 0.5 oz. or more (about 11 to 18 g.)	Almond or oval. 1 × 0.25 in. (2.5 × 0.5 cm.). About 0.1 oz. (2 to 3 g.)	Round. 1 × 0.5 in. (2.5 × 1.25 cm.). About 0.2 to 0.5 oz. (8 to 16 g.)	Elongate, flattened, and oval. Less than 1 in. (2.5 cm.) long and 0.5 in. (1.5 cm.) thick. About 0.1 to 0.4 oz. (3 to 12 g.)	Like dog but smaller (8 to 9 mm. long)
Position	Ventral to 4th or 5th lumbar vertebra. One larger than other and left usually caudal to right. About 20 to 22 in. (50 to 55 cm.) from vulva	Usually on lateral wall of pelvic inlet. Right usually larger than left. About 16 to 18 in. (40 to 45 cm.) from vulva. Varies in position with number of parturitions	Usually on lateral wall of pelvic inlet. About 7 in. (17.5 cm.) from vulva. Varies in position with number of parturitions	On lateral wall of pelvic inlet. Varies in position with number of parturitions	Near posterior pole of kidney below 3rd or 4th lumbar vertebra	As dog
Ovulation fossa	Ovulation fossa on free border. Ovarian bursa formed by mesosalpinx	No ovulation fossa. Ovarian bursa present.	As cow	As cow Hilus present on ovary	As cow	As cow. Ovarian bursa extremely small
Broad ligament	Broad ligament attached in sublumbar region	Broad ligament attached to flank and lateral pelvic wall	As cow	As cow	Broad ligament attached in sublumbar region	As dog
Surface	Corpora lutea do not project from the surface	Follicles and corpora lutea both project	As cow	As cow	As cow	As cow

UTERUS

	Horse	Cow	Sheep	Pig	Dog	Cat
Length	Body about 10 in. (25 cm.). Horns about 7 to 8 in. (18 cm.) ×4 in. (10 cm.). Cervix about 2 to 3 in. (6 cm.)	Body about 1.5 in. (4 cm.). Horns about 15 in. (38 cm.). Cervix about 4 in. (10 cm.)	Body less than 1 in. (2 cm.). Horns about 4 to 5 in. (10 to 12 cm.). Cervix about 1.5 in. (4 cm.)	Body about 2 in. (5 cm.). Horns about 4 to 5 in. (12 cm.). Cervix about 4 in. (10 cm.).	Body about 1 in. (2 to 3 cm.). Horns 5 to 6 in. (12 to 15 cm.). Cervix about 1 in. (2.5 cm.).	Shorter than dog. Body 1.5 cm.
Anterior extremities of cornua	Blunt	Tapered	Tapered	Tapered. Difficult to differentiate from Fallopian tubes	Tapered. As pig	Tapered. As pig
Horns	Large, uniform diameter, and relatively straight	Horns united for 3 to 4 in. (7.5 to 10 cm.) near body. Horns coiled.	As cow, but 1 to 2 in. (2.5 to 5 cm.). Horns coiled	Horns flexuous	Uniform diameter, diverge like a V, and slightly curved	As dog
Round ligament	Short	Reaches internal abdominal ring	As cow	About 6 in. (15 cm.) long	Passes through inguinal canal for short distance	As dog
Internal	Mucous membrane smooth and folded	Cotyledons	As cow	Smooth and folded	Folded	As dog
Cervix	Cervix projects into vagina 1 to 2 in. (2.5 to 5 cm.)	Does not project as much as mare	Similar to cow usually, but may not project into vagina	Does not project	Projects a short distance into vagina	As dog

29

(453)

HEART

	Horse	Cow	Sheep	Pig	Dog	Cat
Weight	About 9 lb. (3.4 kg.) great variation. 0.6 to 0.7% body weight	About 5.5 lb. (2.23 kg.), 0.4 to 0.5% body weight	About 0.5 lb. (220 to 240 g.), 0.4% body weight	1 lb. or less (450 g.) 0.35% body weight. 2.2 to 6.1 g. per kg. body weight	5 to 15 oz. (150 to 450 g.) 0.8 to 1.4% body weight. 5.9 to 13 g. per kg. body weight	3.9 to 8.54 g. per kg. body weight
Shape	Irregularly flattened cone	Relatively longer than horse, with shorter base	Apex more or less pointed than cow	Broad, short, and blunt	Ovoid with round blunt apex	As dog
Vena hemiazygos	Vena hemiazygos does not reach heart	Vena hemiazygos opens into great cardiac vein below posterior vena cava	As cow	As cow	As horse	As horse
Os cordis	Absent	2 ossa cordis	1 os cordis	Absent	Absent	Absent
Brachiocephalic trunk	Brachiocephalic trunk only from aorta	As horse	As horse	Brachiocephalic and left subclavian arteries arise from aorta independently	As pig but brachiocephalic artery may be divided into right subclavian artery and bicarotid trunk	As pig
Fat	Soft, yellow, and oily	Soft and yellow	Hard and white	Softer than sheep and white to cream color	Very little fat unless animal in very fat condition. When white, oily fat present	Generally very little fat

BRAIN

	Horse	Cow	Sheep	Pig	Dog	Cat
Weight	23 oz. (650 g.) $\frac{1}{7}$ of 1% body weight	16 to 17 oz. (450 g.)	4.5 to 5 oz. (130 g.)	4 to 4.5 oz. (125 g.)	Varies from 1 to 5 oz. (150 g.), average 2 to 2.5 oz. (60 to 70 g.) 0.3 to 1% body weight	20 to 28 g. 1.0% body weight
External appearance, cerebral hemisphere	Oval and relatively long. Frontal and occipital poles almost equal in size. Gyri extensive	Short, high, wide, and circular. Frontal poles smaller than occipital. Dorsal prominence—marginal pole. Gyri and sulci simpler pattern than horse	Irregularly ovoid and bean-shaped from side. Flattened rostrally. Frontal and occipital poles more equivalent in size than cow. No dorsal prominence. Gyri and sulci simpler than cow.	Elongate, oval, and widest in caudal third. Bean-shaped laterally. Occipital pole larger than frontal. Gyri simple like sheep.	Triangular from above and broadest in caudal third. Frontal poles narrow and flattened laterally. Gyri simpler than pig	More circular from above and laterally, widest at temporal poles. Frontal lobes not constricted. Gyri simpler than dog
External appearance, mid-brain and hind-brain	Pons prominent and cerebellum not overlapped to great extent. Axis of brain stem relatively straight	Pons smaller than horse and cerebellum overlapped to a great extent. Cerebellum shorter, smaller, but broader. Medulla short and wide. Axis of brain stem bent	Medulla shorter and wider than cow. Pons smaller, cerebellum relatively long and not overlapped by cerebrum to extent as in cow. Axis of brain stem straighter than cow.	Pons very indistinct, medulla short. Cerebellum short, wide, and more overlapped by cerebrum than sheep. Axis of brain stem sharply bent	Medulla broad and thick. Pons small but more distinct than pig. Axis of brain sharply bent	As dog. Cerebellum more exposed
Hypophysis	Ovoid and large	Thicker than horse	Long and large in relation to size of brain	Small and irregularly circular	Small and circular	As dog
Olfactory region	Relatively large bulbs and large striae	Bulbs smaller but lateral stria larger than horse	Bulbs large and ovoid. Lateral stria large	Large bulbs and lateral stria	Bulbs and lateral stria relatively large	Bulbs elongate
Posterior colliculi	Very small in comparison to anterior colliculi	Form large depression in surface of cerebellum	Displaced laterally	Form large depression in cerebellum	Large and displaced laterally	

BIBLIOGRAPHY

ADAMS, O. R.: *Lameness in Horses*, Philadelphia, Lea & Febiger, 1962.

ALEXANDER, GORDON: *Biology*, 8th ed., New York, Barnes & Noble, 1962.

American Institute of Biological Sciences: *Biological Science: An Inquiry Into Life*, New York, Harcourt, Brace & World, Inc., 1963.

American Institute of Biological Sciences: *High School Biology* (Biological Sciences Curriculum Study), Chicago, Rand McNally & Co., 1963.

AREY, LESLIE BRAINERD: *Developmental Anatomy*, 6th ed., Philadelphia, W. B. Saunders Co., 1954.

AREY, LESLIE B.: *Human Histology*, 2nd ed., Philadelphia, W. B. Saunders Co., 1963.

ASDELL, S. A.: *Patterns of Mammalian Reproduction*, Ithaca, New York, Comstock Publishing Co., Inc., 1964.

ATKINSON, DICKSON, HARBAUGH, LAW, LOWE, MOHLER, MURRAY, PEARSON, RANSOM, and TRUMBOWER, *Diseases of Cattle*, Revised Edition, Washington, United States Government Printing Office, 1964.

BARCLAY, ALFRED E., K. J. FRANKLIN, and M. M. L. PRICHARD: *The Foetal Circulation*, Springfield, Illinois, Charles C Thomas, 1945.

BARCROFT, SIR JOSEPH: *Researches on Pre-Natal Life*, Vol. I, Springfield, Illinois, Charles C Thomas, 1947.

BELLING, THEODORE H., JR.: "Bovine Ovarian Palpation I: Normal Ovaries," *Veterinary Medicine, 59*, 161, 1964.

BELLING, THEODORE H., JR.: "Bovine Ovarian Palpation II: Abnormals and Therapy," *Veterinary Medicine, 59*, 289, 1964.

BENESCH, FRANZ and JOHN G. WRIGHT: *Veterinary Obstetrics*, Baltimore, The Williams & Wilkins Co., 1951.

BENJAMIN, MAXINE, M.: *Outline of Veterinary Clinical Pathology*, 2nd ed., Ames, Iowa, The Iowa State University Press, 1961.

BERGER, ANDREW, J.: *Elementary Human Anatomy*, New York, John Wiley & Sons, 1964.

BEST, CHARLES HERBERT and NORMAN BURKE TAYLOR: *The Living Body*, 4th ed., New York, Henry Holt and Co., 1958.

BEVELANDER, GERRIT: *Outline of Histology*, 5th ed., St. Louis, The C. V. Mosby Co., 1963.

BLOOM, WILLIAM and DON FAWCETT: *A Textbook of Histology*, 8th ed., Philadelphia, W. B. Saunders Co., 1962.

BOURNE, G. H., ed.: *The Structure and Function of Muscle*, 3 Vol., New, York Academic Press 1960.

BOWEN, WILBUR PARDON, and HENRY A. STONE: *Applied Anatomy and Kinesiology*, 7th ed., Philadelphia, Lea & Febiger, 1953.

BOYD, WILLIAM: *A Textbook of Pathology*, 7th ed., Philadelphia, Lea & Febiger, 1961.

BRADLEY, O. CHARNOCK, Revised by Tom Grahame: *The Topographical Anatomy of the Head and Neck of the Horse*, 2nd ed., Edinburgh, W. Green & Son, Ltd., 1947.

BRADLEY, O. CHARNOCK, Revised by Tom Grahame: *The Topographical Anatomy of the Limbs of the Horse*, Edinburgh, W. Green & Son, Ltd., 1946.

BRADLEY, O. CHARNOCK, Revised by Tom Grahame: *The Topographical Anatomy of the Thorax and Abdomen of the Horse*, Edinburgh, W. Green & Son, Ltd., 1946.

CARLSON, ANTON JULIUS, VICTOR JOHNSON, and H. MEAD CAVERT: *The Machinery of the Body*, 5th ed., Chicago, University of Chicago Press, 1961.

CASIDA, L. E.: "Fertilization Failure and Embryonic Death in Domestic Animals," *In* Earle Engle, ed., *Pregnancy Wastage*, Springfield, Illinois, Charles C Thomas, 1953, pp. 27-37.

CLEMENTS, JOHN A.: "Surface Tension in the Lungs," *Scientific American, 207*, 120, 1962.

COHN, NORMAN S.: *Elements of Cytology*, New York, Harcourt, Brace & World, Inc., 1964.

COLE, H. H. and P. T. CUPPS: *Reproduction in Domestic Animals*, Vol. I, New York, Academic Press, 1959.

COPENHAVER, WILFRED M.: *Bailey's Textbook of Histology*, 15th ed., Baltimore, Williams & Wilkins Co., 1964.

CROSBY, ELIZABETH, TRYPLENA HUMPHREY, and EDWARD W. LAUER: *Correlative Anatomy of the Nervous System*, New York, The Macmillan Co., 1962.

CRUICKSHANK, BRUCE, T. C. DOBBS, and D. L. GARDNER: *Human Histology*, Baltimore, The Williams & Wilkins Co., 1964.

DAWSON, HELEN: *Lambert's Histology*, 2nd ed., Philadelphia, The Blakiston Co., 1948.

DECOURSEY, RUSSELL M.: *The Human Organism*, 2nd ed., New York, McGraw-Hill Book Co., Inc., 1961.

DEROBERTIS, E. D. P., W. W. NOWINSKI, and F. A. SAEZ: *General Cytology*, 3rd ed., Philadelphia, W. B. Saunders Co., 1960.

DUKES, H. H.: *The Physiology of Domestic Animals*, 7th ed., Ithaca, New York, Comstock Publishing Co., 1955.

EDWARDS, L. F.: *Concise Anatomy*, 2nd ed., New York, McGraw-Hill Book Co., Inc., 1956.

ELIAS, HANS: *An Outline of the Histology of Domestic Animals*, 2nd ed., Waltham, Massachusetts, Middlesex University, 1944.

ELIAS, HANS and JOHN E. PAULY: *Human Microanatomy*, 2nd ed., Chicago, Da Vinci Publishing Co., 1960.

ELLENBERGER, W., H. BAUM, and H. DITTRICH: *An Atlas of Animal Anatomy for Artists*, 2nd ed., New York, Dover Publications, Inc., 1957.

ELLENBERGER, WILLHELM, and HERMANN BAUM: *Handbuch der vergleichenden Anatomie der Haustiere*, 18th ed., Berlin, Springer, 1943.

ELLIOTT, H. C.: *Textbook of Neuroanatomy*, Philadelphia, J. B. Lippincott Co., 1963.

EVANS, HERBERT MCLEAN and HAROLD H. COLE: *An Introduction to the Study of the Oestrous Cycle in the Dog*, Berkeley, California, University of California Press, 1931.

FINERTY, J. C. and E. V. COWDRY: *A Textbook of Histology*, 5th ed., Philadelphia, Lea & Febiger, 1960.

FOLLEY, S. J.: *The Physiology and Bio-Chemistry of Lactation*, Edinburgh, Oliver & Boyd, 1956.

FOUST, H. L. and ROBERT GETTY: *Atlas and Dissection Guide for the Study of the Anatomy of Domestic Animals*, 3rd ed., Ames, Iowa, The Iowa State College Press, 1954.

FRANCIS, CARL C.: *Introduction to Human Anatomy*, 4th ed., St. Louis, The C. V. Mosby Co., 1964.

FREEMAN, JAMES A. and JACK C. GEER: *Cellular Fine Structure*, New York, The Blakiston Co., 1964.

GARDNER, EARNEST, DONALD GRAY, and ROMAN O'RAHILLY: *Anatomy*, 2nd ed., Philadelphia, W. B. Saunders Co., 1963.

GETTY, ROBERT: "The Sense Organs and Integument," *In* Miller, Christensen, and Evans, *Anatomy of the Dog*, Philadelphia, W. B. Saunders Co., 1964. pp. 837-863.

GIESE, ARTHUR C.: *Cell Physiology*, 2nd ed., Philadelphia, W. B. Saunders Co., 1962.

GORBMAN, AUBREY and HOWARD A. BERN: *A Textbook of Comparative Endocrinology*, New York, John Wiley & Sons, Inc., 1962.

GOSS, CHARLES MAYO, ed., *Anatomy of the Human Body* by Henry Gray, 27th ed., Philadelphia, Lea & Febiger, 1959.

GRANT, J. C. B.: *A Method of Anatomy*, 6th ed., Baltimore, The Williams & Wilkins Co., 1958.

GRANT, J. C. B.: *An Atlas of Anatomy*, 5th ed., Baltimore, The Williams & Wilkins Co., 1962.

GREISHEIMER, E. M.: *Physiology and Anatomy*, 8th ed., Philadelphia, J. B. Lippincott Co., 1963.

GREMMEL, FRED: "Coat Colors in Horses," *The Journal of Heredity*, 30, 437, 1939.

GROLLMAN, SIGMUND: *The Human Body*, New York, The Macmillan Co., 1964.

GUYTON, ARTHUR C.: *Function of the Human Body*, 2nd ed., Philadelphia, W. B. Saunders Co., 1964.

HADLEY, FREDERIC BROWN: *Principles of Veterinary Science*, 5th ed., Philadelphia, W. B. Saunders Co., 1954.

HAFEZ, E. S. E., ed.: *Reproduction in Farm Animals*, Philadelphia, Lea & Febiger, 1962.

HAM, ARTHUR W. and THOMAS S. LEESON: *Histology*, 4th ed., Philadelphia, J. B. Lippincott Co., 1961.

HERMAN, H. A. and F. W. MADDEN: *The Artificial Insemination of Dairy Cattle—A Handbook*, 2nd ed., New York, Lucas Bros., 1964.

KAHN, FRITZ: *Man in Structure and Function*, Vol. I-II, New York, Alfred A. Knopf, 1943.

KING, BARRY G. and MARY J. SHOWERS: *Human Anatomy and Physiology*, 5th ed., Philadelphia, W. B. Saunders Co., 1963.

KITCHELL, RALPH L.: "*Introduction to the Nervous System*," *In* Miller, Christensen, and Evans, *Anatomy of the Dog*, Philadelphia, W. B. Saunders Co., 1964, pp. 464-479.

KON, S. K. and A. T. COWIE: *Milk: The Mammary Gland and Its Secretions*, Vol. I, II, New York, Academic Press, 1961.

LANGLEY, L. L.: *Outline of Physiology*, New York, McGraw-Hill Book Co., 1961.

LEACH, JAMES W.: *Functional Anatomy: Mammalian and Comparative*, 3rd ed., New York, McGraw-Hill Book Co., Inc., 1961.

MARSHALL, F. H. A.: *Physiology of Reproduction*, edited by A. S. Parkes, 3rd ed., Vol. II, London, Longmans, Green & Co., 1952.

MAUGER, H. M.: *An Introduction to Veterinary Anatomy*, 3rd ed., Columbus, Ohio, 1953.

MAY, NEIL, D. S.: *The Anatomy of the Sheep*, 2nd ed., Brisbane, University of Queensland Press, 1963.

MAYNARD, LEONARD A. and JOHN K. LOOSLI: *Animal Nutrition*, 5th ed., New York, McGraw-Hill Book Co., Inc., 1962.

MCGRATH, JOHN T.: *Neurologic Examination of the Dog*, 2nd ed., Philadelphia, Lea & Febiger, 1960.

MCLEOD, W. M.: *Bovine Anatomy*, 2nd ed., Minneapolis, Burgess Pub. Co., 1958.

MEYER, HERMANN: "The Brain," *In* Miller, Christensen, and Evans, *Anatomy of the Dog*, Philadelphia, W. B. Saunders Co., 1964, pp. 480-532.

MILLER, MALCOLM E., GEORGE C. CHRISTENSEN, and HOWARD E. EVANS: *Anatomy of the Dog*, Philadelphia, W. B. Saunders Co., 1964.

MURRAY, MARGARET R.: "Skeletal Muscular Tissue in Culture," *In* G. H. Bourne, ed., *The Structure and Function of Muscle*, Vol. I, New York, Academic Press, 1960, pp. 111-136.

NALBANDOV, A. V.: *Reproductive Physiology*, San Francisco, W. H. Freeman & Co., 1958.

NELSON, OLIN E.: *Comparative Embryology of the Vertebrates*, New York, The Blakiston Co., Inc., 1960.

NETTER, FRANK H.: *The CIBA Collection of Medical Illustrations*, Vol. I, Summit, New Jersey, CIBA, 1958.

NICKEL, R., A. SCHUMMER, and E. SEIFERLE: *Lehrbuch der Anatomie der Haustiere*, Berlin, Paul Parey, 1954.

PATTEN, BRADLEY M.: *Embryology of the Pig*, 3rd ed., Philadelphia, The Blakiston Co., 1953.

PATTEN, BRADLEY M.: *Foundations of Embryology*, 2nd ed., New York, McGraw-Hill Book Co., Inc., 1964.

PERRY, ENOS J., ed.: *The Artificial Insemination of Farm Animals*, 3rd ed., New Brunswick, New Jersey, Rutgers University Press, 1960.

PORTER, KEITH R. and MARY A. BONNEVILLE: *An Introduction to the Fine Structure of Cells and Tissues*, 2nd ed., Philadelphia, Lea & Febiger, 1964.

PROSSER, C. L. and F. A. BROWN: *Comparative Animal Physiology*, 2nd ed., Philadelphia, W. B. Saunders Co., 1961.

RASCH, PHILIP J. and ROGER K. BURKE: *Kinesiology and Applied Anatomy*, 2nd ed., Philadelphia, Lea & Febiger, 1963.

RHODIN, J. A. G.: *An Atlas of Ultrastructure*, Philadelphia, W. B. Saunders Co., 1963.

ROBERTS, S. J.: *Veterinary Obstetrics and Genital Diseases*, Ann Arbor, Michigan, Edwards Bros., 1956.

ROGERS, T. A.: *Elementary Human Physiology*, New York, John Wiley & Sons, 1961.

ROMER, A. S.: *The Vertebrate Body*, 3rd ed., Philadelphia, W. B. Saunders Co., 1962.

RUCH, THEODORE C., and JOHN F. FULTON, eds.: *Medical Physiology and Biophysics*, 18th ed., Philadelphia, W. B. Saunders Co., 1960.

ST. CLAIR, L. E.: "The Nerve Supply to the Bovine Mammary Gland," *American Journal of Veterinary Research*, 3, 10, 1942.

SALISBURY, GLENN W. and NOLAND L. VANDEMARK: *Physiology of Reproduction and Artificial Insemination of Cattle*, San Francisco, W. H. Freeman & Co., 1961.

SCHEER, BRADLEY T.: *Animal Physiology*, New York, John Wiley & Sons, Inc., 1963.

SISSON, SEPTIMUS and JAMES D. GROSSMAN: *The Anatomy of the Domestic Animals*, 4th ed., Philadelphia, W. B. Saunders Co., 1953.

SMITH, SIR FREDRICK: *A Manual of Veterinary Physiology*, 4th ed., London, Balliere, Tindall, and Cox, 1912.

SOMERS, R. K.: *The Lymph Glands of Cattle, Hogs, and Sheep*, United States Department of Agriculture, Circular No. 866, Revised January, 1951, Washington, D. C.

SPECTOR, WILLIAM S.: *Handbook of Biological Data*, Philadelphia, W. B. Saunders Co., 1956.

STEEN, EDWIN B. and ASHLEY MONTAGUE: *Anatomy and Physiology*, Vol. I-II, New York, Barnes & Noble, 1959.

STEINDLER, ARTHUR: *Kinesiology of the Human Body*, Springfield, Illinois, Charles C Thomas, 1955.

TAYLOR, JOHN A.: *Regional and Applied Anatomy of the Domestic Animals*, Vol. 2, Philadelphia, J. B. Lippincott Co., 1959.

TRAUTMANN, ALFRED and JOSEF FIEBIGER: *Fundamentals of the Histology of Domestic Animals*, 9th ed., Ithaca, New York, Comstock Publishing Associates, 1957.

TRUM, BERNARD F.: "The Estrous Cycle of the Mare," *The Cornell Veterinarian*, 40, 17, 1950.

TURNER, C. DONNELL: *General Endocrinology*, 3rd ed., Philadelphia, W. B. Saunders Co., 1960.

TURNER, CHARLES W.: *The Comparative Anatomy of the Mammary Glands*, Columbia, Missouri, Univ. Cooperative Store, 1939.

TURNER, CHARLES W.: *The Mammary Gland I: The Anatomy of the Udder of Cattle and Domestic Animals*, Columbia, Missouri, Lucas Bros., 1952.

Turtox Biological Supplies, 65 Catalog, Chicago, Illinois, General Biological Supply House, Inc., 1963.

TUTTLE, W. W. and B. A. SCHOTTELIUS: *Textbook of Physiology*, 14th ed., St. Louis, The C. V. Mosby Co., 1961.

VILLEE, CLAUDE A.: *The Placenta and Fetal Membranes*, Baltimore, The Williams & Wilkins Co., 1960.

WEBER, ALVIN F., R. L. KITCHELL, and J. H. SAUTTER: "Mammary Gland Studies I: The Identity and Characterization of the Smallest Lobule Unit in the Udder of the Dairy Cow," *American Journal of Veterinary Research*, 16, 255, 1955.

WELLS, KATHARINE E.: *Kinesiology*, 3rd ed., Philadelphia, W. B. Saunders Co., 1960.

WESTERFIELD C.: *Histology and Embryology of the Domestic Animals*, 3 vols., Ann Arbor, Michigan, Edwards Brothers, Inc., 1957.

WILSON, G. B. and J. H. MORRISON: *Cytology*, New York, Reinhold Publishing Co., 1961.

WITSCHI, E.: *Development of Vertebrates*, Philadelphia, W. B. Saunders Co., 1956.

YOUNG, WILLIAM CALDWELL, ed.: *Sex and Internal Secretions*, 3rd ed., Baltimore, The Williams & Wilkins Co., 1961.

YOUNGMANS, W. B.: *Fundamentals of Human Physiology*, 2nd ed., Chicago, The Yearbook Publishers, Inc., 1962.

ZIETZSCHMANN, O. and O. KRÖLLING: *Lehrbuch der Entwicklung geschichte der Haustiere*, 2nd ed., Berlin, Paul Parey, 1955.

INDEX

Italicized figures indicate illustrations

A

A BAND, 173, *174*
A-D galactose, *283*
A-D glucose, *283*
A-V node, *233*
Abdominal aorta, *207*, 209, 210
  breathing, 247
  cavity, 32
  tunic, *406*
Abduction, *145*, 146, 159
Abnormal electrocardiogram, *234*
  presentations, *359*
Abomasum, *267*, 269, 294
Abortus, Brucella, 358
Abscess, 193
Absorption, 41, 297, 298
AC globulin, *196*, 197
Accessory pancreatic duct, 279
  sex glands, 369, 382
Accommodation, 112
Acetabulum, *133*, 148, *406*
Acetic acid, 304
Acetylcholine, 100, 171, 178, 231, 309, 320
Acetylcholinesterase, 178
Achilles tendon of, 150, 166
Achondroplastic dwarf, 136, 142
Acid acetic, 304, *305*, 306
  alpha lipoic, 309
  ascorbic, 309, 425
  butyric, 306
  citric, *304*
  deoxyribonucleic, 40, 45, 50, 345 380,
  fatty, 304
  folic, 288, 309
  fumaric, *305*
  hydrochloric, 299, 435
  isocitric, *305*
  ketoglutaric, *305*
  lactic, 177, *305*, 308
  malic, *305*
  nicotinic, 308
  oxaloacetic, *305*
  oxalosuccinic, *305*
  pantothenic, 309
  phosphoglyceric, 304, *305*
  prorionic, 306
  pteroylglutamic, 309

Acid pyruvic, 304, *305*
  ribonucleic, 47, 50, 192, 345, 380
  6 8 dithio N octanoic, 309
  succinic, *305*
  thiodic, 309
  urine, 321
Acidophils, 30, 193
Acidophils (Pituitary), 423
Acids amino, *45*, *285*, 297, 304, *305*, 306, 419
  essential amino, 285
  fatty, *305*, 306, 418
  glycogenic amino, 304
  iodinated amino, *431*
  ketogenic amino, 304
  saturated fatty, 286
  unessential amino, 285
  unsaturated fatty, 286
Acini, *279*
Acinous gland, *35*, 36
Acromegaly, 424
ACTH, 412, *419*, 424
Actin, 174, *176*
Actinomycosis, 193
Action, potential, *94*
  reflex, 95
  synergistic, 422
Activation, heat of, 177
Active reabsorption, 320
  transport, 55
Acusticae, maculae, 108
Adanine, 63
Adaptation, light, 114
Addison's disease, 426
Adduction, *145*, 146, 159
Adenine, *63*
Adenoids, 263
Adenosine diphosphate, 50, 58, 175, 304
  triphosphate, 50, 175, 302
  triphosphotase, 175
ADH, 319, 320, 416, 426
Adipose tissue, 27
Aditus laryngis, *261*
ADP, 48, 50, 58, 175, 304
Adrenal cortex, 345
  corticoids, 412, *419*
  gland, 426, *427*
  medulla, *66*, *429*
Adrenaline, 100, 178, 320, 417, 427
Adreno-corticotrophic hormone, 412, 424